D1286707

A Geography
of
Spain and Portugal

A Geography of
Spain and Portugal

BY

RUTH WAY

ASSISTED BY

MARGARET SIMMONS

LONDON

METHUEN & CO LTD

36 ESSEX STREET · WC2

First published in 1962
© *1962 Ruth Way*
Printed in Great Britain
by Butler & Tanner Ltd, Frome and London
Cat. No. 2/4246/10

Contents

Illustrations

PLATES

vii

*

LINE DRAWINGS

CHAPTER I

Geology and Landforms

THE IBERIAN PENINSULA consists basically of a hard crystalline core, around which have occurred several periods of sedimentation each followed by orogeneses. The age of this core is extremely difficult to determine; there are traces of Huronian folding in the north-west and Caledonian folding in the Sierra Morena, Estremadura, and Montes de Toledo, but metamorphosis at geologically recent dates accounts for some of the crystalline rocks of these areas. There is a complete range of sedimentary rocks, dating from lower Cambrian times onwards, which implies that for extensive periods parts at least of the peninsula were below sea level. In general, however, it was the Hercynian orogenesis that gave to Iberia its most characteristic geomorphological features.

It has been suggested that at this time an extensive range of mountains trending from south-east to north-west arose, starting where the Guadiana is today and continuing through north-west Spain into what is now the Atlantic. Separated from this main mass of highland by a narrow strait was the *rodilla* of Asturias, while highlands arose in the positions of the present Pyrenees and south-west Mediterranean. Apart from initiating three of the main highland areas of Iberia, the Hercynian orogenesis is important in connexion with mineral resources. The coal seams of Asturias (which were marginal deposits of the *rodilla*[1]), the silver-lead ores of Linares and La Carolina, and the copper-filled igneous dykes of the Rio Tinto district all occur in rocks associated with this period.

[1] *Rodilla:* a complex area of Carboniferous rocks encircled by Silurian and Devonian strata, probably the eroded remnant of a Hercynian syncline. There is a slight resemblance on a topographical or geological map to a knee-cap, hence the Spanish term, which means 'knee'.

By the end of the Primary era subaerial denudation had brought about the partial peneplanation of these highlands and earth movements caused fracturing and foundering. The Guadalquivir fault came into existence and there was a general submergence of the peninsula. During the succeeding millions of years sedimentation continued unhurried and unchecked. In Jurassic times a vast geosynclineex tended to the west, in which sediments up to a thickness of 5,000 feet were laid down, as can be seen from rock evidence near Torres Vedras and in the Serra da Arrabida. The rocks forming the Cintra hills, the bare limestone plateaus (upper Cretaceous) and lower fault-edged slopes (lower Cretaceous) of the hills around Soria, and the rocks which generally form the *muelas* (molar-tooth-shaped summits) of the Cuenca hills were all laid down in Mesozoic times. Tertiary marls now provide the rich soils for the vineyards of Jerez and the olive groves of Cijarefe near Seville.

During the Alpine orogenesis the vast accumulations of sediments were buckled up into mountains folded around the Hercynian massif. The mountain ranges emerged slowly, over a period of perhaps 25 million years. The Cantabrians were formed in the Eocene era, the Betic Cordillera at a later time during the Miocene period, while the Pyrenees, already in existence, were crushed by the movements and partly covered with fresh strata. The main trend of these mountains was from west-south-west to east-north-east; between each major range there occurred depressions which in some cases helped to shape the pattern of the present river system of Iberia. By the end of the Miocene era the basic 'ground plan' of Iberia had been created; the peninsula extended further north and west than it does now, but the main ranges of highlands (Montes de León, Cantabrians, Pyrenees, Central Sierras, Iberian mountains, Catalan hills, Sierra Morena and Betic Cordillera) were already in existence, separated by depressions which filled gradually with lacustrine or, occasionally, with marine sediments.

During the succeeding years from late Tertiary times onwards, the Iberian peninsula gradually changed its shape to a pattern strongly resembling that of today. The Balearic Islands, a continuation, in part, of the Betic Cordillera, were still joined to the

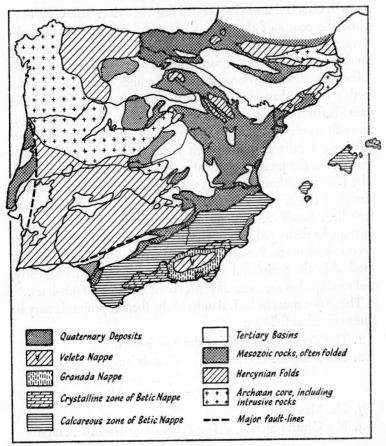

Fig. 1. Geology

mainland; but the great expanse of the land to the north and west of Spain and Portugal was gradually submerged beneath a proto-Atlantic. This isostatic movement slightly altered the watershed of the peninsula, moving it eastwards and causing several cases of river capture. The Douro acquired headwaters at the expense of the Ebro, and the Guadiana captured a southern tributary of the Tagus, the elbow of capture being visible in the latter case at Helechosa. In some parts vulcanicity occurred; there are extinct volcanoes near Olot, and basaltic dykes have cut sharply across Palaeozoic rocks in the region of Campo de Calatrava. Along the coasts of Galicia foundering created drowned river valleys or 'rias', while the coasts of the south-east were likewise partially submerged, thus opening the Strait of Gibraltar and producing conditions suitable for the formation of alluvial plains.

Iberia is situated on one of the major lines of weakness of the earth's crust, that associated with the great trench dividing Laurasia from Gondwanaland. It has, therefore, always been liable to earth movements, of great magnitude during orogenesis, or relatively localized during such epeirogenic activity as earthquakes. At the present moment only the latter are experienced. The Lisbon earthquake of 1755 was one of the most violent of historical times, and was associated with the Oporto–Abrantes fault-line. Small tremors are still occasionally felt – in 1902 an earthquake destroyed part of Cuenca cathedral and several shocks occurred in north Portugal in 1958. Crustal instability is most marked in the peripheral regions, formed geologically recently, and earthquakes are generally associated with local fault-lines.

The major morphological units of the Iberian peninsula may be summarized as follows:

1. The Crystalline Massif of the North-West
2. The Marginal Ranges. a The Cantabrians
                     b The Pyrenees
                     c The Betic Cordillera
3. The Mesetas
4. The Central Sierras. a The Estrêla–Guadarrama Range
                     b The Toledo Mountains
                     c The Sierra Morena
                     d The Soria–Teruel Group
5. The Depressions. a The Ebro
                     b The Guadalquivir
6. The Coastal Plains

I. THE CRYSTALLINE MASSIF OF THE NORTH-WEST

This area is, geologically, the most ancient part of the peninsula. Formed basically of a pre-Palaeozoic block, covered with Palaeozoic sediments which have undergone extensive metamorphosis due to granitic intrusions, the present-day surface presents a limited series of rocks. Granites, gneiss, some Palaeozoic sediments, including slates, help to heighten the effect of greyness in this damp and cloudy countryside. With a present-day annual rainfall ranging from 40 to 80 inches, and a prehistoric rainfall during the Ice Age possibly greater, there has been extensive and rapid subaerial denudation, accentuated in part by rejuvenation. This has resulted

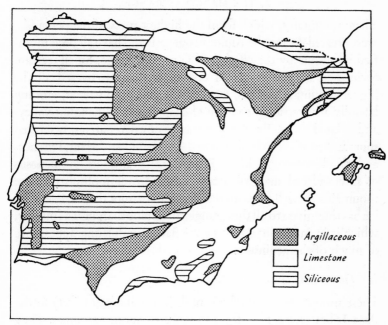

Fig. 2. Dominant Surface Rocks

After María de Bolós y Capdevila (*Enciclopedia de Gasso*, Geográfica de España, Gasso Hnos; Barcelona)

in markedly undulating relief, with rounded outlines but fairly steep slopes. The extreme hardness of the rocks, however, has counterbalanced denudation to such an extent that despite very active erosion the average elevation remains surprisingly high at about 2,000 feet. There are higher mountain masses rising to 5,599 feet (Peña Seixo) and 3,398 feet (Pico de Cuadramon). The gradient from the hills to the sea remains steep, and rivers here maintain steep-sided V-shaped torrent or upper courses for most of their lengths. Practically all drainage to the Atlantic follows a definite trend line from north-east to south-west; this direction is attributed by some geographers to faulting, the rivers having eroded along the fault-lines. The mouths of these rivers were drowned during slight isostatic movements in Pliocene times, thus creating rias.

2. THE MARGINAL RANGES

These mountains, which form the highest parts of the peninsula, were created during the Alpine orogenesis and have all been modified in outline by the effects of the great Ice Age. Small ice-caps formed of accumulations of compressed snow covered all the higher mountain regions, and glaciers filled the valleys, eroding laterally and vertically to form U-shaped valleys, hanging valleys and striated rocks. Excellent examples of cwms, arêtes, truncated spurs and erratics can be found in the higher Cantabrians, Pyrenees and, to a lesser extent, in the Betic Cordillera. Enormous deposits of fluvio-glacial materials occur in the lower foothills of these mountains as well as scattered deposits of moraine. Erosion by ice has thus given to all these ranges an Alpine sharpness of outline, which is in marked contrast to the flat or undulating appearance of much of the peninsula.

(a) The Cantabrians

These mountains extend from peak Miravilla (6,461 feet) to the Peña Labra (6,566 feet) for a distance of about 120 miles. They reach their maximum height in the eastern section, in the peaks of Peña Vieja (8,573 feet) and Peña Prieta (8,301 feet), which are sometimes referred to as the Picos de Europa. From the Peña Rubia (8,167 feet) the range of mountains changes its east–west direction, and continues in two semi-circular lines, via the Sierra de Picos and Sierra del Caurel (highest point Pico Pia Pajaro, 5,300 feet) in the west and the Montañas de León (highest point El Teleño, 7,178 feet) in the east. These two lines unite in the Peña Trevinca (6,707 feet). The enclosed circular enclave 'El Bierzo' is composed of pre-Cambrian rocks, and is, geologically, the oldest element in this mountain zone; all the other ranges are formed basically of Palaeozoic sediments, including limestone, sandstone, slate and coal. The only exception is the Peña Trevinca, which is composed of intrusive granite. To the east, beyond the

Peña Labra, the Mesozoic rocks begin, and the high mountain peaks no longer exist, their place being taken by hill country.

The highest parts of the Cantabrians still show the effects of glaciation, and are snow-covered and frost-shattered every winter. In general, however, fluvial erosion is now more active. The Cantabrians provide water for the short torrents that flow rapidly through deeply carved V-shaped valleys to the Bay of Biscay, and for the much longer rivers to the south, which start as swift-flowing torrents similar to the northerly streams, but eventually flow across the flat and arid meseta country to join the Douro. These streams dissect deeply an already broken landscape and divide much of Asturias into small virtually isolated zones, so producing difficulties in communications. There are only two main passes through these mountains; one, the pass of Pájares (4,513 feet high), leading to Asturias, and the other the pass of Puerto del Manzanal (4,034 feet high), leading to Galicia. In this way the Cantabrians and León ranges have helped to accentuate isolation and independence in Galicia and Asturias.

(b) The Pyrenees

The Pyrenees are broader and higher than any other mountain range in the peninsula. Their maximum coast-to-coast length is about 260 miles, but really high mountainous country extends only for about 150 miles. Their maximum width is approximately 60 miles, including both French and Spanish sides, and the whole of the central area is well over 4,500 feet high. The general alignment today is from west-north-west to east-south-east; the relationship of this alignment to trends in the folded strata has yet to be determined. The central mass of the Pyrenees is formed entirely of ancient material; crystalline rocks such as granite and gneiss indicate intrusion and metamorphism, and the sequence of sedimentary rocks includes Silurian slate, Devonian limestone, sandstone and conglomerate, as well as other strata of Palaeozoic and Mesozoic age. Ice has carved and fretted these resistant rocks into a series of high jagged peaks and arêtes, their rugged topography accentuated by corries, nivation hollows, U-shaped valleys and hanging valleys. Post-glacial effects of frost-shattering, chemical weathering of limestone rocks and extensive erosion by rivers (which frequently exhibit signs of rejuvenation due to slight isostatic oscillation which is, apparently, still in progress) combine with glacial features to give an extremely complex morphological pattern.

The region of high mountains begins to the west of the pass of Roncesvalles; here the Franco-Spanish borderline follows the line of higher peaks – Pic d'Orhy (6,618 feet), Pic d'Anie (8,215 feet), – bends south of the Pic du Midi d'Ossau (9,480 feet), but rejoins the wild crests of the Balaitous (10,319 feet) and Pic de Vignemale (10,820 feet). From this point onwards the boundary line passes between or on one side of the main peaks; thus Monte Perdito (10,998 feet) lies in Spain, the Pic de Neouvielle (9,435 feet) in France; Posets (11,047 feet) and the Maladetta range, culminating in the highest point of the Pyrenees, the Pic d'Aneto (11,168 feet), are entirely within Spain, while further east the Pic d'Estats (10,302 feet) and the Pic de Montcalm (10,105 feet) form the boundary, with the Pic Carlitte (9,584 feet) and Mont Canigou (9,137 feet) lying within France.

The Iberian side of the Pyrenees is characterized by extensive foothills, formed primarily of Secondary and Tertiary sediments. These rocks, sometimes contorted, but often occurring in broad horizontal strata, lie parallel to the high central mass, and have been subjected to much denudation. In most cases the alternation of hard and soft rocks has induced differential erosion, and the drainage pattern is, therefore, of the trellised type, with consequent streams at right-angles to, and subsequent streams parallel with, the general alignment. This arrangement of steeply scarped sierras alternating with flat-floored valleys naturally focusses lines of communication on the consequent southward-flowing streams; these, however, lead upstream only to the high peaks, through which it is almost impossible to pass. Furthermore, the lower foothills at either end of the range exhibit similar difficulties of terrain; though less high, they are deeply dissected by rivers which generally lead west to the Bay of Biscay or east to the Mediterranean; the valleys themselves therefore offer no easy passage across the main range. It is a significant fact that only one main road crosses the higher parts of the Pyrenees (that over the Bonaigua pass, 6,796 feet, which leads into France via the Val d'Aran), and that only two railway lines penetrate the whole range, that at Canfranc (Somport tunnel) and that at Puigcerda. Apart from the road already mentioned only three secondary roads cross the higher ranges, entering Spain at Canfranc, Sallent and Puigcerda, and two cross the lower foothills, one following the pass of Roncesvalles, and one rising over the Montes d'Albères in the east. The difficulty and complexity of Pyrenean morphology has always limited both communication and settlement and made these mountains a more formidable barrier to man than their higher counterparts, the Alps.

(c) The Betic Cordillera

The Betic Cordillera (which derives its name from Baetis, the old Roman province of south Spain) extends from the Gibraltar highlands to Cape de la Nao, a distance of just under 400 miles. In former epochs it was longer, continuing into the Balearics, where its eroded remnants still form the major highlands. Its greatest width is about 80 miles, but it is by no means a continuous range. A great longitudinal fault, extending from the upper course of the Genil to the middle course of the Segura river, divides it into two different sections. To the south are the series of ranges sometimes called penibetic, formed of a variety of older rocks in which diversity is revealed by several well-formed nappes, which give to the geology a definite alpine character. Crystalline rocks, particularly micaceous schist, form the Veleta zone which is the highest area and contains such peaks as Mulhacén (11,420 feet), Veleta (11,128 feet) and Tetica (6,822 feet) in the Sierra de Los Filabres. Around this zone, reaching the coast between Motril and Granada, is the Granada nappe, containing Triassic rocks which form the Sierra de Gádor (7,117 feet), Palaeozoic rocks which appear in the Sierra de Contraviesa, and several areas of crystalline formations. The Granada nappe is bordered by the crystalline rocks of the Sierra de Alhama and Sierra de Tolox (6,294 feet). The eastern and western extremities of this penibetic system generally reveal Tertiary rocks, although at Cape de la Gata there are signs of vulcanicity.

To the north of the fault-line lies a zone of much more recent material, though folded as are the rocks to the south. Jurassic,

Cretaceous and Tertiary deposits are abundant, and the predominant rock is limestone. The Jurassic limestone massif of Sagra
(8,416 feet) is outstanding and forms a central nucleus of highland
from which extend sierras, all progressively decreasing in altitude
towards the coast. To the west they include the Sierra de Magina
and Sierra Parapanda (north-west of Granada), the Sierra de
Yeguas, with a huge salt lake, and the Sierra de Algodon (3,704
feet). Eastwards the ranges include the Sierra de Taibilla, Sierra de
Espuña (5,190 feet), and the coastal sierras near to Cape de la Nao.

The highest range of this area, the Sierra Nevada, is a deserted
rocky wilderness, with a generally rounded summit level which
drops precipitously on the north-facing slope to a series of deeply
carved valleys. Some of these valleys have their headstreams in
deep *hoyas* which are thought to be vestigial cirques and are an
indication of Pleistocene glaciation. Despite the alpine characteristics of geology, the relief presents very few alpine features;
the main peaks are rounded or have at least one slope so gentle that
it can be ascended with ease. (A motor road reaches the top of
Veleta.) Although there are steep slopes and occasional precipitous
drops of up to 100 feet these are more the exception than the rule.
There are no U-shaped or hanging valleys, few cirques, no arêtes;
the scenery of these snowy heights is unique but not picturesque.

Throughout the whole of the lower ranges the effects of aridity,
with its corollary of sporadic but torrential rain, are pronounced.
The long suave crests of the sierras (*lomas*) have been deeply
etched by torrents, giving rise to *barrancas* or deep transverse
valleys which at times are occupied by no more than a trickle of
water and at infrequent intervals by raging streams. Elsewhere an
infilling of soft Quaternary marls and limestones, horizontally
placed, has been eroded into typical 'badland' scenery (*cárcavas*),
scarred with gullies which slowly recede into fertile but uncultivated summit areas. It is significant that the phrase 'the steppe and
the sown', normally applied to Egypt, is equally applicable to
these barren ranges. Only where perennially flowing rivers have
built up a flood plain, however small, is cultivation possible.
Otherwise the landscape borders on the Saharan.

3. THE MESETAS

The 'Meseta' (Spanish *mesa*, from Latin *mensa* – a table) is the general name given to the vast tablelands which form the desolate, monotonous hinterland of Spain. The land is universally flat, except where there is an abrupt change from one height to another. Level surfaces are generally associated with a particular rock series, and the break of slope, frequently made of marl, is referred to by Spanish geographers as a 'cuesta', which has an average gradient of from 1 : 1 to 1 : 4 and a height varying from 50 feet to 200 feet.

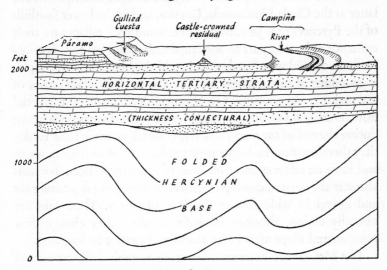

Fig. 3. Typical Meseta Country

(It should be noted that a salient feature of aeolian denudation is the steepening of the base of slopes.) Where the higher level is utterly barren, as happens most frequently on limestone, it is called a *páramo*, and often represents the original height of the Meseta, while the smaller hills are referred to as *alcores*. The lower tracts in general have been excavated by rivers which have carved flat steep-sided valleys. Such fertile alluvial plains or *campiñas* facilitate, but at the same time limit, irrigation; if more capital were available some of the higher regions could be irrigated, but such a development is impossible at the moment.

Development of the typical meseta landscape, due basically to the practically horizontal strata, also reveals clearly the effects of subaerial denudation under semi-arid conditions. The cuestas and other steep slopes have a harshness of outline that would inevitably be softened and rounded in a wetter climate. Mesas (small, isolated tablelands, capped by resistant rock, with steep sides, and slightly more vegetation than the *páramos*) and buttes (isolated flat-topped hills sometimes crowned with the ruins of an ancient castle) are found in both Old and New Castile, while the extensive limestone and sandstone deposits provide suitable conditions for the formation of rock pillars. There are striking examples of the latter at the Ciudad Encantada, Cuenca, and in the lower foothills of the Pyrenees near Jaca. Mesas, buttes and rock pillars owe their existence at least in part to aeolian abrasion and are features normally associated with hot deserts. In addition, badland topography is encountered in Andalusia and the Cuenca hills. Tributaries of the major rivers are subject to alternate drying up and torrential flow. During flood time their power of vertical abrasion is great; during the rest of the year there is no rainfall to erode their banks; they therefore flow in deep gorges reminiscent of Moroccan wadis and have an adverse effect on lines of communication. Torrents also scar the cuestas, causing extensive gullying and depositing silt and gravel in wide fans at the base of slopes. These fans are virtually useless, although often fertile, since they change their position and shape after every storm and cannot be irrigated.

The Mesetas are extensive, covering roughly half the area of Spain (about 98,000 square miles). Old and New Castile are predominately of meseta type, but characteristic features can be found in the Ebro depression and in the foothills of the Pyrenees and the Betic Cordillera. The central Castilian nucleus, with an average height of 2,000 feet, slopes almost imperceptibly to the west. It seems probable that extreme aridity and aeolian erosion are, to a certain extent, products of man's destruction of the original vegetation cover, for the Mesetas were never before the barren lands they are today. In Palaeolithic times the vegetation must have afforded pasture for abundant game where today only a few flocks of goats manage to live on scanty dried-up herbage; even in the fifteenth century writers described woods and forests in regions which today are rocky wildernesses.

4. THE CENTRAL SIERRAS

The Central Sierras are characterized by the predominance of granite as a basic rock, which, owing to its resistance to denudation, forms the higher peaks. The Sierras form part of the Hercynian block of Iberia and were faulted during Alpine orogenesis; the lower slopes reveal extensive Palaeozoic sediments. These mountains trend from east to west and form further barriers to north–south movement across the peninsula. This is offset to a certain extent by the dislocation of the general alignment of the ranges by faulting or erosion, giving rise to numerous easy passes.

(a) The Estrêla–Guadarrama Group

This group of mountains consists of a series of dislocated sierras, and is unusual in that, although the general trend is roughly from east to west, each individual sierra trends from south-west to north-east. In Portugal the group is represented by the Serra da Estrêla (6,530 feet) and the Serra de Lousã (3,942 feet), separated by the river Zêzere, which originates in the Serra da Estrêla, from the Serra do Moradal and Serra Guardunha (4,015 feet). Palaeozoic sediments form the lower much-dissected country which marks off the Portuguese section from Spain and gives rise to the Sierra de Gata (4,895 feet) and Sierra de Peña de Francia (5,635 feet). Granite re-emerges just east of this point and forms the highest ranges of all the Central Sierras – the Sierra de Gredos (Pic d'Almanzor, 8,502 feet) and the Sierra de Guadarrama (Pic Peñalara, 7,872 feet). The high pass of Somosierra (5,800 feet) separates the Sierra de Guadarrama from the primarily Palaeozoic mass of the Sierra de Ayllon.

All these sierras present a similar landscape of rugged but seldom alpine relief; rounded slopes, strewn with granite blocks, alternate with steep rocky glens, which in turn give way to gently undulating hillsides. It is only in the highest regions that really mountainous country is encountered. Here the effects of frost-shattering and previous ice action are much in evidence; cirques, a few small U-shaped and hanging valleys, nivation hollows and screes all occur on the Gredos and Guadarrama ranges. Lower down morainic mounds exist (as low as 2,300 feet on the Serra da

Estrêla), although post-glacial erosion has washed away some of this deposit. This series of sierras is the highest of the group, and, situated centrally in Iberia, it creates a definite barrier, broken in Spain only by relatively high passes (Somosierra, 5,800 feet; La Cañada on the Madrid–Ávila route, 4,454 feet; Tablada on the Madrid–Segovia route, 4,194 feet; and Pizarral on the Plasencia–Salamanca route, 3,312 feet), while in Portugal no major routes either cross or even penetrate into the rugged highlands.

(b) The Montes de Toledo

These uplands occur immediately south of the river Tagus, trend from east to west and include all ranges from the Sierra de Yebenes to the Serra de Mamede. South of Toledo intrusive granites and gneiss form the Sierras of Yebenes and Calderina, with extensions into the massif of Corocho de Rocigalgo (4,746 feet) and the Sierra de Tejadilla (4,565 feet). The nucleus of the group is the Sierra de Guadalupe (5,695 feet) where Palaeozoic sediments, including sandstones and limestones, form the highest peaks. The range continues westwards, composed primarily of Palaeozoic rocks, but with intrusive granite forming some of the higher peaks. The westerly sierras are generally lower than those in the east; they include the Sierra de Montanchez, Sierra de San Pedro, and the higher Serra de Mamede.

These mountains, fractured and isolated as those in the north, present an extremely rugged outline. Though not very high, slopes are steep, and the country is deeply dissected by rocky valleys which give the appearance of high relief. On the northern slopes of the Montes de Toledo there is an abrupt change to the Rañas of San Bartolomé, an extensive plain covered with coarse detritus laid down in Pliocene times. Their mountainous nature is, in fact, more real than their cartographic presentation suggests and, although they offer little difficulty to communications, they mark the boundary line between the provinces of Toledo and Ciudad Real.

(c) The Sierra Morena

Altitude and the prevalence of intrusive granite tend to decrease southwards over central Spain. The Sierra Morena group of hills is lower than those previously mentioned; the main ranges are, from east to west, the Sierra Madrona (4,342 feet), Sierra de Almadén (3,630 feet) and the Sierra de Alcudia (3,632 feet). Though Palaeozoic rocks predominate the granitic intrusions are economically more important. In the Rio Tinto area these are associated with many copper workings; at Almadén occur some of the richest mercury mines in the world, while lead is fairly widespread throughout the region. Carboniferous rocks provide coal at Puertollano, and in the Campo de Calatrava several extinct volcanoes provide stone for local constructional work.

The general relief of this area is less abrupt than that of the more northerly sierras. Undulating, rock-strewn uplands take the place of the scree-covered ridges of the Guadarrama. The southern slope is deeply dissected by streams running south to the Guadalquivir, but northwards the land descends gently, with wide, shallow valleys leading to the Guadiana. Viewed from the north the sierras appear as sinuous swellings rising above a rolling plain; viewed from the south the mountainous effect is far more obvious. The whole Hercynian block ends abruptly at the Guadalquivir fault, descending by steps from land over 1,500 feet to land under 300 feet, and to sea level at Cape St Vincent. It presents the appearance of a steep escarpment, marginally dissected, and frequently a burnt tawny yellow colour due to the effects of aridity, or a dark brown colour due to underlying rock type; hence the name Sierra Morena – the Brown Mountains.

(d) The Soria–Teruel Group

This extensive mass of hill country is sometimes known as the Iberian mountains, and includes the land centred around the two towns of Soria and Teruel. The dominant rocks here are limestones of Jurassic and Cretaceous age, amongst which have been revealed by erosion the basic Palaeozoic strata. In many instances the younger rocks have remained unfolded, or very slightly tilted, giving rise to meseta-like features. The average height is 5,000 feet, and the rivers Jalón and Henares divide the area into two sections. To the north is the Soria mass with two outstanding ranges formed primarily of Palaeozoic sediments; the Sierra de la Demanda (Picos de San Lorenzo, 7,225 feet) and the Sierra de Cebollera

(Picos de Urbion, 7,356 feet). The Cretaceous limestones of the Sierra de Moncayo form an eastern boundary, rising to 7,804 feet. The southern group of sierras are generally lower, and are composed of Jurassic and Cretaceous limestones which surround the small Tertiary basin in which Teruel is situated, and the Quaternary deposits flanking the valley of the Jiloca. The most important ranges include the Sierra de Albarracin, Jarallón (5,549 feet), Sierra de Javalambre (6,625 feet) and Sierra Palomera (5,015 feet). To the north-east and south-east these highlands make a rapid, terraced descent to the Tertiary basin of the Ebro and to the coast respectively. Some geographers see in these abrupt slopes the fractured edges of the Hercynian massif, but much geological study is required in this little-known region before any precise ideas on its geomorphology can be expressed with any authority.

Since limestone predominates in this region, karstic scenery is to be expected, but many of the features associated with British or Jugoslav limestone uplands are missing, as, for example, solution hollows such as dolina, and large trenches like the Jugoslav polja. There are scarcely any swallow holes or gorges due to collapsed caverns, while clints occur infrequently. This is primarily due to extreme aridity which has tended to produce desert rather than karstic scenery. Cuestas, mesas and rock pillars are much in evidence, and the general outline is one of high, flat and incredibly barren *parameras*, broken only by the slightly more rugged slopes of the higher sierras which were locally glaciated during the Ice Age. Taken as a whole the Soria–Teruel ranges, covering almost 8,000 square miles, provide the largest single 'area of difficulty' in the Iberian peninsula. Fortunately for the inhabitants rivers break up the highlands into distinct units and help to provide means of communication. The most important routes follow the rivers Henares and Jalón, linking the Meseta lands to the Ebro depression, while a secondary route provides a link with the Valencian coast via the river Jiloca.

5. THE DEPRESSIONS

The two major depressions of Iberia have in common several basic characteristics. They are both bounded on the side away from the Meseta by fold mountains of Alpine origin; they are both floored by Tertiary deposits and each is occupied by a river flowing nearer to the Meseta than to the mountain limits; if there is a fault-line marking the edge of the Meseta beneath the Soria–Teruel Secondary deposits, then both depressions are asymmetrical rift valleys, with the steep edge of the Meseta forming the inner and the younger fold mountains forming an outer line of demarcation. If no such fault-line exists the Ebro basin is another of the large depressions formed after the Hercynian orogenesis, and thus more comparable with the Tertiary basins of Castile.

(a) The Ebro Depression

The wide hollow has a roughly triangular shape, its south side being about 200 miles long, its south-east side about 100 miles long and its northern edge about 230 miles in length. It has an average height of about 1,500 feet, sloping gradually from Haro to the lower regions of the Llanos de Urgel near Lérida in the south-east. The river flows near the Meseta edge, either because it originally started here and continues along its old course or because its Pyrenean streams, having greater flow due to higher rainfall and increased erosive power due to steeper gradients, have pushed it progressively away from the Pyrenees by the coalescence of their alluvial fans. The tributaries have cut deeply into the horizontal Tertiary strata (these include marls, clays, a few sandstones and conglomerates – all laid down in an enclosed sea), and have separated the area into a series of masses of meseta type. Between the Aragón and the Arba are the barren heights of Las Bardenas; between the Aragón and the Gallego is the region named El Castellar; between the Gallego and the Cinca occurs the Sierra de Alcubierre, and the rocky slopes of Los Monegros, while between the Segre and the coastal ranges occurs the lower steppe land of the Llanos de Urgel, now partially irrigated. All these hills have features closely resembling those of the real meseta country, giving place in the north to the sierras which form the Pyrenean foothills. To the south there is a similar merging into the bleak *parameras* of the Soria–Teruel group. The soil fertility of the region is quite high and much of the land is flat; at the moment, however, arid conditions prevent systematic farming except on the lower alluvial fans, or in regions where extensive irrigation works have been undertaken. For the most part, therefore, this area presents a landscape as barren and monotonous as the Spanish Mesetas.

(b) The Guadalquivir Depression

This depression in the form of an elongated triangle is as long but less broad than its northerly counterpart, measuring along the northern edge 230 miles, along the south 200 miles and across the base about 55 miles. It is formed mainly of Miocene and Pliocene marls and limestones deposited in a sea which once extended eastwards. On the north side the Palaeozoic and crystalline rocks of the Meseta form a long line of bordering sierras abruptly terminated in geological sequence by the Guadalquivir fault. To the south the Tertiary deposits are, in places, overlain by Quaternary clays and limestones, which are fluvial in origin, possibly connected with outwash from the Sierra Nevada range during Pleistocene glaciation. These more recent deposits form terraces which become wider towards the mouth of the river Guadalquivir.

The general height is about 500 feet, and a major difference between this depression and that of the Ebro is its wide funnel-shaped opening to the sea. The river Guadalquivir flows in close juxtaposition to the fault-line which takes its name; it has not yet been determined to what extent it has followed the original fault-line or been deflected by the action of left-bank tributaries greater in both number and erosive power than those from the north. The appearance of the southern slopes of the Sierra Morena has already been described; south of the river the land is either gently or moderately undulating. The southerly tributaries of the Guadalquivir have eroded wide V-shaped valleys which alternate with irregular masses of highland; occasional outcrops of limestone bedrock give rise to barren heaths. In general contours are rounded rather than lineal, and the scenery less meseta-like than in the Ebro valley, though many of the hills are gullied. The limestone rock has weathered in many places to give a characteristic *terra rossa* type of soil, while the higher rainfall provides sufficient water for extensive cultivation of vines and olives. Steppe and semi-desert areas are infrequent and localized, limited mainly to younger rocks, for example gypsum, which have undergone extensive gullying and developed a badland type of topography. Towards the sea there is a wide expanse of salt-marsh, created by the damming up of the original outlet of the Guadalquivir by a sandspit which exhibits well-developed sand-dunes along the coast.

6. THE COASTAL PLAINS

The coastal plains of Iberia are few in number and small in extent, yet they form important centres of agriculture and their population density is higher than in the rest of the peninsula – over 130 people per square mile rising to 300 per square mile in some areas. Despite diversity of origin, there are certain features common to them all; they are flat and low-lying, floored with fertile alluvium, watered by at least one perennial stream, isolated from each other by intervening ranges of hills, susceptible to marine influences which often result in a slight increase in rainfall, separated from the centre of Iberia orographically, but open to communication and trade by sea. With fertile soils and a moderately humid climate these areas have tended to become the richest agricultural lands of the peninsula; in Spain, however, where the plains are smaller, separation has limited their importance and induced a certain regionalism of outlook.

The three largest littoral plains, those of Valencia, the lower Tagus and Aveiro, are all basically small Tertiary basins, surrounded by Mesozoic or Palaeozoic rocks. The largest is that around the lower Tagus; it covers about 2,200 square miles and is bordered to the north by Mesozoic limestones of the Serra de Candeiros and to the north-east and south by Palaeozoic crystalline rocks of the Hercynian block. The Tertiary rocks of the basin cover the Oporto–Abrantes fault-line, and are themselves covered in places by recent alluvium deposited by the Tagus, which flows close to the northerly boundary of the Tertiary basin.

The plain of Valencia, facing the Mediterranean, covers about 450 square miles, and is surrounded on the landward side by the Mesozoic limestones of the Central Sierras, which are geologically a continuation of the Soria–Teruel group of hills. The rivers Turia and Júcar have covered the seaward edge of the plain with alluvial deposits, while sand-dunes along the coast have cut off the marshy lagoon Albufera from the sea.

The coastal plain of Aveiro is approximately the same size as that of Valencia, but is more elongated along its coastal extension. Inland it is bounded by Mesozoic rocks which form the foothills of the Caramulo and Lousã group of uplands, themselves based on crystalline or Palaeozoic rocks. It is the river Mondego which has here deposited surface alluvium and provided material for the formation of extensive coastal sand-dunes.

Other coastal plains occur in the peninsula on a much smaller scale. Those along the south and east coasts include the small tectonic basin of Ampurdán, of about 80 square miles, which is open to the Mediterranean, and is partially floored by horizontal Tertiary strata covered with alluvium deposited by the river Fluvia. Further south there is another small Tertiary basin, similar in size and appearance, centred around Tarragona. The Ebro delta, formed almost entirely of alluvium, covers about 100 square miles and is still being extended by the river. There is a narrow, alluvially covered, coastal plain from Castellón de la Plana as far as the Valencian plain. Murcia is situated on the inland edge of an alluvial plain, which covers about 200 square miles of land from Murcia to the sea. A similar, though smaller area of 150 square miles occurs just north of Cartagena. Finally there are the plains of Almería (20 square miles), Málaga (100 square miles), and other smaller ones at Motril and Vélez Málaga. The coastal plain of Algarve in south Portugal can be included here as typical – it covers about 300 square miles, is backed by hills formed of Jurassic and Cretaceous rocks, and is fringed by dunes and sand-spits. A characteristic of all Mediterranean plains is the sudden abrupt transition from flat cultivated land to steep, rocky, often limestone sierras; the contrast in rock type, slope, cultivation and settlement is sharp and fundamental.

Along the west coast of the peninsula differences in geology and climate give rise to another type of coastal plain. The basic rock underlying all is of non-porous crystalline material or Palaeozoic sediments; on top of this rivers have deposited a mantle of alluvium. Although there is a contrast in slope between the plain and surrounding hills, this contrast is not so marked as in the southeast of the peninsula, while a more pluviose climate provides sufficient water for cultivation at all levels. Contrasts are, therefore,

i

ii

I i Mulhacén, the central peak (11,420 ft.) dominates the small village of Guejar
   Sierra. Olive terraces cover the lower slopes, and the river Geníl flows past
   the village in a rocky gorge.

  ii The Maladetta range from the S.W. The highest point is the Pic d'Aneto,
   11,163 ft.

i

ii

iii

II i Gullied cuesta, with poplars marking the course of the Arlanzón,
near Palencia, Northern Meseta.

ii High plains and distant Sierra de la Demanda, beyond the spires of
Burgos Cathedral.

iii The river Arlanzón, village of Venta de Baños, and distant páramos
of Torozos, north of Valladolid

less noticeable and less abrupt than in the south-east. A further point of comparison is that the north-westerly plains are all much smaller in size (5 to 30 square miles), and are riverine in character. In Galicia subsidence has caused the drowning of many alluvial plains to form rias, thereby giving to the province an extremely indented coast. Only at the heads of rias is there any appreciable area of flat land, and in many cases these could more accurately be termed alluvial patches rather than alluvial plains. Such patches occur near Túy on the river Miño, around Pontevedra and Padrón near the river Ulla, around Noya on the river Tambre, and near Betanzo and El Ferrol. In Asturias there is a small plain along the Nalón river near Avilés. In the Basque provinces there is a similar paucity of coastal plains, the best examples occurring near Bilbao, Pedernales and San Sebastián.

CHAPTER II

Rivers and Coasts

THE LONGER ATLANTIC coastline of Iberia and the slight tilting of surface to the west ensure that the majority of the precipitation falling on the peninsula is eventually returned to the Atlantic Ocean, whence it came. The rivers which form the terrestrial component of this climatic cycle show a wide diversity of type. Very few Iberian rivers have a typically graded 'thalweg', or valley profile. In the north and west the upper or torrent type of course is characteristic, the rivers flowing down a steep gradient to the sea. They are perennially fed by abundant precipitation, their powers of vertical corrasion are great, and their valleys thus present a steeply sloping V-shaped appearance, which continues for most of their course until they reach a drowned estuary, or ria. Shorter and swifter streams predominate in Asturias; in Galicia rivers are generally longer and slightly less rapid in flow.

The river Miño is the largest of these Galician rivers; it starts in Lake Fuenmiña at the foot of the Sierra de Meiro. It is 212 miles long and drains an area of approximately 6,866 square miles. Its importance lies in the fact that it annually discharges 7,700 million cubic metres of water, a total exceeding that of the Ebro, Guadalquiver, Guadiana, Tagus or Douro, although these rivers have greater lengths and catchment areas. The explanation lies in the climatic differences between the perennially wet north-west region and the seasonally arid central and southern regions of the peninsula.

On the Mesetas occur old well-established rivers. Flowing along courses delineated during Alpine orogenesis, the rivers Douro, Tagus and Guadiana traverse the arid Meseta and lower coastal plains until they reach the Atlantic in wide estuaries. All negotiate the steep edge of the Meseta by a series of rocky gorges carved deep in Palaeozoic or crystalline outcrops. As a result their courses show a double profile; the first or upper section is predominantly 'old' or 'lower' course in type, characterized by gentle gradient, wide alluvial plains and little active erosion except of bluffs, with deposition of load and development of wide meanders and braiding. This section ends abruptly at the edge of the Meseta, and the river has a rejuvenated appearance as it makes its way across this escarpment by a series of rapids, often through steep gorges. In the case of the Douro this period of active flow continues to the sea; the other rivers pass again into a 'lower' course type of river, flowing placidly across flood plains until reaching the Atlantic in estuaries. The river Ebro shows similarities to these rivers in length of flow, and in a double or triple profile; but it drains into a sea with a daily tidal range of only about 3 feet and has, therefore, formed a delta. Furthermore it receives much water from well-fed, perennial tributaries flowing from the Pyrenees, whereas the Meseta rivers receive tributaries from arid sierras.

Rivers on the south and east coasts of the peninsula generally have one profile and are well graded. They start either in the Betic Cordillera (where in the centre the gradient is very steep, and the rivers short, swift, and fed from the perennial water table of the Sierra Nevada), or from the more arid central sierras of Spain; here the rivers are longer, show the effects of summer drought and sudden equinoctial floods more obviously, and debouch on to wide alluvial plains. Such rivers form valuable sources of irrigation water although they are liable to occasional disastrous floods.

The Segura is one of the larger rivers of this type; 140 miles long, it drains approximately 6,315 square miles of arid country, reaching the sea across the plains of Murcia. The water level is generally low, but after a sudden storm it can rise with amazing rapidity, producing disastrous floods, such as that of 1879, when 1,000 people were killed and the vegas of Lorca, Murcia and Orihuela were utterly devastated. The Júcar is similarly liable to sudden floods, especially in spring and autumn; the town of Alcira was destroyed by floods in 1472. The Turia (or Guadalaviar) is a river of similar type, but its waters are stabilized to some extent by extensive irrigation and filtration through limestone rocks (at

Villar del Cabo the river flows underground for 4 miles). Nevertheless floods still occur; the most disastrous of recent years being that of 1957, when 77 people died and damage was extensive.

The five major rivers of the peninsula merit fuller treatment.

The Ebro

The river Ebro drains an area which is larger, but similar in shape to the Tertiary basin formed during and after Alpine orogenesis. The great earth hollow was originally an inland lake, cut off from the coast by the emergence of the Catalan hills. The extreme antiquity of the river is believed, by some geographers, to be indicated by the fact that the river has successfully cut through this coastal barrier, proving that vertical erosion kept pace with uplift. Another interesting feature connected with the Ebro valley is the asymmetrical position taken by the river in regard to the Tertiary basin; it lies much closer to the Meseta than to the Pyrenean edge.

In general the river takes a remarkably straight course southeastwards; at the town of Caspe, however, there is a general change of direction, the river forming a right-angled bend and flowing north-eastwards. This direction of flow brings its course into alignment with the extension of the original Tertiary basin; the precise significance of this trend, however, has yet to be determined.

The Ebro starts near Fuentibre as a small swift-flowing stream in the Peña Labra, an easterly extension of the Cantabrians. Rainfall here is high and perennial, although a combination of an average spring rainfall and snow-melt can give rise to spring floods, which lower down are augmented by tributaries often swollen at this time of year by the spring maximum of rain on the Meseta. This upper course of the river is fairly swift-flowing, with several meanders, and at first passes over rocks of Jurassic and Cretaceous age. There is no marked flood plain here, but beyond the hill country around Reinosa the river becomes less swift and signs of deposition appear on an increasingly large scale. At this point the river is passing through the greatly dissected hill country of the Santander hinterland; this is a zone of transition from pluvial coast to arid meseta and rainfall is both irregular and limited in

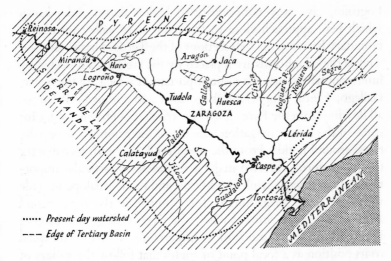

Fig. 4. The Ebro Basin

amount. A series of insignificant tributaries flow from these hills
to the Ebro and by the time it reaches Miranda del Ebro it has
become a wide, but still quite swiftly flowing, river.

At Haro, some 10 miles downstream from Miranda del Ebro,
the river leaves the Mesozoic zone and enters the Tertiary basin.
As it does so it passes through a rocky gorge, which marks the end
of the hill country, and emerges on to the flat, almost undisturbed
Tertiary sediments. The change of scenery is abrupt, and a slight
change of climate is also apparent; this part of the river's course
is lower and more sheltered than its upper course, and olives are
grown on the higher land. The alluvial fans of tributaries are
utilized for wheat growing; spring floods provide water which,
in normal years, is retained in the alluvium for sufficiently long
to nourish the wheat until it is harvested in August. This upper
basin of the Ebro receives fewer and smaller tributaries than does
the lower basin; those from the wetter Pyrenean side are longer
and more important and include the Arga and Aragón. The
Iregua and Cidacos are two of the more important southern
tributaries.

Near Tudela the river enters the lower part of the Tertiary
basin; the wide, flat plains, typical of the Rioja region around

Logroño, give way temporarily to higher sierras and *páramos* which here approach close to the main river valley forming a boundary between the two sections of the Tertiary basin. Beyond Tudela these highlands are replaced by flat tablelands dissected by numerous tributaries, the most important of which are the Segre, Gallego, Cinca, Noguera Ribagorzana and Noguera Pallaresa, all flowing from the Pyrenees. These tributaries provide water for some of the largest irrigation schemes of the peninsula, especially those around Lérida. From the south the Jalón, with its tributary the Jiloca, forms the two major tributaries, of particular importance as routeways, while the Martín and the Guadalope provide much water for irrigation, as, for example, in the vega around Alcañiz. Zaragoza, situated where the rivers Gallego and Huerva join the Ebro, owes much of its importance as a regional capital to its position as a focal point of routes that follow the valleys of the Ebro and its tributaries. Below Zaragoza the river flows less swiftly, braiding is of frequent occurrence and very large meanders have developed. Near the village of La Zaida a small hamlet has been built in the middle of each of four meanders, thus ensuring water supply and, in earlier times, a natural means of defence.

At the town of Fayón the river leaves the flat strata of the Tertiary basin and begins its third stage, that of the gorge carved in the Catalan hills. The rocks consist mostly of Jurassic and Cretaceous sandstones and limestones and have, in parts, been eroded into cliffs with fantastic shapes; their porous nature has helped to maintain the steep sides of the gorge in many places. The river in this third stage forms two almost right-angled bends, giving two stretches where it flows approximately south-eastwards linked by one section of south-westerly flow parallel to the coast. This latter direction is due primarily to structure; at this point there is a small interior valley in the Catalan hill system filled with soft Quaternary deposits. The river follows the more easily eroded bedrock for some distance until deflected once more south-eastwards by the Sierra de las Razas to flow across Cretaceous rocks to the coast.

The fourth and final stage is completely flat consisting of the Ebro delta. The river emerges from the Catalan hills at Tortosa, and, although canalized, has sufficient water to maintain its sluggish course to the sea. The delta is arcuate and typical of those made by a main river with few distributaries in that its length (17 miles) exceeds its breadth (average 10 miles), although today, because of the demands of irrigation, very little deposition can be observed. Currents have swept the mud and silt from Cape Tortosa either north or south, and two well-formed 'hooked' sandspits have been formed, enclosing marshy lagoons which, to the south, are used for saltings.

The river Ebro extends for 465 miles from its source near Fuentibre to the Mediterranean Sea, the catchment area (33,593 square miles) is great, and its tributaries help to water the largest irrigated zone of Spain – that around Lérida. Its usefulness to man is otherwise limited. The river bed is generally wide but the river is irregular in flow; it sends annually an average of 7,500 million cubic metres of water into the Mediterranean, but floods are likely from October to March (for example that of 1787, when as many as 85 victims were drowned at Tortosa), and drought may occur in summer, creating shallows that prohibit navigation by large craft. In addition it cuts across the main north–south routes of Spain. There are fifteen main bridging points for major roads and railways; the upper course in particular is frequently bridged since here the links between Madrid and the northern industrial areas are numerous. There are, for example, five bridges between Miranda del Ebro and Logroño, yet in the similarly sized but less frequented reach downstream between Caspe and Fayón there is only one bridge.

The Douro

The Douro (Latin – *Durus*, Spanish – *Duero*) is the most northerly of the three Meseta rivers and drains an area of approximately 38,281 square miles. It starts at a height of 7,389 feet in the Soria group of highlands. This is a region where porous Cretaceous rocks, frequently limestone, outcrop, and rainfall is scant. The upper course of the river is in no way a torrent course; the gradient is gentle, the flow is placid, so that erosion is restricted to the gradual undercutting of bluffs, and there is ample evidence, as at Soria, of the steady accumulation of alluvium, particularly on the convex sides of meanders. Once firmly established, these alluvial patches form valuable horticultural sites. This upper course was formerly a tributary of the Ebro, and the 'elbow', or bend, of capture (by the rejuvenated Douro in Pliocene times) can be seen near Soria.

South of Soria the river enters the second stage, and begins to cross the horizontal sedimentaries of the Tertiary basin. Its course now runs approximately westwards over arid country with frequent porous outcrops; evaporation is high, especially throughout the long dry summer. The major right-bank tributaries, however, come from the well-watered Cantabrians to the north and help

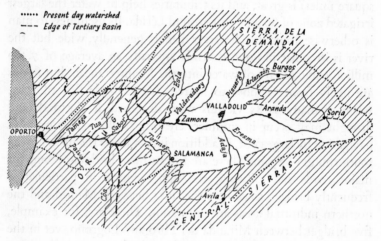

Fig. 5. The Douro Basin

to maintain a steady regular flow of water over this meseta section. The important rivers in this connexion are the Pisuerga, with its tributaries the Carrión and Arlanzón, and the Esla which drains a wide area in León and receives the waters of the Tera and Órbigo. Between these two systems runs the river Valderaduey and its tributary the Sequillo. Left-bank tributaries of the Douro drain from the Central Sierras, and are more irregular in flow; they include the Cega, Eresma and Guareña. This section of the river is one where irrigation is most urgently needed and, although there are a few major irrigation works, the river Douro is at present by no means fully utilized; barrages actually under construction or projected will eventually make this the largest irrigated zone in the peninsula.

Beyond Zamora, the lowest bridging point on the river in Spain, the Douro leaves the Tertiary basin and crosses the uptilted edge of the Meseta, where Palaeozoic rocks now come to the surface. There is a sudden change of scenery; the river, slow, placid and shallow on the Meseta, has been partly rejuvenated as a result of minor isostatic oscillation, and now flows rapidly over granite, shale and schist, carving a deep V-shaped valley, and being augmented by tributaries which often come from well-watered highlands. The boundary follows the river where it flows in a south-westerly direction; the only tributary here is the Tormes which starts in the Sierra de Gredos. In Portugal the major tributaries come from the north and include the Sabôr, Tuella and Tâmega, while of the left-bank tributaries only the Côa has a comparable length. The Douro finally enters the Atlantic at Oporto, in a wide estuary.

The main value of this river to man is in providing water for irrigation schemes, though these in general only affect Spain. The average annual amount of water reaching the Atlantic is about 4,883 million cubic metres. The Portuguese section of the river is far more liable to sudden flooding which normally occurs from December to March. All sections of the river suffer frequently from summer drought, the months of August and September being critical. The poverty of surrounding regions is clearly indicated by the paucity of bridging points necessary for major routeways which have to cross the river; the frontier zone is entirely devoid of bridges; of the six bridges in Portugal worthy of note the most important include those at Oporto, Pêso da Régoa and Pocinho; in Spain there are also six important bridging points concentrated in the central area around Valladolid. Navigation, as would be expected, is limited entirely to small river craft, except at Oporto. Here small ocean-going ships can enter the estuary, but a submarine sandbar at the mouth of the estuary has led to the building of the outport of Leixôes, which caters for larger vessels.

The Tagus

The source of the Tagus lies high in the Montes Universales, at a point about 5,000 feet high called the Muela de San Juan. This is

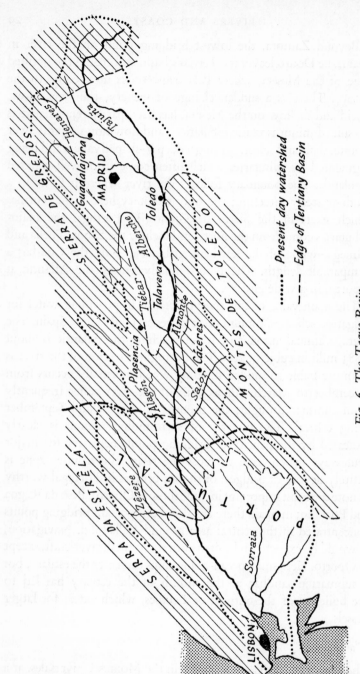

Fig. 6. The Tagus Basin

arid country developed on porous Jurassic and Cretaceous rocks, and the river flows at first due north-east, and then curves south-westwards. This section of the river has a gentle gradient and shows features similar to those of the upper Douro; erosion and deposition, particularly in connexion with meander development, continue steadily, but there is no marked torrent stage. A little upstream from the village of Trillo the river flows on to a long and narrow Tertiary basin.

This section of its course is similar to the tableland course of the Douro, with characteristic meanders, often entrenched, and frequent development of braiding. The Tagus receives a large number of right-bank tributaries, all coming from the wetter Central Sierras; these include the Tajuña, Henares and Jarama which enter the river near Aranjuez and help to provide irrigation water for the gardens and vegas around this town. Beyond Aranjuez the river shows similar features to the Ebro and the Guadalquivir in that it flows asymmetrically over the Tertiary basin, and has its longest tributaries coming from the highest mountains, in this case the Central Sierras to the north. The river flows so far to the south of the Tertiary sediments that at Toledo it has carved a deep, rocky gorge through granite and Palaeozoic outcrops. From Toledo the river curves slightly north-west, thus passing over the Tertiary basin again until Talavera de la Reina is reached, where it bends south-west. The Tagus finally leaves the Tertiary rocks near a village called Almaraz. Before doing so it reveals, in a short bend to the north-west, the point at which it originally received the river Guadiana. The course taken by the latter can be traced via two small tributaries which flow at the foot of the Sierra de Altamira and help to establish the link with the 'elbow' of capture on the Guadiana. In this lower tableland zone there are few large tributaries; the Alberche joins the Tagus from the north, and a series of short streams comes from the Montes de Toledo to the south.

In the third section the river flows over the Palaeozoic rocks which form the core of the Meseta and come to the surface along its western edge. These rocks have none of the horizontal stratification seen in the Tertiary sequence; folded and crushed, they have presented a hard, resistant block to the agents of subaerial denudation, and have been only gradually eroded to form a gently rolling peneplain. The rocks are non-porous and surplus water occasionally lies for a time in hollows on the surface until dried up in summer. The major tributaries consist of the Tiétar and the Alagón from the north, and the Almonte and the Salor from the south. At Alcántara the river passes through a deeply cut gorge, and this continues for some distance as the river flows over the edge of the Meseta and into Portugal.

The fourth section of the Tagus occurs just before Abrantes, where it re-enters a region of comparatively undisturbed Tertiary sediments. The main direction is now south-westerly and the river is extremely wide, exhibiting many of the features characteristic of rivers in their lower courses. There are several meanders and much braiding; the main feature of the river at this stage, however, is its singularly sheltered bottle-necked estuary. Before entering the sea beyond Lisbon the river receives several tributaries (the Ocreza, Zêzere and Tera) from well-watered Portuguese highlands; thus augmented it fills a wide shallow hollow and forms an extensive tidal lake, the Rada da Lisboa, of great value to shipping. For many centuries the town of Lisbon has benefited from this unique natural feature.

As a river useful to man the Tagus has little to commend it. It is 565 miles in length and drains 31,620 square miles of country that is arid and mainly of meseta type owing to the horizontal stratification of its rocks, which makes irrigation difficult. The river is utilized for transport only in its lower reaches which accommodate large ocean-going vessels in safety; otherwise only small river boats can navigate the more sluggish reaches. Both irrigation and navigation, however, are subject to irregularity of flow. The average annual discharge is 6,065 million cubic metres; but floods, which are at their worst in December and February (for example that of 1941, when the water level at the Roman bridge of Alcántara reached a record height of 95 feet), can greatly add to this figure. Conversely, a year of exceptionally low rainfall creates a very low water level, which reaches a minimum in September and can give rise to a disastrous lack of irrigation water. Large-scale water conservation schemes would help to stabilize the flow and minimize the effects of flooding (which are worse in the lower reaches of the river), but at the moment the capital for such schemes is not available.

The Guadiana

The source of the Guadiana lies in the Triassic limestone country of the Campos de Montiel which has several karstic characteristics. At first a chain of pools, the Lagunas de Riudera, indicates where the subterranean water table reaches the surface, but the pools

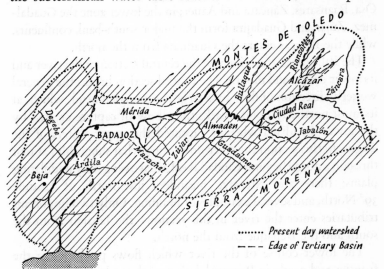

Fig. 7. The Guadiana Basin

cease after a brief 15-mile course and the river disappears underground. Shortly afterwards it reaches the surface again in the Ojos de Guadiana, and is soon joined by the Záncara. In fact the water appearing at Los Ojos (the 'eyes') has been found to come by complex subterranean passages from the Záncara, and not from the Lagunas de Riudera. The Záncara is, therefore, the main headstream.

The Guadiana has four separate sections, a tableland zone followed by a Palaeozoic zone, this pattern being repeated in the lower course. The first tableland zone includes the whole of the upper reaches of the river as far as the bridges north of Ciudad Real; the second tableland zone extends roughly from a point a few miles upstream from the confluence of the Zújar and Guadiana, as far as the Portuguese boundary. Both zones are similar in appearance, the river flowing in a well-defined bed between flat-topped plains which remain extremely arid unless irrigated. In both the upper and lower zones there is some irrigation, but there are extensive schemes for irrigating much of the lower zone around Badajoz; construction of some of the projected barrages has already commenced. It is in the tableland areas that the river receives its major tributaries; in the upper zone these include the Osa, Riansares, Záncara and Azuer; in the lower zone the Guadalmez, Zújar and Guadajira form the major south-bank confluents, while the Ruecas enters the Guadiana from the north.

The Palaeozoic zones include the central section of the river and its lower course and mouth. The central section breaks the general westerly direction of flow by a large right-angled bend, which, at its most northerly point, marks the elbow of capture created by the lower Guadiana when it captured the upper waters of the Tagus. In this section the river flows somewhat sluggishly, at first through a gorge beyond Ciudad Real, then over gently undulating plains; there are extensive meanders just north of latitude 39° North, and several examples of braiding. Only two important tributaries enter the river in this section – the Jabalón from the south and the Bullaque from the north.

The lower course of the river which flows partly along the frontier and partly in Portugal drains southwards to the Atlantic. The river is again restricted, flowing in a narrow valley developed on ancient Palaeozoic and crystalline rocks, which, unlike the porous limestones of the Tertiary basins, have a rapid surface run-off after unusually heavy rains and contribute to the frequent flooding. Although there are many small tributaries, the major ones include only the Degebe and the Chanza. The estuary of the Guadiana is wide and shallow; between the frontier towns of Ayamonte and Vila Real de San António the width is a little under a mile; south of this point the estuary widens to 4 miles and contains several small islands, the largest of which splits the main stream into two parts as it enters the sea.

Of all the main rivers of the peninsula the Guadiana has the least annual discharge, of 2,260 million cubic metres, despite its length of 510 miles. This is accounted for by the small catchment area

(26,500 square miles), the low annual rainfall (much of the area receives under 20 inches a year), the high rate of evaporation on the Palaeozoic sections, and the use of river water in a few places for irrigation. A very small area, just under 9 square miles, is irrigated at present, but it is hoped to increase this area at some future date to approximately 850 square miles. One of the main difficulties in utilizing the waters for irrigation is the great irregularity of flow. This is more marked in the lower course where floods are frequent from December to March; in the upper course water gradually filters through the porous rock and greater stability ensues. The river is navigable to smaller craft for about 42 miles, as far as the Portuguese town of Mértola. The extreme poverty of the border country through which the river flows limits the number of crossing places; there are two main bridging points in Portugal, near Beja and Mourão; in Spain Badajoz, Mérida and Ciudad Real are the important points, and although there are a few minor bridges, large stretches of the river, especially in the central section, remain unbridged.

The Guadalquivir

The source of the Guadalquivir lies in the Sierra de Cazorla, at a height of 4,475 feet. Mesozoic rocks, predominantly limestones and sandstones, act as massive reservoirs for the scanty rainfall of this area. Near Baeza the river starts to flow over the younger but still porous rocks of the Tertiary basin. Like the Ebro it is asymmetrically placed within the basin, flowing close to the steep faulted edge of the Sierra Morena. The northern tributaries are, therefore, short and sometimes insignificant; they include the Guadalimar, Guadalén and Huelva. Tributaries from the south are longer and generally more important; the Genil, which rises in the well-watered slopes of the Sierra Nevada, is the largest, while other south-bank confluents include the Guadiana Menor, Guadajoz and Corbones.

The river's total length is 512 miles; but in the lower course the drop is only 1,000 feet in some 400 miles, producing a gradient which at Córdoba may be described as gentle, and as non-existent beyond Seville. The river exhibits many of the features compatible with a lower course (or old stage); erosion, particularly

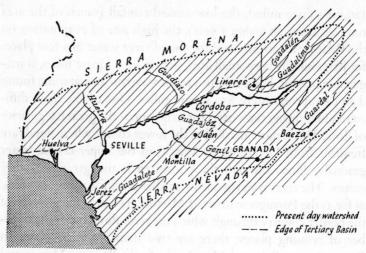

Fig. 8. The Guadalquivir Basin

vertical erosion, has almost ceased, while deposition is active, especially near the mouth. Meanders are particularly noticeable between Córdoba and Seville, and braiding also occurs. From Seville to the sea the river changes its direction, from west-south-west to south-south-west. In this section its course has been diverted by a sandspit, marked by the line of dunes called Arenas Gordas, and the river, brought almost to a standstill, has dropped most of its load to form the marshy swamps known as Las Marismas. Three main distributaries cross this uninhabited fen, giving rise to the 'islands' of Mayor and Menor, and reuniting before entering the sea past the Salinas de Levante and the small port of Sanlúcar de Barrameda.

The Guadalquivir drains approximately 22,312 square miles of land, and has an annual discharge of 5,760 million cubic metres. Since the time of the Moorish occupation of Iberia this river has been used for irrigation; at the moment approximately 320 square miles are irrigated, but it is hoped to increase this amount to 2,500 square miles at some future date. Flooding in the Guadalquivir valley is traditional, particularly in February and March; great devastation was caused in 1603, 1649 and 1684. Recently, however, several schemes have been completed which help to control floods; the meanders have been straightened to speed up the discharge of flood waters, barrages help to stabilize the flow, and drainage channels in the lower courses safely canalize some of the surplus water. Tidal influence, which is sometimes felt as far inland as Córdoba, also presents a considerable problem at flood time. Small craft of not more than 1,500 tons can reach Seville; Arab ships once reached Córdoba, but the river now contains more sandbanks and navigation between Seville and Córdoba is restricted to small river boats. Bridging points of importance occur at Seville and Córdoba; elsewhere there are several bridges of minor importance which link the cultivated regions on either side of the river, as for example at Lora de Rio and Villaverde del Rio.

Apart from the more normal fluvial drainage patterns there are a few small centres of inland drainage. These predominate in Spain, where the wide distribution of almost level land, with a porous bedrock eroded under semi-arid conditions, produces suitable terrain for their formation. Such areas are small, widely scattered, seldom visited by travellers, and frequently overlooked by geographers. In general the water collects either in a lake, often saline, or in a depression sometimes floored with salt deposits. One such area occurs south of La Roda, on the western side of the Betic Cordillera; the waters of an area approximately 46 square miles in extent drain into Lake Salada, a name which indicates its salinity. In the Teruel highlands, just west of Calamocha, there is a larger area of about 375 square miles, with minor streams, the longest 20 miles long, which drain into the Laguna de Gallocanta, and provide water for several small villages.

THE COASTS

Seven-eighths of the Iberian peninsula is bounded by sea; the Portuguese claim approximately 500 miles of the coast and the Spaniards 1,965 miles. There is great diversity of coastal formations, due partly to basic structural differences, and partly to the unequal powers of erosion of the Atlantic and Mediterranean, coupled with geologically recent isostatic oscillations.

Geographically the coasts of the north-west are most widely known, since they exhibit some of the best examples of rias. (In Spanish the word *ria* signifies an estuary.) These inlets are formed generally along coasts of 'Atlantic' type, that is where the 'grain' of the land, or structural trends, come to the sea at right-angles to the coastline. This type of coast is found in Galicia, where two areas of rias occur; the first area includes the inlets of the extreme north-west of the peninsula – the rias of Vivero, Barquero, Santa Marta, Ferrol, Ares, Betanzos, Burgo (or La Coruña) and Corcubión, which are collectively known as the Rias Altas. Further south the inlets become deeper and more extensive; they include the rias of Noya, Arosa, Pontevedra and Vigo, collectively called the Rias Bajas.

The formation of these long, branching inlets began originally with Alpine orogenesis, which created fault-lines in this region, running roughly in two directions – from north-east to south-west, and from north to south. The Galician coast follows these trend lines and so do the main rivers which help to form these rias. During Alpine orogenesis the rivers carved deep V-shaped valleys, running into the sea a good deal west of their present courses. In Pliocene times the whole of the north-west area was gradually submerged to a depth of, perhaps, 300 feet, the lower courses of the rivers were inundated by sea water, and isolated hills flanking the original valleys protruded as rocky islands. The typical ria is an inlet disproportionately large for the size of the river entering it; for example the river Lerez has a valley 24 miles long, and an estuary of 14 miles, while the river Oitaben and its ria of Vigo have approximately the same length of 18 miles.

The rias form sheltered anchorage for storm-driven ships, and their existence has done much to facilitate the fishing industry off this dangerous coast. The Galicians, like the Cornish people, have a long tradition of seafaring, and one of Spain's large modern naval bases is at El Ferrol del Caudillo. Improvements in transport and accommodation are annually drawing more tourists to these undoubtedly lovely stretches of water; but they also have disadvantages. The length of each inlet is so great that coastal road and rail traffic is forced inland to convenient bridging points; any use the rias have as harbours is thus offset by difficulties of hinterland communication.

The north-west coast is in general rocky, steeply shelving, and devoid of a coastal plain. In the Basque provinces Mesozoic limestones and sandstones form the major headlands, and every river

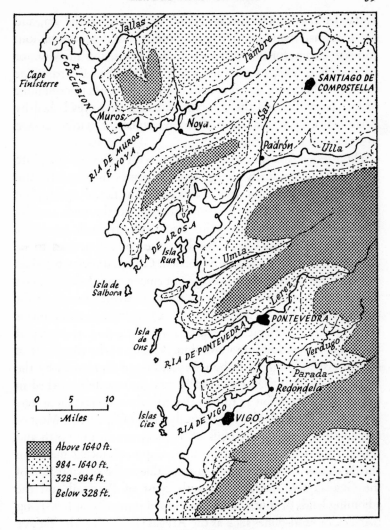

Fig. 9. The Rias Bajas

enters the sea through a small and often narrow estuary, similar to
a ria. Sand has sometimes accumulated along these rias or at the
heads of bays to form well-known beaches such as those of Deva
and Concha (San Sebastián). Cape Machichaco is one of the most
outstanding headlands of this area; a little to the west of it occur
the three small rias of Bilbao, Laredo and Santander. Beyond

Santander the Cantabrian mountains lie parallel to the sea, and the coast is, therefore, fairly smooth in outline throughout Asturias, except for the headland of Cape Peñas, and a few minor inlets such as those of Villaviciosa, Avilés and San Esteban. The coast of Galicia is deeply indented by rias; the resistant crystalline rocks have withstood the constant battering of waves lashed by Atlantic storms, so that there has been insufficient marine erosion to straighten the coastline.

This rugged Atlantic coastline continues for a short distance into Portugal, but gradually the gradient becomes more gentle and inlets narrower and less deep. Cliffs extend as far as Oporto, but south of this town there is a rapid change to the wide marshy lagoon of Aveiro, fringed with two sandspits, each nearly 12 miles long. Beyond Cape Mondego the coast continues to be cliff-edged and very sparsely populated. Cape Carvoeiro provides slight shelter for the fishing village of Peniche, and the cliffs, caves and general scenery near Cascais afford pleasant attractions for tourists from Lisbon. Cape Roca (38° 47′ North, 9° 29′ West) is the most westerly point of Iberia and the bottle-necked estuary of the Tagus is the most important single feature of the west coast of the peninsula. South of Lisbon, beyond the cliffs formed by the Serra da Arrabida, lies a practically straight coastline marked in the north by a sandspit 15 miles in length which diverts the waters of the river Sado, and by the centrally placed Cape Sines. Most of this coast has bare rocky cliffs of Tertiary age in the north and folded Palaeozoic rocks in the south. Cape St Vincent marks an abrupt change in direction of coastline, due to the continuation of the Guadalquivir fault. The south coast of Portugal and the adjoining lands of south Spain are formed primarily of low-lying marshes, or sand-dunes such as the Arenas Gordas (i.e. the 'fat', or wide, sands). The rivers Guadiana, Odiel, Tinto and Guadalquivir bring down quantities of material which annually help to augment the muddy islets which are dotted about their estuaries. The wide embayment which extends from Cape Santa Maria to Sanlúcar is referred to as the Gulf of Cádiz, while Cádiz Bay is the small stretch of water which lies to the north and east of the promontory on which Cádiz stands. From Cádiz the coast is rocky as far as the Strait of Gibraltar. Limestone predominates and helps to form the prominent headlands of Cape Trafalgar and Point Marroqui, the most southerly point of Spain.

The Mediterranean coasts of Spain are well known to tourists, who visit the Costa Brava (the rugged coast) or the Costa del Sol (the sunny coast). There is no continuous coastal plain except that north of Valencia, which is an extension of the Valencian lowland; there is instead a predominantly rocky coastline, with many headlands alternating with small patches of alluvial lowland which tend to decrease in size from north to south. The diurnal tidal rise is seldom more than 3 feet, so that fluvial sediment is deposited at the mouths of rivers (for example the Ebro, and the Andarax at Almería) to form deltas, while the less stormy climate minimizes the erosive power of waves. Longshore drift is particularly noticeable along these coasts and has helped to form large numbers of sandspits, many of which enclose salty lagoons.

The Catalan coast from the French frontier to Blanes has been termed the 'Costa Brava'. Formed of a wide variety of rocks ranging from Palaeozoic schists and sandstones to crystalline rocks and from Cretaceous and Jurassic limestones to conglomerates, it presents a diversity of attractive scenery for the tourist. There is a succession of minor headlands and bays which give place to the promontory of Cape Creus, itself succeeded by the deeply embayed Gulf of Rosas which marks the seaward end of the tectonic basin of Ampurdán. Another series of capes and bays continues this rugged coastal scenery as far as Blanes; from this point the coast becomes sandy, and from Calella to Barcelona there is a narrow coastal plain, corresponding to a small Tertiary basin lying a little inland. This section of the coast is referred to as the Costa del Levante, and is noted for its wide sandy beaches.

South of Barcelona there occur, in quick succession, the partially drained delta of the Llobregat, the beaches of Castelldefels, and the hills of Garraf which create a rocky coastline at this point. Beyond Sitges extends a long sandy beach as far as Cape Salou, but the immediate hinterland consists of cultivated hills rather than a coastal plain. Deeply dissected country around Cape Salou gives rise to a rocky coastline, but this is replaced by a low, sandy section which continues until Tortosa and the Ebro delta are reached. Beyond the wide expanses of the delta the Sierra

Montsia reaches the sea in a series of rocky headlands; Vinaroz and Benicarló have sandy beaches from which projects the rock of Peñiscola, a *tombolo* accessible from the mainland at low tide by a sandspit.

From Vinaroz to Cape San Antonio extends the largest coastal plain of this Levant littoral. The hinterland is composed of undisturbed Pliocene and Pleistocene sediments, mainly calcareous, which produce extensive beaches of fine sand. Along this coast longshore drift has played a prominent part in building up sandspits, and in many cases has created lagoons; these are often called *albuferas* from the original Arabic El Buhera. The largest is that of Valencia; it covers an area of approximately 18 square miles, and is fed by the river Turia and the channel Acequia Real, having access to the sea by the outlets of Perelló and Perellonet which cut the sandbar in two places. These outlets have sluice gates and the water level is generally maintained a few feet higher than that of the Mediterranean, to facilitate flooding of rice fields. At this height the water reaches a depth in the centre of from 12 to 16 feet, and affords a very favourable environment for fish, especially eels, and water fowl.

From Cape San Antonio to Gibraltar the coastline is influenced by the Betic Cordillera, and is rocky and indented. Beaches become smaller in number and size, and are generally associated with the streams and rivers which carve their way to the sea through limestone highlands. Cape de la Nao is the outstanding promontory of this region; to the south, beyond the Peñon Ifach, are the bays of Calpe and Benidorm, noted tourist centres. The coastal plains of the Murcia region give rise to sandy beaches, with several lagoons or *albuferas* such as that of Elche, which, however, is not completely cut off from the sea. The largest lagoon, the Mar Menor, covers an area of approximately 60 square miles, and was formed by two sandspits, one extending from Cape Palos and the other from the sandbank of San Pedro del Pinatar. These two sandspits have not quite joined, leaving a small entrance, the Mango or Boca de las Golas, open to the sea. Within the lake there are several islets of volcanic origin, while a series of small coastal streams enter it on the landward side and help to maintain a central depth of 21 feet.

Beyond Cape Palos the coast is again very rugged as far as Cape Gata. Cape Tiñosa and Point Peñon are the outstanding headlands, but there are no extensive beaches since only one large river, the Almanzora, comes to the sea along this coast, mainly due to the extreme aridity of this rain-shadow area. The hard volcanic rocks which have been eroded to form Cape de Gata mark the beginning of the Costa del Sol, an apt name for such a sheltered south-facing coast only a few miles from Africa. The predominant feature is the high rocky outline of the coast, which is broken only by small sandy bays such as those of Almería, Motril, Vélez Málaga, Málaga and Estepona. The eastern coast of Spain terminates characteristically in the abrupt limestone crags of the Rock of Gibraltar, facing the Bay of Algeciras. It is, perhaps, significant that the terminal point of the British possession is called the Punta de Europa, while the terminal point of Iberia is named Punta Marroqui.

CHAPTER III

Climate

P OSITION EXERTS A profound influence on the climate of the Iberian peninsula. Lying between latitudes 36° North and 43° 45′ North, it is situated in a transition zone between the westerly air stream of the North Atlantic, which brings a constant supply of relatively warm moist air to North West Europe, and the warm dry air stream which blows less frequently from the Sahara. Both these air masses are related to areas of low pressure; but a third pressure region, the Azores high, on occasions extends its influence to western Europe. A further point connected with latitudinal position is the intensity of insolation. It has been calculated that, taking into account such factors as length of day and angular elevation of the sun, maximum insolation on June 21st is experienced along latitude $43\frac{1}{2}°$ North; on other dates the latitude is further south. It follows that the effects of the sun are greater over Iberia than over many countries of Europe, and a general lack of cloud cover increases the effect of solar influence, especially in summer.

The shape and size of Iberia also exert an influence on its climate. The compact quadrilateral mass, with a highland rim to the north and south, is large enough to produce its own pressure systems. In summer great insolation in the interior causes a slight updraught of air over the Meseta; this intensifies, creating a minor low-pressure system with inblowing winds which come from regions of higher pressure surrounding the peninsula. The winds blow for the most part from the Atlantic or Mediterranean, but any moisture content is rapidly dispersed, for as the air reaches the scorching interior its moisture-holding capacity is raised, and the clouds, often prevalent along the west coast, disappear literally into thin air. This is particularly the case off south-west Portugal

44

and Spain, where the prevalence of the cold Canaries current out to sea gives rise to air masses which are cooler and therefore less saturated with moisture. The instability of air conditions in summer tends to produce small local thunderstorms, often of short duration but of great intensity.

In winter the Mediterranean area as a whole experiences low pressure, but the interior of the Iberian peninsula loses its heat rapidly, and cold is accentuated by altitude. There is occasional temperature inversion, the very cold air of the mountains flowing down to the plains, where it stagnates to form a dense freezing mass which gives rise to high pressure. This air mass is frequently so large that depressions from the Atlantic are deflected northwards or southwards and enter the Mediterranean either through the Strait of Gibraltar or through the gap of Carcassonne. Where no depressions occur winds blow steadily outwards, bringing dry cold air to the warm coastlands and causing a series of cold spells. The anticyclonic conditions of winter are character-istic of the Iberian peninsula, and give rise to a climate quite different from that generally associated with the Mediterranean. The annual reversal of the pressure system has been compared, in a small way, with that of Asia; but it should be emphasized that Iberian monsoons are distinctly dry, any violent precipitation being localized.

The complexity of weather conditions is further increased by the geomorphology of the peninsula. The highlands to the north and south limit oceanic influence to the coasts. The western littoral in general has no such physical barrier, but the scarped edge of the Meseta nevertheless acts as a frontier zone, beyond which the Atlantic influence penetrates but rarely. It is significant that this climatic 'no man's land' also forms the boundary between Spain and Portugal. The east coasts are throughout their length high enough to form a barrier to all but the most pervading of Mediterranean influences, and in the south-east quadrant of Spain the Betic Cordillera creates a rain-shadow where annual precipita-tion in some years reaches the Iberian minimum. The great table-lands of the Meseta are cut off both from each other and from the sea by highlands, and are affected to some extent by their altitude, which reduces temperatures, while porous bedrock absorbs only too readily such scanty precipitation as falls, and increases the aridity of the Mesetas, making them the most drought-stricken areas of the peninsula.

A detailed analysis of weather records for Iberia reveals six major types of weather sequence, which affect the peninsula at different times of the year. Two have already been mentioned – the well-established winter anticyclone and the summer low-pressure system, both due in part to terrestrial configuration. The critical times in Spanish weather, at least as far as agriculture is concerned, are spring and autumn, when there is no well-established pressure system, and conditions of instability prevail. In these seasons a third type of weather sequence associated with secondary depressions is likely to occur, sometimes connected with primary depressions over the Atlantic. In autumn such secondaries form off the south-east coast of Spain; here the precipitation associated with the warm front reaches the Levant coast, which remains cloudy and rainy. Under these conditions the updraught over the hot dry sierras of the littoral is occasionally so great that it counteracts the effect of gravity on falling raindrops to such an extent that enormous quantities of moisture accumulate in the atmosphere, to be dropped suddenly, with disastrous effects, when the winds slacken. Such cloudbursts are responsible for the serious, though infrequent, floods of the rivers Segura, Turia, Júcar and others along the Levant coast. The worst floods of such a nature in recent years include that of 1957 (October 19th) when much of the huerta of Valencia was damaged and 77 people were killed by the floods of the Turia; and that of 1959 (September 30th) when excessive rain occurred along the Catalan coast in connexion with a deep depression over the North Atlantic. Then, 3 inches fell during one hour in Barcelona, while continuous lightning during the night aided the fire brigade in its rescue of people from flooded buildings.

In winter and spring secondary depressions frequently occur further north, and provide the fourth type of weather sequence. Those depressions associated with low pressure over the Gulf of Genoa tend to divert southwards the colder air lying over north Europe. At such times the north-east coast of Spain may at first experience mild, humid conditions as the warm front of the depression passes, with a rapid change to cold, blustery weather similar to a line squall as the warm is succeeded by the cold front. If pressure north of Spain is high, the north winds thus indrawn are extremely strong, and may blow continuously for two or more days. In Huesca province these winds are locally termed the *cierzo*, or in Basque *ipargorri* (Basque *ipar* means north, and *gorri* rough), while along the Catalan coast, where they are more frequent and even more violent, they are called the *tramontana*. Both winds are similar in origin to the well-known *mistral* of the Rhône valley.

A fifth variety of weather sequence, again due to secondary depressions, occurs during the winter half of the year over the Bay of Biscay, so producing a definite factual basis for the renowned storminess of this region. Such secondaries are frequently associated with a large parent depression passing to the north over Brittany, and give rise to persistent rain and gales over the Basque littoral and the western Pyrenees. Such is the configuration of the hilly coast that, whether the warm or cold front passes over the area, rainfall is certain and often excessive in amount. The high annual precipitation of such towns as San Sebastián (65 inches) and Bilbao (46 inches) can be explained in part by this type of depression.

The western coasts of Iberia are influenced primarily by the sixth type of weather, that associated with a large Atlantic depression which passes over the north-west part of the peninsula. Such depressions in summer take a more northerly track and affect only Galicia and north Portugal; in winter the whole of the west coast is subjected to the cloud, fog, hill mist, drizzle and rain that accompanies a typical warm front. If the depression is deep and vigorous it is strong enough to disperse the high pressure of the Meseta, bringing warmth and rainfall to the cold, arid interior. These conditions may persist for several days, and the frequency of such low-pressure systems is greatest in autumn, a fact revealed in the autumnal rainfall maxima of most towns along the west coast.

Apart from these major types of pressure systems, with their associated weather conditions, there are less frequently occurring varieties of Iberian weather. The great area of high pressure prevailing in winter over Eurasia seldom affects Iberia, which is to some extent protected from intrusive air masses by its own small high-pressure system. Occasionally this protective cover is removed by passing depressions and its place is taken subsequently by cold north-easterly winds blowing from Europe. This was the case in February 1956, when late frosts along the Levant coast of Spain caused extensive damage to orange and other fruit trees, reducing the expected exportable surplus of 1·3 million tons to 0·55 million tons in reality, and necessitating a government compensation of £30 million. Such visitations are fortunately rare, although similar frosty conditions in south-east Spain caused much damage in 1953.

The central area of Spain experiences widely varying weather conditions during spring and autumn, when the normal pressure systems are disrupted. In autumn but particularly in spring the Mesetas often have cold spells as a result of the passing of a cold front. On March 14th, 1950, Madrid's midday temperature stood at 59° F.; a depression was approaching from the Atlantic, and on the 16th, as the cold front passed over Madrid, the midday temperature dropped to 23° F. By next morning, however, it had risen to 48° F. In early summer the Mesetas are rapidly heated, but once again depressions may cause a drop in temperature. On May 21st, 1949, Madrid's midday temperature was 55° F.; by the 25th it was 64° F., and by the 28th had reached 72° F. A small depression then crossed the country and caused a temporary drop in temperature. This sequence was repeated in May 1959 when on the 5th Madrid's midday temperature was 70° F.; a small depression off south-west Spain passed over the Mesetas during the night, becoming partially occluded, and by midday next morning the temperature at Madrid was only 57° F. A similar occurrence took place in 1949, when as late as June 4th the passage of a minor cold front caused Madrid's midday temperature to drop from 75° F. to 68° F. by the following day. In autumn Atlantic depressions frequently cross the peninsula, with no well-established pressure system to act as a barrier, and, as the cold front passes, freezing, cloudy conditions prevail. Very occasionally polar air is diverted southwards over the Mesetas. This happened on October 28th, 1959, when strong winds from Iceland travelled due south, in connexion with the cold fronts of two depressions centred over central Europe, and caused a drop of more than 10° F. in all parts of northern and central Iberia.

A map of the peninsula showing actual summer isotherms marks off the south and east regions, where the average temperature is over 72° F., from the north and west, where it is more moderate. Certain areas of Estremadura and Andalusia have an average temperature of over 80° F. Such average figures, if translated into actual conditions experienced from day to day, reveal the much higher diurnal temperatures of south-east Spain. The mean maximum temperatures for the hottest months at Málaga and Jaén are 86° F. and 93° F. respectively, while midday temperatures of 104° F. have been recorded occasionally at Murcia, and Seville's absolute maximum is 122° F. The interior, despite its height, is likewise extremely hot; the absolute maximum temperatures at Madrid and Zaragoza stand at 111° F. and 117° F., while Valladolid and Burgos have both registered over 100° F., the latter, at a height of 2,800 feet, having an absolute maximum of 104° F. A characteristic of the Meseta, however, is the great diurnal range of temperature; this is seldom less than 20° F., and night temperatures bring welcome relief after the intense heat of the day.

More moderate conditions prevail in the north and west, due to marine influence. Lisbon's temperature rises to the mid eighties on occasions, seldom higher, while further north, as at Santiago de Compostella, temperatures of 70° F. to 75° F. are rarely exceeded and the diurnal range fluctuates between 5° F. and 12° F. Along the Cantabrian coast, summer temperatures are a little cooler; the average temperature for the hottest months in San Sebastián is 71° F., which is almost the same as that for Coimbra, 70° F. On the Catalan coast, the mean temperature for the hottest month at Barcelona is 74° F. and there is a rapid increase southwards, the average maximum temperature for the hottest month at Valencia being 86° F., although the mean summer temperature is 75° F., while at Alicante the average maximum temperature for the hottest month is 91° F.

Winter isotherms bring out clearly the differences between the equable littoral and the cold interior of the peninsula. Most of the

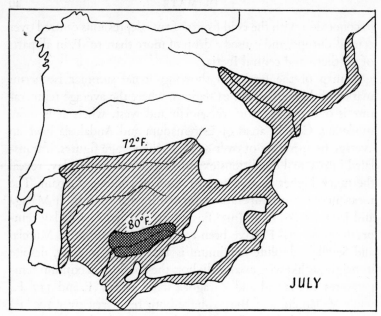

Fig. 10. July Temperature

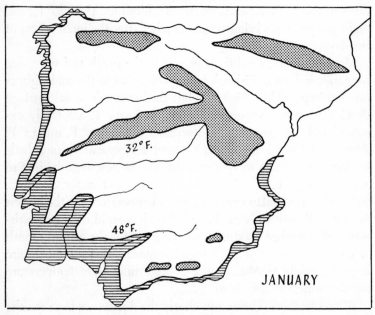

Fig. 11. January Temperature

coastal areas have an average temperature of over 48° F., and the average minimum temperature for the coldest months at Barcelona, Valencia, Murcia and Cartagena are 40° F., 40° F., 40° F. and 44° F. respectively. Frosts are extremely rare and spring normally comes early. Along the west coasts the winter temperatures are similar but more equable; monthly averages for Lisbon over the past 10 years have ranged from 48° F. (1957) to 56·5° F. (1948). Midday temperatures seldom rise above 55° F. or fall below 45° F., while the diurnal range is approximately 10° F. The average temperature of the coldest month at Coimbra is 47° F., and the average minimum temperature at San Sebastián is 37° F. Although the absolute minimum at Santiago de Compostella is 23° F., frosts along the Galician coast are rare, becoming more noticeable in Asturias and the Basque provinces, although even here their occurrence is infrequent. In Andalusia there is almost continuous warmth; Seville's average winter temperature is 52° F., Gibraltar's 55° F., while the average minimum temperature at Málaga, Seville and Jaén respectively are 48° F., 41° F. and 39° F., the two latter showing the cold influence of the Meseta in winter.

Winter temperatures of the central part of the peninsula show remarkable differences when compared with those of the periphery. The average temperatures for Madrid, Burgos and Zaragoza are 40° F., 36° F. and 41° F. respectively, but the average minimum February temperatures for Burgos, Logroño, Valladolid, Salamanca and León are 11° F., 7° F., 13° F., 30° F. and 28° F. respectively, Salamanca receiving slight influence from the Atlantic and León benefiting from occasional inversion of temperature. In the Ebro basin Zaragoza and Huesca experience 21° F. and 20° F. as their average winter minimum, and Zaragoza has registered one of the lowest temperatures in the peninsula, 3° F. The absolute minimum for Ciudad Real is 9° F. and for this town and for Madrid the average minimum for the coldest month is 32° F. Further south Badajoz and Cáceres register average minima of 33° F. and 37° F. for the coldest month, thus revealing a slight maritime influence.

In dealing with the temperatures of the peninsula altitude must be considered also. Under normal conditions temperatures vary inversely with altitude to the extent of 1° F. for every 300 feet. The main highland masses of Galicia, the Cantabrians, Pyrenees, Soria–Teruel complex, Central Sierras and the Betic Cordillera are well over 3,500 feet. There is therefore at least 12° F. difference between sea level temperatures and mountain temperatures, while the really high zones show differences of approximately

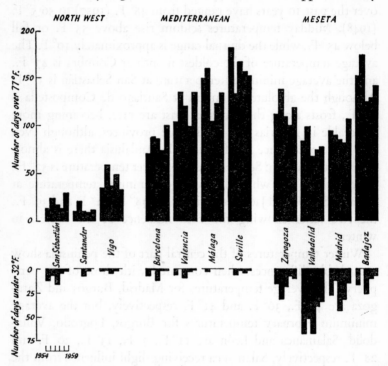

Fig. 12. Regional Temperature Extremes

20° F. to 30° F., corresponding with heights of 6,000 to 9,000 feet. The influence of altitude is less marked on summer temperatures, but is extremely important in spring and autumn for two reasons: firstly, the irregularity and general lateness of the coming of spring, which limits the growing season and hence affects the yields of crops such as vines, almonds, olives and oranges; and secondly, a similar uncertainty surrounding the advent of winter frost and snow, which seriously affects the flocks of sheep and goats annually taken to summer pasture in the mountains.

i   ii

iii

III i The deep gorge of the Júcar at Cuenca.

    ii The Douro in the Paiz do Vinho region, near Régua, with terraced vineyards and 'rabelo' sailing upstream. Compare with III iii.

   iii The Douro at Zamora; note the wide, shallow course winding between typically flat-topped meseta country.

i

ii

IV i Sheep seeking shade under the bridge over the partially dried-up Turia, Valencia, during August.

   ii A March shower, Barcelona; note palm trees.

Winters are universally cold, with temperatures well below freezing point (an average of 20° F. or below on all high mountains), and moderate drifts of snow which even at the lower levels lie well into April or May, while regions over 5,000 feet have temperatures below freezing point for four or five months of the year.

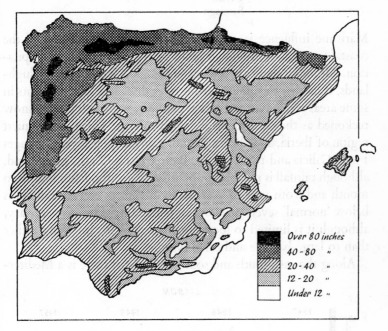

Over 80 inches
40 - 80 "
20 - 40 "
12 - 20 "
Under 12 "

Fig. 13. Rainfall

The precipitation of the Iberian peninsula shows, in common with its temperature, extreme variation both in amount and in seasonal distribution, and affords the most important single criterion for a regional climatic division. The north-west is characterized by copious rainfall which falls throughout the year but reaches a maximum in the winter months. This precipitation is generally of the drizzle type, locally called *cala bobos* (literally 'dolt's drench'), and it causes constant cloudiness and humidity, frequently accompanied by fog and mist (*bretama*). The general annual average for north and west Iberia is between 40 and 80

c

inches; the annual average amount for some of the larger towns is
listed below:

San Sebastián	65 inches
Bilbao	46
Santander	50
Oviedo	38
Corunna	32
Orense	33
Santiago	65

Maritime influence is emphasized in the higher rainfall of the
coastal towns, but mountain peaks receive much more precipitation. Although there are few meteorological stations on the highlands, it has been estimated from river discharge that amounts in
some areas reach over 100 inches per year, with 10 inches of snow
reckoned as the equivalent of 1 inch of rain. This is the rainiest
region of Iberia, and the number of rainy days per year averages
150 in Galicia and 165 along the Basque coast. On the other hand,
although rainfall is reliable, amounts vary greatly, from month to
month and from year to year. Even in Galicia average rainfall is
below 'normal' seven years out of ten and irrigation is necessary,
although it is limited to local distribution of stream water rather
than to large barrage and canal systems.

Along the east, south and south-west coasts there is a Mediter-

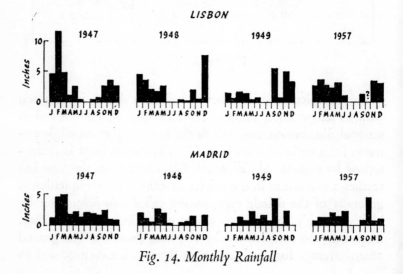

Fig. 14. Monthly Rainfall

ranean rainfall régime; here pronounced summer droughts alternate with rainy winters. The prevalence of equinoctial storms
frequently produces a spring or autumn maximum of rainfall, but
maximum precipitation occurs in the winter half of the year,
between the months of October and March inclusive. Average
figures, however, tend to obscure the great fluctuations from
year to year. Graphs showing the monthly amounts of rainfall at
Lisbon for a series of years are appended, and illustrate clearly the
two or three months of summer drought, which consistently
occur, and the winter maximum which is composed of widely
differing monthly totals. The type of rainfall is sometimes torrential, very sharp showers being followed in quick succession by
bright periods. During thunderstorms hailstones may occur, but
these seldom reach any outstanding size. Average annual amounts
of rain for the main coastal towns are as follows:

Barcelona	21 inches
Valencia	$17\frac{1}{2}$
Cartagena	$13\frac{1}{2}$
Málaga	19
Gibraltar	$35\frac{1}{2}$
Cádiz	$18\frac{1}{2}$
Lisbon	$29\frac{1}{2}$
Coimbra	36

while corresponding figures for inland towns are:

Seville	23
Córdoba	24
Murcia	15

The rainfall of the central tablelands is both sparse and
irregular, with marked continentality of régime. There is usually a
double maximum in spring and autumn, and the summer half of
the year is the more pluviose. Slight rain or snow is brought by
winter depressions and torrential downpours of convectional rain
occur in summer, sometimes accompanied by hail and thunderstorms. The prevalence of extensive highlands in this area tends
to increase rainfall amounts on the windward side and creates
marked aridity on the leeward, or rain-shadow, side. The general
average amount over the whole area varies from 12 inches to

20 inches annually; individual towns receive the following yearly amounts:

Zaragoza	13 inches
León	14
Valladolid	12½
Salamanca	13
Madrid	16½
Ciudad Real	18
Badajoz	15
Cáceres	30

Of all these towns Cáceres alone is open to Atlantic influence via the Tagus valley, and its rainfall is more reliable. All the other stations suffer, not only from extremely low rainfall amounts, but also from great irregularity in amount, both monthly and annually. (See the appended graphs for Madrid, which also show a slight annual similarity in pattern to those for Lisbon.) Agriculture, difficult enough in such an arid climate, is made even more hazardous by this unreliability of rainfall, which in some years may be as little as 6 or 8 inches. Since the tablelands form Spain's main granary, droughts considerably affect bread supplies and can cause great distress and hardship.

On the highlands of Iberia rainfall is generally heavy; the highlands of the north and west are extremely wet (average precipitation of 80 inches and over, with an average annual total of 113 inches on the Serra da Estrêla), and since the maximum precipitation occurs in winter snowfall is great. Snow depth averages 5 to 7 feet and drifts are deeper, while isolated hollows retain their snow cover even until early June. The western Pyrenees have similar precipitation amounts, but these decrease eastwards, so that in the Catalan mountains average amounts range from 40 to 80 inches. Both sections, however, have a tendency to violent thunderstorms in August and September, explained in part by the intrusion of moist Atlantic air into a region of unstable atmospheric conditions. The highest parts of the Iberian ranges and the Sierras Morena and Nevada all have annual amounts varying from 40 to 80 inches, with average snow cover to a depth of 4 to 6 feet, and deeper drifts in north-facing hollows. Annual amounts of snow are liable to great fluctuations, but often are sufficient to block the higher passes in the north for two to three months every year.

The Iberian peninsula can be divided into three major climatic zones; the north and west coastal area which, with continuous rainfall but a winter maximum and moderate, equable temperatures, is a southern variant of the oceanic type of climate found in north-west Europe; the typically Mediterranean east, south and south-west coasts, with summer drought, mild winters, and hot summers; and the interior zones of high tablelands, with annual and diurnal extremes of temperature, scant and unreliable rainfall, and a marked similarity to the southern steppes of Europe (compare Odessa, January average temperature 26° F., July 73° F., 16 inches of rain per year, and Budapest, January 28° F., July 70° F., 25 inches of rain per year).

These three major climatic regions can be further subdivided as follows:

(A) NORTH AND WEST COASTS:			
Type station	Jan. av. temp. °F	July av. temp. °F	Av. an. rainfall inches
1. Galicia and Asturias			
Santiago de Compostella	45	66	65
2. Basque Provinces			
Bilbao	46	70	46
(B) MEDITERRANEAN:			
1. North-east			
Barcelona	47	74	21
2. South and east			
Murcia	50	79	15
3. Andalusia			
Seville	52	85	23
4. South-west			
Lisbon	50	71	30
(C) THE MESETAS:			
1. Old Castile			
Valladolid	35	70	12½
2. New Castile			
Madrid	40	77	16½
3. Ebro Basin			
Zaragoza	41	76	13

It is a remarkable, but widely acknowledged, fact that the most typical 'Mediterranean' climates occur in areas far removed from the Mediterranean Sea. The average criteria for the Mediterranean 'norm' are as follows:

Temperature: 45° F. to 55° F. in winter,
                      70° F. to 75° F. in summer.
Rainfall: 20 to 35 inches per year, with winter maximum and summer drought of approx. 3 months.

Meteorological stations at Capetown, Perth, Adelaide and Sacramento (California) all record similar statistics. Within the Mediterranean basin, however, there are many deviations from this established norm. In Spain the Mediterranean coast is affected by the Meseta and the Betic Cordillera, which create a rain-shadow particularly noticeable in the Murcia–Levant area. Catalonia, though slightly wetter, is subjected in winter to the cold air of the *tramontana*, which helps to reduce the average December and January temperatures. By contrast the winter warmth and intense summer heat and drought of much of Andalusia introduce an African motif into the general climatic pattern. The coast of south Portugal, where the influence of the Atlantic is regular and unimpeded, is the only Iberian area of 'pure' Mediterranean climate.

North of this zone a more pronounced oceanic influence is indicated by heavy and continuous rain, coupled with more equable temperatures. Corunna alone experiences summer drought (in July, which has an average rainfall of 0·9 inches) and this is due in part to local topography; most of the area receives at least 30 inches of rain a year, if not more, and, although there is a winter maximum of precipitation, appreciable amounts (normally 2 inches or more) fall each summer month. The only exceptions occur in small localized rain-shadow zones. Temperatures are rarely extreme, the annual range fluctuating around 20° F., ranging from an average of 45° F. to 65° F., while in Galicia, more exposed to the warm sectors of Atlantic depressions, the range is even less (Corunna 16° F.). (See the appended graphs showing temperature deviations.)

The Mesetas of Iberia, on the other hand, experience unusually wide ranges in temperature, both diurnal (often as much as

20° F.) and annual (30° F. to 35° F.). This continental characteristic is also revealed in the annual rainfall figures, which seldom exceed 20 inches and in some regions (for example Zaragoza and Valladolid) are as low as 12 inches. There is a summer drought throughout the whole of central Spain, coupled with drying winds and heat haze. Winter, however, is also dry. Zaragoza has four months of absolute winter drought, and three months of absolute summer drought; and, while both the north and south Mesetas are slightly more pluviose in the winter, they, too, have a secondary rainfall minimum in January and February.

Most authors divide Iberia into two regions; pluviose and arid. Statistically this is feasible; a generalized isohyet of 30 inches separates the northern and western areas from those to the centre, south and east, and a map based on the indices of aridity for selected stations shows a similar arrangement. Geographically, however, such a classification is limited in value. It ignores the causal relationships of position, topography and climate, and tends to present a misleading picture of natural vegetation and agriculture. The tripartite climatic division of Iberia is reflected in natural plant growth, and has been recognized throughout the centuries by man, whose choice of crops is limited by climate.

CHAPTER IV

Soils, Flora and Fauna

SOILS

SOIL REPRESENTS THE surface of the rock-waste which generally covers the earth. There is a definite cycle of soil evolution which enables the soil profile to reach maturity if the ground is left undisturbed by man. Types of soil vary according to the nature of the parent bedrock, the climate and the natural vegetation. Of all these factors climate is the most important; not only does it control the type and amount of weathering of the rock-waste, but it determines the type of natural vegetation, and can cause either leaching or capillary action which leads to deposits of salts in the surface layers. It has been estimated that one inch of good rich mature soil is produced in 900 years if natural processes are left undisturbed. Soil depth varies widely in the Iberian peninsula, but with an average of 10 inches or more in many areas, it appears that the present soil of Iberia has been made over a period of at least 9,000 years. During this time slight climatic oscillations have taken place due to minor changes in the extent of polar ice, and these changes have altered the natural vegetation and affected soil evolution.

Most soils of the peninsula were evolved under a forest cover. Those in the north-west are associated with a cooler variant of a temperate forest, and have to some extent been enriched in the upper layers by the addition of manure. The original humus came from leaves of deciduous trees, and the upper 2 inches, or 'A' horizon, is leached of lime and other soluble substances by the downward movement of slightly acidic water. The colour is generally brown, due to staining with iron, while the 'B' horizon (between 2 and 3 inches below the surface) is yellowish brown and heavier in texture due to the downwashing of particles from the 'A' horizon. These soils form good agricultural land if limed or manured regularly; in parts of Galicia, however, the presence of large particles of sand, derived from granite, reduces the fertility. The general name for this type of soil is Podsol, derived from the Russian под – under, and соль – salt.

Over much of the peninsula dry forest soils predominate. There is still some leaching from the upper layer, despite the arid climatic conditions now prevailing, but the humus content, unless artificially increased, is fairly low. The colour varies from grey-brown to chestnut brown on the more arid steppe lands, and in all cases the lower layer becomes greyer. Such soils need careful cultivation and are moderately fertile. Where the parent rock is calcareous a red soil, *terra rossa*, is formed, mainly from inorganic material, and is characteristic of Mediterranean lands. Such soil, of average fertility, is improved by the addition of humus, but is highly susceptible to soil erosion.

In certain extremely arid regions where underlying rocks have a high saline content, for example, gypsum, the excessive surface evaporation of salt water brought up by capillary action has the effect of creating extensive surface deposits of soluble salts. These reduce plant growth to a minimum, and render the ground useless agriculturally. Such encrustations are fortunately rare – restricted to a few isolated tracts of La Mancha, and the gypsum beds in Andalusia and the Ebro basin. In certain semi-arid regions soil cover is discontinuous, and the parent rock protrudes; an extremely scant vegetation helps to retain such patches of soil as remain. *Calveros* (cf. Spanish *calvo*, bald) is the name used to denote this type of soil, which is well developed in the arid steppe-lands of La Mancha and in the eastern part of the Betic Cordillera.

In all mountain regions there are relatively infertile soils. These vary widely in colour, texture and mineral compounds. Some are formed from roughly weathered scree, others from the graded deposits of outwash fans. On some steep slopes a cover of coniferous forest gives rise to thin soils, dark brown in colour, acidic, sometimes almost peaty in waterlogged regions, with the upper layers somewhat leached. Humus content is generally high, but unless carefully limed such soils are of little use agriculturally. In the south and east mountain soils developed originally under a forest cover have reddish or grey-brown colourings, a higher calcareous but lower humus content, and are only slightly leached.

A few select parts of the Iberian peninsula benefit from soils derived from alluvium, and usually developed under an original forest cover. The forests have now vanished, and with them the annual collection of humus from decaying leaves, but today this is provided artificially in the form of dung. These alluvial soils are rich, possessing a wide mixture of minerals and a variety of particles, so that neither sand nor clay predominates, and a rich loam or marl results. Such soils, which form the best agricultural land of the peninsula, are found around Aveiro (Portugal), the lower Guadalquivir, and in patches along the east coast. In Andalusia they are similar in appearance to the rich black earths of the Mississippi valley.

Soil erosion is one of the major problems in the peninsula. This dates from the days of the first pastoralists and settled agriculturalists, who upset the delicate balance of soil, climate and vegetation, a balance which has never been readjusted. Ploughing on dry marginal land, or the *año y vez* (one year's growth and one year fallow) method of cereal production, give conditions highly conducive to soil erosion; the topsoil is without cover, occasionally ploughed to conserve moisture, and left in a dry powdery state, unconsolidated enough to be blown away by strong winds. Such erosion occurs on a small scale on the Spanish Mesetas, but most soil erosion in the peninsula is the result of gullying. This occurs everywhere in regions receiving under 35 inches of rain annually. Where soil cover is unprotected by vegetation, gullying proceeds rapidly, and 'badland' topography results, as in parts of La Mancha and around the river Horce in Andalusia. On mountain sides goats make tracks which soon become gullies; parts of the eastern Pyrenees show advanced stages of gullying for this reason, but goats are still allowed to wander at will over such areas, and the writer has seen olive groves in the upper Segre valley and parts of the Sierra Nevada threatened with extinction because of the unchecked wanderings of these animals. Soil erosion could be restricted in a variety of ways – by educating the local farmers in soil conservation, controlling pasturage, building dams across gullies to prevent downwash, and planting trees and grasses to bind the soil together. Few of these methods are practised in the peninsula; the capital expenditure on dam construction would perhaps be too great for present finances, but the other methods could be adopted in many more places than is the case at present.

NATURAL VEGETATION

The Iberian peninsula is particularly rich in its variety of natural vegetation; this is in part explained by the gradual change in climate during the last twenty-five millennia. In the last glacial phase (Würm) the peninsula was covered by steppe grasses interspersed with deciduous and coniferous forest, while large areas flanking the ice-capped highlands were covered by alpine and tundra plants. There has been a gradual warming and desiccation of the climate since those times; the alpine flora retreated upwards, and is now found only on the higher northern slopes; the steppe grasses diminished in extent, and the coniferous forests gave way to deciduous forests, these in turn retreating north and west as the climate became drier, so that only drought-resisting species could survive. Man has almost succeeded in deforesting the peninsula – only 10 per cent of Spain and 25 per cent of Portugal is forested. The degeneration of vegetation which frequently accompanies unrestricted deforestation is evident in the poor scrub growth referred to as *matorral* which occupies much of central Spain.

The abundance of species can also be ascribed to the widely differing climatic types found within the peninsula, and the general distribution of vegetation is closely related to the climatic regions. In the north and west, high average rainfall combines with warm or hot temperatures to give conditions eminently suitable for deciduous forest. The lower and coastal areas have extensive groves of oak (*Quercus robur*) with which man occasionally plants pine trees (*Pinus pinaster*), walnut and sweet chestnut (*Castanea sativa*), the latter formerly used in lean years as an article of food. In drier regions an oak tree more adapted to drought, the *Quercus pyrenaica*, can be found, and in higher areas beech (*Fagus silvatica*) takes the place of oak, with alders and willows flanking the numerous streams. Within the woodlands grow a great variety of grasses and wild flowers, some of them bulbous,

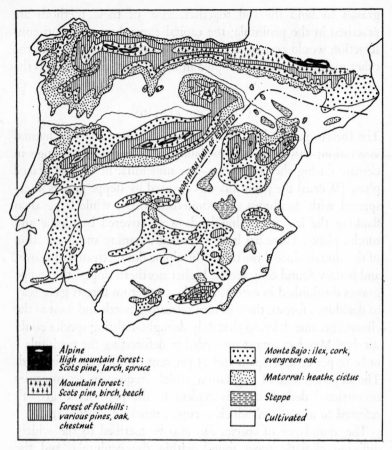

NORTHERN LIMIT OF ESPARTO

■ Alpine	Monte Bajo: ilex, cork, evergreen oak
High mountain forest: Scots pine, larch, spruce	Matorral: heaths, cistus
Mountain forest: Scots pine, birch, beech	Steppe
Forest of foothills: various pines, oak, chestnut	Cultivated

Fig. 15. Natural Vegetation

and these smaller plants are particularly noticeable in north Portugal and Galicia. Where the original forests have been destroyed a degenerate type of scrubland has developed, locally called *dehesas*, containing either heaths (*Erica cinerea, Erica ciliaris*) or gorse and furze (*Ulex europaeus, Ulex nanus*). Most of these plants shed their leaves or become dormant during the winter, in contrast to the evergreens found in other parts of the peninsula.

Summer drought in the rest of Iberia limits vegetation to xerophytic (drought-resisting) species. Adaptation to these unusual conditions varies from plant to plant; some, like the evergreen oak, have small, thick-cuticled leaves which minimize evaporation; others have a thick bark, like the cork oak, while some, such as the vine, have long tap roots which find water at low levels even during protracted periods of drought. Such plants also include hardy species of grasses, which are quick to take advantage of spring rains, and resist summer droughts by requiring a very short growing season. Other grasses, such as esparto, survive because of their extensive root system and tough, wiry leaves.

The most characteristic of xerophytic trees is the evergreen oak (*Quercus ilex*). Once this tree was to be found throughout Iberia; now, due to deforestation, it is restricted mainly to the east and south coasts, preferring the warm Mediterranean to the colder and drier meseta climate. Other trees which flourish in the Mediterranean region are sweet chestnuts, several varieties of oaks (*Quercus faginea, Quercus coccifera*), the dwarf palm (*Chamaerops humilis*) which, though not very abundant, is the only wild palm of European origin, the wild olive (*Olea europaea*), the Aleppo pine (*Pinus halepensis*), juniper trees (*Juniperus oxicedrus* and *Juniperus phoenicea*), and the cork tree (*Quercus suber*), which is, however, limited to soils with a high silica content. This collection of trees, referred to as *monte bajo*, once occupied the more arid parts of Spain, but only remnants are now found, along the coasts, leaving barren heaths in the central areas. Pine trees along the Mediterranean littoral frequently have their lower branches removed for firewood; Théophile Gautier, in his *Voyage en Espagne* (O.U.P.), describes them as '. . . pins . . . (qui) . . . se rapprochent de la forme de parasol'.

The Iberian tablelands, where not cultivated on an extensive basis, have a scant cover of *matorral*, or heath plants such as *Erinacea anthylies*, rosemary, lavender, and aromatic Labiatae such as thyme. The name *tomillare* is applied to steppe areas with a plant cover consisting primarily of the latter species, while steppe-lands where rosemary predominates are called *romerales*. Wide expanses of *jarales*, or cistus scrub, occur in the mid-Tagus and mid-Guadiana basins, and the ladanum bush (*Cistus ladaniferus*) is prominent in the Sierra Morena. Leguminosae such as the Spanish broom (*Sparteum junceum*) and other furzes occur in the slightly wetter areas and along water courses. A characteristic of most forms of steppe vegetation is the extremely sparse distribution of the actual plants; in general the number of plants per 4 square yards varies from one to six.

On the mountains of north and central Iberia distinct species of natural vegetation are found, type varying with altitude. In the Pyrenees there is a wooded zone from 4,250 feet to 5,250 feet, with ash, beech, oak and spruce, while box and pine trees flourish in drier valleys. Beneath the trees there is a fairly dense carpet of grasses, bulbous flowers and fruits such as the wild strawberry, raspberry, red currant and bilberry. From 5,250 feet to 7,000 feet only the hardier pines, for example *Pinus mugo* species *unciata*, with some rhododendron bushes, are able to survive the long hard winter. Above this height the pasture, or sub-alpine zone, begins; it occupies in general the flatter 'benches' above the U-shaped valleys, and provides hay as well as being used for transhumance. Apart from grasses there is a profusion of flowers of both cool temperate and alpine variety; wild carnation, campanula, saxifrage, scabious, anemones, foxgloves, rock roses, a few gentians – all thrive on the well-watered slopes. On the higher rocky crags at a height of about 9,000 feet, a few patches of grass, rock rose and other hardy alpine species may be found; the eidelweiss (locally known as *pie de león*) is now only found on the Soasa and Diazas slopes in the national park of Ordesa.

Further south the truly alpine species are often replaced by hardy xerophytic plants, and in the Betic Cordillera steppe vegetation is predominant, particularly on calcareous rock. In the Sierra Nevada it is possible to distinguish five zones of vegetation, as follows:

1. 0–2,600 feet: little natural vegetation, mainly of steppe type; cultivation of tropical plants.
2. 2,600–5,250 feet: 'mountain' or woodland vegetation; walnut, sweet chestnut, common and holm oak, poplar, some grass and flowering plants. Cultivation of olives, vines and citrus fruits.
3. 5,250–7,500 feet: sub-alpine region; berberis, pine (*Pinus silvestris*), rosemary, broom, bracken,

thistle, thyme and esparto in drier regions; some oaks, sweet chestnuts, willows, patches of meadowland near lakes or in wetter areas; maize, rye, beans and potatoes main cultivated crops, with a few vines and olives.

4. 7,500–9,000 feet: alpine region; a few dwarf bushes and scanty pasture for sheep and goats; gentians on the western slope of Mulhacén, saxifrage, violet (*Viola nevadensis*), *Ranunculus glacialis*.

5. over 9,000 feet: perpetual snow in a few north-facing patches, much bare rock; occasional tufts of hardy grasses.

It will be obvious from the above summary of Iberian natural vegetation that, apart from the great variety of species, there is also a wide diversity in origin. It has been estimated that 25 per cent of all Iberian species are endemic, most of them to be found in the central and southern regions; 20 per cent are common to most Mediterranean countries, and 33 per cent are of central European origin. Only 8 per cent are of African or Atlantic origin, illustrating clearly the effects of the Quaternary Ice Age in restricting the encroachment of all types of desert plants until postglacial times. The transverse mountain barriers in central Spain have also played their part in restricting plant migration.

FAUNA

Iberian fauna, like the flora, exhibits two basic characteristics; the peninsula has, through climatic changes since the Quaternary Ice Age, formed a zone of passage and transmission for species entering from either the north or the south, but more often from the former. In addition, the size and shape of the country, and diversity of environment within the peninsula, have combined in the evolution of certain types of creatures now reckoned as indigenous.

A few small bears still roam the northern highlands of Iberia, particularly in the Cantabrians. Living on fruits, nuts and edible roots and grasses, they generally manage to avoid human beings, but two were caught in 1952 and installed in a stout cage in Oviedo for the amusement of visitors. Such animals once inhabited the Pyrenees, but none have been seen there for many years, despite hunters' tales to the contrary. On the other hand, the chamois, or *isart* as it is known in the central Pyrenees (from the Basque *izar*, a star, a reference to the star-like mark on its forehead), and the *rebeca* (*Rupicapra pyrenaica parva*), as the small variety is called in the remoter parts of the Cantabrians (compare the Basque word *beka*, meaning bleating), can be seen by mountaineers in the wilder parts of both Cantabrians and Pyrenees, although numbers are dwindling. A hundred years ago it was possible to see up to 150 chamois browsing together, whereas now only herds of twenty or thirty are to be found. Excessive hunting, encroachment by man on natural food supplies and possibly the ravages of small carnivores are reasons for this diminution. In addition to these larger animals there are squirrels (*Sciurus vulgaris alpinus*), wildcats, mountain goats (*Capra pyrenaica*), martens, and wild boars in the central Pyrenees, as well as central European varieties of foxes, moles, rabbits and hares.

In central Iberia the Spanish wolf (*Canis lupis signatus*) haunts the higher sierras and northern hills of Portugal. In the Sierra Guadarrama a large squirrel (*Sciurus vulgaris infuscatus*) lives among the pine trees, while the Spanish fox (*Vulpes vulpes silaceus*) and Iberian weasel (*Mustela iberica*) prey on hares, rabbits and other small creatures. Further west there is a slightly different type of mountain goat (*Capra pyrenaica lusitanica*).

Of all the animals in south Spain the Barbary Ape (*Macacus sylvanus*) is probably best known and is exclusively restricted to Gibraltar. It is believed to have entered Spain, without human assistance, after the final retreat of the Sierra Nevada ice-cap. There are also a genet (*Genetta genetta*), weasel and dormouse of African origin, and a mountain goat native to the area (*Capra pyrenaica hispanica*), all of which provide food for the Andalusian wildcat (*Felis sylvestris artesia*) and the Spanish lynx (*Lynx pardellus*). Rabbits and hares are also found in the region.

The Mediterranean coastlands possess fewer wild animals than most parts of the peninsula, certain species (e.g. squirrels) being entirely absent. The larger carnivores, too, avoid this arid area which does not produce sufficient pasture for the small animals forming their staple diet. The Balearic Islands, separated from the mainland in early geological times, have even fewer species, all types of ungulates, squirrels and moles being totally absent. Only a small vole, dormouse and genet can be termed native to the islands.

Iberia has a unique position as outpost, bridging point, migration centre and common meeting place for a very wide diversity of avifauna, of which only the most outstanding can be listed here. Along the northern coasts in winter, especially in Asturias, flocks of gannets and guillemots can be seen, waiting for spring to return to their northern nesting places. In the Pyrenees and Cantabrians several birds of prey are to be found, including the buzzard, eagle owl (*Bubo bubo hispanis*) and the Spanish imperial eagle (*Aquila heliaca adalberti*). Furthermore, several varieties of pheasant make their home in the Pyrenees; one, the white pheasant, changes the normal grey-brown of its plumage to white in the winter, and makes its nest between rocks at a height of 8,000 to 10,000 feet.

In the Mesetas the steppe birds such as the red-legged partridge (*Alectoris rufa*) and the sand grouse (*Pterocles orientalis*) are sometimes hunted, while the stork makes its nest every spring on the crumbling bell-tower of some Castilian village church. In summer the flamingo nests in the Guadalquivir marshes; other aquatic birds, particularly duck, can be found in the marshes of Aveiro and the lagoons along the Mediterranean coast as well as in the lake of Ibars, Lérida. The bearded vulture (*Gypaetus barbatus grandis*) is sometimes found in the south, while there is a more general distribution of the royal cuckoo (*Cuculus canoris minor*), the green woodpecker (*Picus vividus sharpeii*) and the azure-winged magpie (*Cyanopica cyanus cooki*), the latter being peculiar to Spain and eastern Asia.

Reptiles are represented in Iberia by relatively few species; the grass snake inhabits the wetter areas of the north and west, and the only dangerous snake is the common viper which haunts sandy hill slopes and the wetter regions of the Mesetas. The largest reptile is a lizard (*Coelopeltis monspessulanus*), which has been known to reach a length of 5 feet or more, but is less common than the smaller varieties. In the central and southern districts the Iberian land tortoise (*Testudo iberico*) and the European pond tortoise (*Emys orbicularis*) exist, while the chameleon, of African origin, is occasionally seen in south Spain.

Fish in the inland waters of the peninsula are limited mainly to tench, bream, barbel, carp, trout and salmon. The river Minho is often taken as marking the southern limit of the salmon in Iberia, and there are fishing preserves in the rivers Eo, Narcea and Deva in the provinces of Galicia and Asturias, while similar preserves for trout are reserved in the river Tormes, Ávila province. Lake trout reach their greatest size in the mountain lakes of the north. In the Mediterranean the size and variety of fish is not so great as in the Atlantic. The more stagnant submarine conditions of the former sea prevent the mixing of water of different salinity and temperature, and thus give rise to a uniformity which precludes a great variety of fish; there is also less fish food in the Mediterranean which limits the number of fish and their rate of growth.

Typical Mediterranean fish include sardines (often smaller than in the Atlantic), anchovies, tunny, octopus, squid, cuttlefish, sea trout and, closer to the shore, eels, lobsters, crabs, cockles and mussels. Off the Atlantic coast there are similar species, but in greater profusion. Here tunny may reach a great size, 5 feet long, and with an average weight of 500 to 600 lb. Hake, codling, whitebait, sole and pilchards are species found along the more northern shores, and molluscs are an important article of food; clams, lobsters, crabs, limpets, mussels, oysters (inferior to those of more northern waters) are all caught around the Atlantic coasts.

CHAPTER V

Historical Geography

'TOROS! TOROS!' cried Maria to attract the attention of her father, the Marquis de Sautola, when he was exploring the cave of Altamira. In this way a five-year-old child of the nineteenth century heralded the discovery of 25,000-year-old cave paintings of the late Palaeolithic age. They include magnificent polychrome roof frescoes which have inspired later visitors to call one chamber in this cave the Sistine Chapel of the Ice Age.

These paintings represent the culmination of Ice Age art, which included sculpting in clay, painting with brushes or spraying by tube, and engraving on bone and cave walls. Men of this epoch were organized to such an extent that they maintained 'art schools' where rough engravings were practised on pebbles, later to be translated into more majestic drawings in the innermost recesses of caves. They portrayed with extraordinary plasticity the animals of the chase – bison, deer, reindeer, wild ox, horse, bear, mammoth and woolly-haired rhinoceros. Spear marks in the animals sculpted from clay and arrows painted on the cave drawings suggest that the primary aim of this art was an attempt to acquire magical control over hunting and game supply. The two known centres of this type of art lie in the Cantabrians and at Lascaux, in the Dordogne district of France, both regions where local limestone strata is honeycombed with potholes and caverns. Its distribution was more widespread, however, since painted caves occur in the provinces of Málaga and Guadalajara.

A different type of Palaeolithic art occurs along the Spanish Levant. Here the engravings and paintings occur in rock shelters once occupied by hunting communities, who frequently drew human beings in matchstick style, and depicted hunting scenes which show the bow and arrow as the dominant weapon for

71

killing ibex and wild boar. These paintings can be measured in inches, are visible in rock shelters and are artistically inferior to those of the older cave art, which can be measured in feet, are well hidden in inaccessible caverns and very rarely depict the human form. Both types of art find their best expression in Iberia, where a Palaeolithic population existed for some 500,000 years.

Even at this early stage of settlement the influence of geography was marked. Much of the peninsula lies between the Greenwich Meridian and 10° West, and forms, together with Ireland, the most westerly extension of Europe. The majority of its Palaeolithic inhabitants were not autochthonous, but were driven forward by stronger races or by climatic deterioration which caused diminution of food supply. Once established within the peninsula they had reached their ultimate line of retreat. On the other hand, penetration into this peninsula was slow, since it was restricted to three vital zones of passage, one at each end of the Pyrenees, and one via the Strait of Gibraltar. Iberia's geographical position thus allowed settlement by a mixture of races, except during maximum glaciation periods, such as Mindel, Riss and Würm, when the Pyrenean zone was less than inviting. Archaeological finds frequently point to mixed racial origin, and one may quote as an example that at Parpallo, Valencia province. Here the lower series includes Gravettian tools, made by a technique derived from south Russia and brought to Spain by tribes from the north, while the upper series contain every variety of Solutrean tools, of African origin. This transitional position of Iberia between African and European influences remained a constant and vital factor in early human settlement, even after the cutting of the land bridge across the Strait of Gibraltar.

After the last phase of glaciation the climate steadily improved and natural vegetation slowly changed in character, forests in particular becoming lighter, with less undergrowth, as rainfall decreased. Neolithic peoples found little difficulty in practising subsistence agriculture, and their numbers rose with improved living conditions, as ubiquitous megalithic remains prove. Equable temperatures combined with adequate rainfall made the south-west coastlands of the peninsula the best farming zone, the wide funnel-shaped valley of the Guadalquivir proving of particular fertility. Even here, however, summer droughts must have caused critical conditions, until the idea of irrigation was introduced. It has been suggested (*vide* Miss E. C. Semple) that the use of water for crops followed its use in mining. Whatever the origin of the idea, there can be no doubt that irrigation in south-west Iberia provided, as in Mesopotamia and Egypt, a sound basis of agriculture which in turn encouraged urban growth.

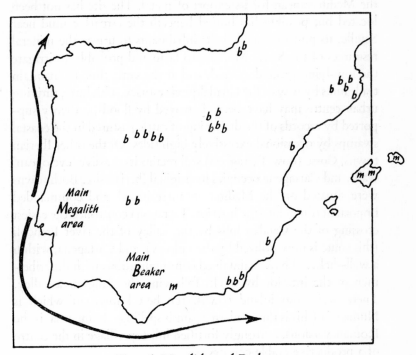

Fig. 16. Megaliths and Beakers

The walled cities of the peninsula are reputedly the work of the Iberians, whose identity, origin and language are a matter of conjecture. They were probably of north African descent, were described by the Romans as being fairly small, dark and wiry, with small face and prominent cheekbones, and their language, of which Basque is the probable descendant, may have been of a Hamitic type, possibly written in a primitive form of script just before the Roman invasion. Their tenacious resistance to invading Roman armies is frequently quoted as an example of the fierce independence of spirit and love of freedom still associated with modern Spaniards.

The Iberians had overseas links with Mediterranean traders from the Middle East, and their town sites reflected this maritime interest. Tartessus (Tarshis, Tarsis; *cf.* Basque *tarte*, interval, *arresi*, walled), situated in the lower Guadalquivir valley, took pride of place. It was an important trading centre, renowned throughout the Mediterranean for its export of metal. The site has not been located but possibly lies buried beneath the estuarine mud near Seville; its position enabled the inhabitants to utilize the mineral resources of the Sierra Morena, to farm and probably to irrigate the low-lying ground around, and at the same time to maintain trade links by way of the Guadalquivir estuary. This busy, thriving urban centre may have been destroyed by floods, a theory supported by records of the drowning of cattle pastured in the coastal swamps by occasional excessively high tides. Of the other Iberian towns, Cosse (now Tarragona) still retains its massive 'cyclopean' walls, and Cartagena occupies its original Iberian site. Both towns were situated on the Mediterranean seaboard, and commanded important routes into the interior. Tarragona controlled the easiest crossing of the Catalan hills by the valley of the river Francoli (this route is now utilized by the railway), and Cartagena, within a well-sheltered bay, maintained communications with the tribesmen of the interior by tracks following the Sangonera valley. There were also inland towns, the best known of which is Numancia (this is the modern Spanish spelling; 'Numantia' is the Roman version), a strongly fortified hill-top village in the centre of a productive arable country.

The Iberians began the task of city-building within the peninsula, but their work was soon taken over by groups of merchants from the more highly civilized countries of the eastern Mediterranean. The Phoenicians are believed to have discovered the Strait of Gibraltar in the eleventh century B.C., and, to maintain their hold on the Strait, established the trading stations of Carteia (near Algeciras), Gades (now Cádiz) and Onoba, near Huelva. The Greeks came more as colonists and founded Hemeroskopeion (now Calpe), Mainake (now Málaga), Saguntum (now Sagunto) and Emporion (now Ampurias). These towns, situated

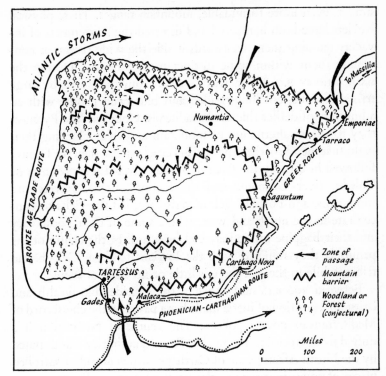

Fig. 17. Geographical Influence on Early Settlement

mainly on the east and south coasts, were limited to the periphery, as was the influence of their founders, and illustrate the increasing importance of the peninsula as a supplier of raw materials (corn and metals) to the Mediterranean world. Small-scale expeditions were still made along the north and west coasts, but these were exposed to Biscayan weather, and maintained contacts only with remote and barbarian lands, for example Gaul and Britain.

To the human geographer, however, the interior is of equal importance, since here the influence of geography on population distribution is more clearly apparent. Access and penetration into the peninsula are made difficult by the mountainous nature of the terrain. Along the south and Levant coasts a broad mountainous belt effectively limits the settlement of agriculturalists to the scattered alluvial flats around the mouths of such rivers as the Ebro, Segura and Júcar. Along the north and west coasts there are similar, even more formidable, mountain ranges. These physical barriers have both hampered and directed the movements of invaders, guiding them westwards beside the wide rivers, or containing them within some distinct natural region. During the sixth century B.C. Iberia was invaded from the north by large tribes of Celts, tall long-headed and blue-eyed people with an admixture of darker thickset broadheads. Once past the Pyrenees they found an alternation of mountain and river blocking their path; first the Ebro, then the Soria–Teruel ranges, then the Douro, followed in turn by the Central Sierras, river Tagus, Montes de Toledo, river Guadiana and the Sierra Morena. Rivers and mountains, and possibly lack of resistance, led the Celts to concentrate in the north and west, where some of their vocabulary and their bagpipe music may still be heard. In the centre of the peninsula they mingled with the Iberians to form Celt-Iberian tribes, while in the east there is little or no trace of them.

Between 300 B.C. and 150 B.C. the considerable wealth and latitudinal position of Iberia made her a pawn on the chessboard of Mediterranean power politics. The centre of civilization had shifted from Greece to Rome, but Roman authority was disputed by the North African state of Carthage, which already controlled places of sovereignty along the peninsular coast. To counteract this growing threat in the west Scipio invaded Spain in 209 B.C. and occupied much of the north-east coast. Saguntum was accepted by Carthage and Rome as the neutral centre of the marchlands, but in 218 B.C. Hannibal besieged it, and eventually captured its smoking ruins after the occupants had committed their goods and themselves to the flames. This provocative attack was followed by the Carthaginian invasion of northern Italy via the Alpine passes, and by protracted warfare which only ceased in 150 B.C. when Cato's reiterated dictum 'delendum est Carthago' was effected by the besieging, burning and ploughing over of the unfortunate town.

Roman occupation of the peninsula, often a painful process, was accomplished in 130 years. Resistance was fierce, heroic but hopeless. Viriatus, the shepherd king of Lusitania, the arable farmers of Numantia, the horse-breeders of Baetica all fell before the irresistible wave of conquering legionaries. By 20 B.C. only the virile

Fig. 18. Tribes – Fifth to Second Centuries B.C.

Cantabrian highlanders remained unsubdued. During this struggle a crude form of Latin evolved which developed later, despite many vicissitudes, into Castilian, Galician and Portuguese, while another Romance language, Catalan, was introduced at a later date. The word Spain, however, was adapted by the Romans from the Phoenician *Span*, meaning 'hidden', while 'Iberia' comes from a more ancient language, possibly the precursor of Basque, in which *ibai* means river, and *erri* people of, or country of, the whole word signifying 'land of the river' (Ebro).

There were other changes of far-reaching importance, particularly in the sphere of agriculture. Ready markets in Imperial Rome for all types of farm produce gave added incentive to the improvement of both output and quality. Irrigation works were extended wherever possible, especially in the Guadalquivir valley and on the alluvial plains of the Levant coast, and there was a certain amount of specialization. Around Tarraco and the Roman colonies of Tortosa and Saetibis (Játiva) rich deep soil and perennial moisture provided excellent crops of flax, which led to a flourishing linen industry. The spartum reed, used in the manufacture of cordage, was a crop of the irrigated delta of the Tader, near Carthago Nova, and one enterprising market gardener near Corduba made a fortune from growing artichokes (*vide* Miss E. C. Semple). Stock-rearing was also encouraged; wild horses were reared in the central Mesetas, pigs and mules in the damper pastures of Galicia and Asturias, while sheep were kept in the south, and those near Corduba provided a fine wool noted for its russet colour. At this time forests were far more extensive than they are today; pigs were acorn-fed on either side of the Guadalquivir, and Strabo describes the Sierra Nevada range as thickly wooded with gigantic trees. In the north new Roman settlements were built on the Pyrenean foothill terraces in order to facilitate irrigation, while the Ebro basin was devoted to olives and pasture land. In the south large estates (*latifundia*), worked by slaves, produced quantities of high-quality cereals, grapes, olives and peaches. Salted fish formed an alternative to meat for the poorer classes and fishing and salt production were subsidiary occupations. The following list of Iberian exports for this period reveals the high and varied productivity of land intelligently managed; timber, hides, leather, wool and fine cloth, linen, high-grade olives, wine, roots and cochineal insects for dyes, pitch, honey, wax, salt, breeding rams, wild horses and pack mules.

Minerals formed a second important source of wealth. Pliny mentions Vizcayan iron ore, and in the Sierra Morena 40,000 slaves were at one time employed in the extraction of copper, mercury, silver and lead. Small amounts of gold were obtained in Galicia and north Portugal, and the silver-lead mines near Linares (once the dowry of Hannibal's wife) were extended by the Romans who used much lead in the construction of aqueducts, badges, fish-net weights and ammunition. Mines leased from the Emperor to *conductores* were minutely organized, and living conditions, except for slaves, were such as to attract more settlers. These communities provided baths, laundries, shoemakers and barbers; schoolmasters in such areas were free of tax, and exploitation and overcharging were punishable offences. Onoba, near the modern Huelva, was the chief metal-exporting port.

During the days of the Empire peace followed in the footsteps of the legionaries. Hispania had much to offer, and received much in return. Corn, wine and olive oil were sent to Rome, and mining centres were specially organized so that the welfare of all workers was ensured. Iberia also provided hardy soldiers as well as poets and rhetoricians; Spaniards living during the later days of the Empire included the emperors Trajan, Hadrian and Marcus Aurelius, while Martial, Quintilian and Pomponius Mela, the geographer, all came from Spain. The benefits of Roman civilization, superimposed on the peasant population, soon showed material results; urban centres increased in size and number as roads were built and aqueducts and bridges constructed.

The influence of geography on political and municipal organizations was great; the original division, during the occupation, into Hispania Ulterior (south and west Iberia) and Hispania Citerior (north-east and central Iberia) was later reorganized, and, under Augustus, three provinces were recognized:

Tarraconensis, covering the whole of the north and east parts of Iberia, with Tarraco (now Tarragona) as its capital and a legion stationed at Legio (now León) to defend the northern marches against Cantabrian tribes; (this province was later subdivided for greater ease of administration into Gallaecia, Carthaginensis and Tarraconensis);
Lusitania, roughly approximating to modern Portugal; and
Baetica, which included south central Spain.

This division utilized the unpopulated zones of difficult environment as border territory. The boundary of Baetica coincided with the barren, arid hills of the Sierra Morena, or La Sagra, while Lusitania had the Sierra Morena, Sierra de Toledo and Sierra de Gredos ranges as its eastern boundary, and the gorge of the river Douro as its line of demarcation to the north. These divisions cut across the central Meseta lands where resistance to Rome occupation had been long and fierce, and put into effective practice the maxim 'divide and rule'. Furthermore, by singling out the Ebro and Guadalquivir basins as local administrative centres and maintaining close contact with coastal towns, the Romans revealed the fundamental geographical disadvantages of Iberia – a land possessing rich and varied peripheral regions but with no real central nucleus.

During urban development the pattern of routeways began to take shape. Many Roman towns arose on a Celtiberian or Carthaginian site, while others were of purely Roman origin. The modern Tarragona, Badajoz, Segovia, Jaca and Toledo are examples of towns of Iberian origin, if not of earlier date; Cádiz was

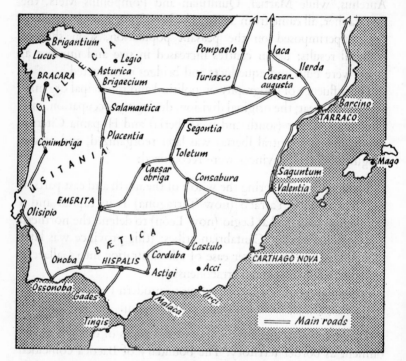

Fig. 19. Roman Iberia

Phoenician and Cartagena of Carthaginian origin, though rebuilt on a ruined Iberian town. León takes its name from Legio Septima Germina, the legion assigned to this border country as a defence against raiding Cantabrian tribesmen, and Mérida, founded in 25 B.C., of great importance in Roman days, was the place to which the faithful servicemen ('emeriti') of the Augustan period retired. To link these centres the Romans constructed the first good roads in the peninsula, either converting previous trackways or building straight new lengths of road as more and more land was subjugated. Although the Roman method of road building tended to ignore relief in other countries, the high, rugged nature of the land in many parts of Iberia forced Roman roads to make use of natural gaps and follow the tracks that had been used previously by prehistoric peoples. Relief features still dominate communications; the Roman pattern remains practically unaltered, except for slight deviations due mainly to the centripetal influence of Madrid.

The main road into the peninsula, the Via Augusta, as might be expected, came from the north-east, and followed the coast, linking the northern regional capital, Tarraco, with Carthago Nova, the regional centre of the south-east. There was no link except by sea beyond Carthago Nova; the great aridity and mountainous nature of the foothills of the Betic Cordillera made settlement extremely difficult and a routeway unnecessary. Today the same factors hold good; the coast from Cartagena to Málaga is devoid of a continuous railway line. In the west the coast route linked Bracara, the capital of the Gallaecia region, with Olisipio and Ossonoba in the south. Today the main Portuguese railway line runs from Lisbon (formerly Olisipio) to Oporto, a little south of Braganza (formerly Bracara), with less important branches to Faro and to the Spanish border. Gallaecia was served by one main road passing through a gap made by the Sil in the highlands encircling the area, reaching Asturica (now Astorga), then, as now, an important route centre. Until recently this route formed the only way of ingress by rail to the isolated north-west province. From Asturica another Roman road crossed the peninsula from north to south, passing through Salamantica (now Salamanca), Emerita (now Mérida) and Onoba (a little to the north of modern Huelva), terminating at Ossonoba (near the modern Faro, in Portugal). This route today is followed by a railway line although there is no complete through service.

Roads radiating from Hispalis (now Seville) to Italica, Astigi (now Ecija), Corduba (now Córdoba) and Gades (now Cádiz) all have their modern rail counterparts, although the direct route, passing north of the Guadalquivir, is now followed between Seville and Córdoba. The road from Emerita due east to the coast anticipated, at least in part, the modern line from Badajoz to Valdepeñas and thence via Alcázar and Albacete to Alicante. In Roman times the nodal point of the central Mesetas was Toletum (now Toledo), with roads radiating to Emerita, Segontia (now Segovia), Bibilis (now Calatayud) and Caesaraugustus (now Zaragoza). If Madrid be substituted for Toledo then the railways linking Segovia, Calatayud, Zaragoza and the La Mancha region follow similar tracks. In the Ebro basin the cruciform pattern of modern railways with the intersection at Zaragoza and with extensions to Tudela, Soria, Palencia, Calatayud, Lérida and hence to Barcelona, are modern counterparts of the Roman road system, except that today Barcelona is more important than Tarragona, and although it utilizes the same gap in the coastal hills as did the original road, the railway branches off some miles north of Tarragona to continue directly to Barcelona.

The Moorish occupation (A.D. 711–1492), though not always peaceful, re-introduced an intelligent agrarian policy into the peninsula after the economic disruption of the Visigoth rule (A.D. 415–711) which followed the decline of Roman power in Iberia. The first forty years were administratively chaotic, as first one emir and then another rose to power through treachery or battle. With the reign of Abd-ar Rahman (A.D. 755–788) of the Omayyad dynasty, stability was achieved and the link with Damascus severed by the founding of the independent Caliphate of Córdoba. There were long periods of internal peace, broken only at intervals by Norse raids off the coasts of Galicia and Portugal, and by the expedition of Charlemagne in north Spain, where the slaughter of his rearguard by the Basques in the pass of Roncesvalles provided a theme for the epic poem *Le Chanson de Roland*. The Africans and Asians settled on Iberian territory lived peaceably with the native inhabitants, who enjoyed a period of increased prosperity.

The Moors, as they became known after A.D. 1000, brought more material benefits to the peninsula than did any previous or succeeding rulers. The government took one-fifth of the land and allotted it to local cultivators who paid rent on the *métayer* system; the rest was distributed among its own adherents, who had a personal interest in improvements. In this way the great estates were broken up and agriculture improved. In Murcia and Valencia especially, large irrigation schemes were initiated, and even in outlying districts the use of the *noria* (Arabic *na ura*) or water wheel, was soon adopted. Several modern Spanish words derived from Arabic are still used in connexion with irrigation, for example, *acequia*, from *as-sâqia*, the conduit, and *azud*, from *as-sud*, the sluice. New products were introduced, such as rice, almonds, pomegranates and oranges, which in Spanish keep their Moorish name – *naranja* (Arabic *naranj*). Stock-breeding and mining were encouraged, and many new industries started, including wool- and silk-weaving, glass-blowing, paper-making, metal and leather working – the English word 'cordwainer' is derived from Córdoba, where such work was especially important. New systems of weights and measures also added to the Spanish vocabulary – *azumbre* is derived from *ath-thumn*, an eighth, and *arroba* from *ar-rub*, a quarter.

With such a favourable economic position the new state could afford to erect such buildings as the first astronomical observatory in Europe, now called the Giralda (weather vane) of Seville, the Mosque at Córdoba, and the royal apartments of the Alhambra at Granada. For many people of rank there was luxury; *almohada*, the modern Spanish word for a pillow or cushion, dates from this time and comes from the Arabic *al-mukhaddi*, while there was a large import of fine cloth and spices, and, before the Christian reconquest, Córdoba possessed 500 public baths. Education was widespread and not restricted to men alone, and the introduction of paper made the production of books easier and cheaper, although they were still written by hand. Mathematics (the word 'algebra' is derived from the Arabic, *aljebr*, meaning the reunion of broken parts), alchemy, astronomy and medicine were all studied to a high level of achievement, and poetry flourished. In fact it is perhaps true to say that while the rest of Europe experienced an age dark in every respect, the tolerant Moors, under a Spanish sun, kept alight the flame of true culture.

Under the Moors town life flourished, as it had in Roman times, because food supplies were adequate, and the need for market centres in a land of plenty encouraged the growth of urban population. During and after the reconquest, however, municipalities acted as a counterpoise to the powers of the nobility. In return for guarantees of aid, towns were granted royal charters, or *fueros*, which provided economic benefits such as freedom from certain taxes and the right to hold regular fairs and markets. By 1188 the urban influence in government was acknowledged in León, where representatives of the towns appeared for the first time in the Cortes (Grand Council). At Burgos in 1315 the Cortes was attended by 192 deputies (or *procuradores*) from 90 towns, and at Madrid in 1391 by 126 deputies from 50 towns. The economic value of these towns lay in their manufactured goods, for which there was a steady demand abroad, although they often had to be transported by mule over rough tracks through brigand-infested country to the sea. Cordoban leather, Toledo steel, and woollen cloth from Segovia all found their way to the medieval ports of northern Europe. Urban wealth was guided into ecclesiastical coffers and was used to finance the building of churches and cathedrals which still attract tourists; those of Ávila, Burgos, Toledo and Santiago de Compostella are well known.

During the political turbulence of medieval times Iberia was once more divided into the three basic geographical regions of west, central and east. Whether historical accident or the re-assertion of fundamental geographical factors was responsible, is a matter of conjecture. From 920 until 1492 a series of small Christian states shared the government of northern Iberia and led sporadically successful attacks upon the Moors ruling in the south. The main battle zone was in the centre of the peninsula, and the insecurity of land tenure here led to extensive depopulation and a notable decrease in arable farming. It was not so much quality as quantity of land that made Castile a significant new power. The old provinces of León and Navarre, geographically contiguous with this vast central province, were eventually incorporated, León in 1230 and Navarre not until 1521.

The coastal areas, on the other hand, had developed along different lines. The kingdom of Aragón, with its rich legacy of well-tilled farmland along the Mediterranean coast, and the quick commercial aptitude of its seafaring traders, was a smaller state economically better endowed, and was already extending its influence eastwards by annexing the Balearic Islands (1349), Sicily

i

ii

iii

V　i Sheep grazing on coarse grass and scrub at c. 7,000 ft. in the Sierra Nevada.

　ii Typical forested slope, and hay-cart removing grass from upper meadows, near Viella, Pyrenees.

　iii Barren steppe vegetation, with narrow irrigated zone at foot of hills, near Albacete.

VI The Roman aqueduct, Segovia.

(1392) and Sardinia (1409); Catalan is still spoken at Alghero, north Sardinia. Portugal appeared for the first time as a separate entity. It originated as a small tract of land in the north of the peninsula, granted by Alphonso VI (1065–1109) to Count Henry of Lorraine, but the confusion in succeeding reigns allowed this petty holding to be extended and the battle of Aljubarrota (1385) decided the issue. The boundary line was drawn so as to coincide with a 'region of difficulty', the arid marchlands of Estremadura.

The complete unification of these three regions has never been achieved except between 1581 and 1640. Portugal remains a small country on the Atlantic seaboard, looking away from the peninsula to possessions overseas. Aragón, known more generally today as Catalonia, has been a centre of unrest ever since the Castilians, proud, austere and aloof, imposed their language and centralized government on a hard-working, independent people. The marriage of Ferdinand of Aragón and Isabella of Castile in 1469, and the conquest of Navarre in 1521, unified Spain in name only. The local variations in language, temperament, customs and traditional ways of life persist even today, when the relationships between the richer periphery and the government ruling from the interior are exacerbated by the inequality of industrial development.

At the end of the fourteenth century the Roman Catholic church in Spain proclaimed the spiritual necessity of uniform religion. This intolerance, slight at first, steadily increased, and was the cause of occasional anti-Semitic riots, such as those of 1391. The Jews after this date were confined to their own quarters, and forbidden to trade with Christians. The 'Mudejars', or Moors living within Christian communities, retained their freedom a little longer. With the final expulsion of the Moors from Granada in 1492 religious intolerance was officially declared by three edicts, one signed in 1492, which faced Jews with a choice between conversion or banishment, one of a similar nature signed in 1497 which applied to Portuguese Jews, and one signed in 1502, which banished Moors from Castile. The absolute loss of population was considerable enough (the Inquisition gave at least 16,000 souls over to the secular powers for execution during this period, and Torquemada, himself of part Jewish origin, was the prime

D

instigator of the expulsion of both Jews and Moors), but economic loss was of far greater significance. For many centuries the Jews had exerted considerable influence over Iberian trade, financing new farming and overseas ventures, stabilizing currency and forming a solid nucleus of fiscal and banking experts. Many who were not merchants formed, with the urban Moors, an important class of artisans, upon whose skill much of the peninsular prosperity depended. In addition, Moslems frequently performed the somewhat monotonous and menial tasks required by the intensive horticulture that produced the bulk of Iberian foodstuffs. The forcible eviction of these patient workers left a gap in the rural and skilled labour forces not closed until the nineteenth and twentieth centuries, while the decrease in agricultural production led to grave economic disorders.

Until the fifteenth century the latitudinal position of Iberia had proved of importance only inasmuch as it conferred upon the peninsula the benefits of climate and crops normally associated with Mediterranean countries. Iberia was still of purely marginal interest to the rest of Europe. Trading conditions in the eastern basin of the Mediterranean, however, were gradually deteriorating; the Turkish wars, with the fall of Byzantium (1453) and other towns, effectively sealed off oriental sources of supply of such goods as pepper and spice, indispensable for 'flavouring' meat in countries where lack of winter fodder caused an annual autumn slaughter. Europe was faced with the alternative of forgoing luxuries imported from the east, or of finding other supply routes. The problem of discovering a sea-route to the Indies was one to which the Portuguese devoted much of their time and money. Latitude now proved of great significance, and Iberian explorers found that their homeland lay conveniently between two major wind systems; the trade winds, which blew them south past the west coast of Africa and on to the Caribbean region, and the westerly winds which ensured their return on a more northerly course.

Prince Henry the Navigator collected at Sagres the most knowledgeable men of his time – astronomers, traders, sailors and geographers – and his ships carried the mariner's compass and hinged rudders. These improvements were known from the thirteenth century onwards, but their value had not been fully appreciated. Their use enabled large ships to sail far into the ocean with a reasonable degree of safety. Progress was rapid; Madeira was colonized in 1420, Cape Bojador (subject of terrifying legends) was doubled in 1434, the Azores were colonized in 1437 and the Cape Verde Islands in 1462. The first cargo of black slaves reached Lisbon in 1441; three years later a company of slavers was established at Lagos in south Portugal. The economic results of exploration were great; musk, ivory, precious stones, spices, *malagueta* pepper (derived from a grain grown along the West African coast), as well as slaves, were being sold in Lisbon from 1460 onwards at immense profit to the king, who had a virtual monopoly of almost all these goods.

During the latter half of the fifteenth century fresh discoveries revealed the mouth of the Congo (1485); the Cape of Good Hope (originally called the Cape of Storms) was rounded by Bartholomew Diaz in 1487; and this culminated in the 1498 voyage to the west coast of India undertaken by Vasco da Gama, a noble chosen less for his ability as a sailor than for his qualities as a statesman and ambassador. Trading stations set up at Cochin, Calicut, Diu and Cananor proved highly profitable, but were subject to the attacks of Arab raiders sent to oust these Portuguese traders. The east African, Arabian and Persian coasts had to be secured if the full benefits of the Asiatic trading posts were to be gained, and this was achieved in some instances by force, as in the case of Quiloa and Mombasa, and in others, for example the kingdom of Melinde, by more friendly means. In addition the east coast of India, the East Indies, Malacca, as well as many islands between Malacca and China, eventually came under Portuguese domination, as did Brazil, part of which was discovered and annexed by Cabral in 1500. At the beginning of the sixteenth century Portugal, a small European state with a population of approximately $1\frac{1}{2}$ millions, controlled a vast though littoral empire in Africa and south Asia.

In the early stages, on the other hand, Spanish territorial acquisitions appeared less lucrative. Ferdinand and Isabella financed the expedition of Christopher Columbus, a Genoese navigator, who had already offered his services unsuccessfully to

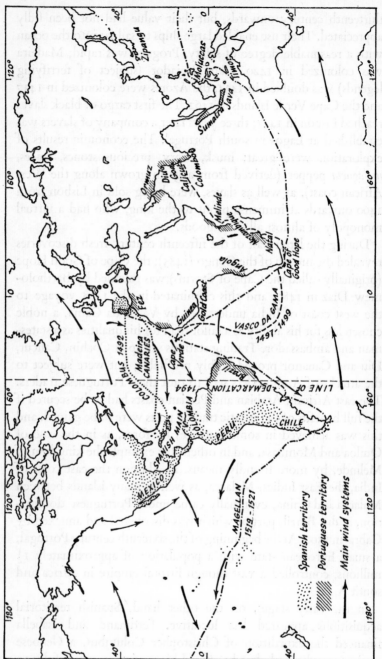

Fig. 20. The World in the Sixteenth Century

Portugal. While the Portuguese aimed at reaching India by way of the Cape of Good Hope, Columbus believed he could achieve this by sailing westwards. Setting out from Palos on August 3rd, 1492, he managed, by great personal qualities of leadership, and some falsification of the log, to stave off mutiny, reached the Bahamas in October, explored parts of Cuba and Haiti, and returned in March 1493, to report progress to the king and queen at Barcelona. There was little to show for his momentous discovery, and Columbus died in disgrace in 1506. His knowledge of navigation and cosmography was inferior to that of the Portuguese (for example, there is nothing in his notes to show that he could calculate latitude from the altitude of the sun, and he made several latitudinal errors) but his discovery eventually produced greater results. Until 1493 Iberia had been regarded as a marginal European country only bordering the vitally important Mediterranean sea. After 1493 Iberia became the geographical centre of the known world, and, lying between the west wind system and the trade winds, was ideally situated for Atlantic exploration.

The exploration of the American continents continued in the sixteenth century; Columbus sailed along the north coast of South America, and in 1513 Nuñez de Balboa crossed the isthmus of Panama and saw the eastern Pacific for the first time, two years after the Portuguese had first sighted the western Pacific near the Moluccas. In 1516 the Plate river was explored, but more important was the expedition of Magellan, a Portuguese serving under the Spaniards. Setting out in 1519 he endeavoured to find the route to the Indies, still considered more valuable than South America. After several attempts, he eventually (1520) negotiated the Strait which now bears his name, and continued across the Pacific, utilizing the trade winds, and reaching the Philippines in 1521, which he annexed to Spain shortly before he was killed by natives. His lieutenant Elcano continued the voyage, and only one of five ships returned via the Cape of Good Hope and only 18 of the original 265 men completed the journey. Although a costly expedition, the new route brought the Spaniards into contact with the Portuguese possessions in the Pacific, and opened up the west coast of South America.

While Magellan was exploring a passage through the gale-swept strait, between Tierra del Fuego and the mainland, at the extreme southern tip of South America, an expedition of conquest was penetrating into Mexico in the extreme south of the North American continent. Cortes landed in Mexico in 1519, with 700 men, a few horses and cannon, and by all means, fair and foul, set out to destroy the kingdom of the Aztecs. This he did so successfully that very little is known of early Mexican history; suffice it to say that the Aztecs were well organized and had a religion which demanded a vast number of human sacrifices. Cortes' victory was the result of superior arms, the belief of the natives in his supernatural powers and the eagerness of many subservient tribes to throw off the Aztec yoke. Spanish rule was one of oppressive exploitation, for, while paying lip-service to the spread of the Roman Catholic dogma, Spaniards were more interested in Mexican silver.

The 'liberation' of Peru from its native oppressors followed. In 1532 Pizarro, of lowly origin and mercenary outlook, attacked the Incas, who had invaded Peru in the thirteenth century. Their king, Atahualpa, was captured, and, despite the payment of a vast ransom, mainly in gold, was murdered in 1533. Their organization was based on the authority of the king, and on his death the defeat of his subjects presented no difficulty. The spoils were fabulous, and led to quarrelling between Pizarro and his subordinates. Almagro, who turned against Pizarro, was defeated and executed at Cuzco. By way of revenge his half-caste son conspired with other malcontents to murder Pizarro at Lima in 1541, but was beheaded at Cuzco in 1542. The conquest of Chile was carried out by another confederate of Pizarro, Pedro de Valdivia, who founded Santiago in 1541.

For many years the Plate river area was not effectively colonized, since warlike Indian tribes proved too strong for such tiny Spanish forces as were landed there. Cattle, horses and sheep imported from Spain often escaped after Indian raids and soon multiplied, spreading far and wide over the extensive plains of the pampas. Only in 1580 was a permanent colony established on an agricultural basis around Buenos Aires, under the energetic leadership of the Basque, Garay. The northern part of South America, then known as New Granada and Venezuela, was colonized between

1530 and 1567, and the towns of Guayaquil, Quito, Bogotá and Caracas established.

The Papal Bull of 1493 was followed in 1494 by the Treaty of Tordesillas which allocated to Portugal all land to the east of the meridian of approximately 48° West. The Portuguese found the colonization of Brazil difficult. Coastal swamps and vast tracts of steaming equatorial jungles – the selvas of the Amazon – made penetration into the interior hazardous. Nevertheless, after the initial discovery in 1501 by Amerigo Vespucci, Rio de Janeiro was founded in 1596, partly to ward off the French, and then its vast hinterland was slowly colonized.

The years following these discoveries mark the apogee of Iberian greatness. In Portugal the exuberant style of Manueline architecture reveals the influence of marine adventure; ropes and globes, tropical plants and beasts adorn in profusion the pillars and arches of fifteenth-century buildings. In Spain architecture was influenced more by Italian workers; the modern tourist can still compare the Casa de los Picos at Segovia with the Piazza de Diamanti of Ferrara. Education, literature and art flourished; there were twenty-nine active universities, the paintings of El Greco, Jusepe de Ribera and Velasquez are now world famous, while Lope de Vega and Cervantes gave to posterity a lasting impression of the generous-minded though coarse-mannered populace of the Golden Age.

Unknown to the rulers of the time, however, two forces were slowly but irrevocably undermining their superior world position. Depopulation continued to weaken insidiously the already crumbling agrarian economy. Religious persecution and eviction played a part, but in addition riches overseas lured many of the abler members of the community to Asia or to the Americas. Unmarried women often entered convents, and the birthrate decreased noticeably. Plague and famine in Portugal (1503 and 1505) took a certain toll as did the constant drain on manpower for wars designed to preserve or extend the imperial limits. 30,000 Portuguese died at the battle of Alcazar Quibir in 1597, and although the Spanish armies in the sixteenth century were the best in the world they suffered severe losses in military and naval engagements against the Turks (Lepanto, 1571), against the Protestants of the Low Countries, and against the English (the defeat of the Spanish Armada, 1588). Furthermore, a large percentage (possibly 30 per cent) of the Iberian population was parasitic, consisting of monks, nuns, friars, courtiers and soldiers who lived off land tilled by a small number of peasants so poverty-stricken that even the slum tenements of the towns provided an alluring alternative to their miserable hovels and caves. As possessions increased abroad, so population decreased at home. By 1550 less than one million people were left in Portugal, while in Spain 6 million Spaniards strove in the seventeenth century to maintain a country which supported 8 million in the sixteenth century. Town life was affected severely; Madrid, which at the beginning of the sixteenth century had approximately 400,000 inhabitants, had only 150,000 one hundred years later; Seville's population was reduced by almost 75 per cent, Toledo and Segovia were almost deserted, and many small hamlets with their surrounding farmland were completely abandoned. The number of agricultural workers in Salamanca province during the reign of Philip III fell from 8,438 to approximately 4,220.

Economic disorders within the peninsula were painfully obvious, although there seemed to be no apparent remedy. The fishing industry was ruined, due to the commandeering of ships for the wars, and the decay of agriculture led to the import of basic foods such as wheat and barley. The indignity of labour (*deshonor de trabajo*) prevented any man with a title (and there were many Spaniards whose carefully carved escutcheons formed the finest part of their estate) from pursuing such mundane occupations as farming, forestry or stock-rearing. Wealth within the country was excessively taxed, monopolies flourished and corruption was rife, as is shown by the fact that the clergy of Castile paid for the upkeep of fifty galleys, whereas in fact only eight existed. Silver, gold and precious stones from overseas did little to improve the basic finances of Spain or Portugal, and inflation, though rampant, went unrecognized. Treaties were signed between Portugal and Britain in 1642, 1654 and 1703 (Methuen Treaty) which allowed trading, religious and certain legal privileges to British nationals in Portugal in exchange for reduction of customs dues on Portuguese wines. Even these measures are regarded by some to have proved disadvantageous to Portugal, since many farmers in north Portugal gave up their grain land to viticulture, thus necessitating imports of corn, while an adverse balance of trade between the two countries was restored by payments of gold from Brazilian mines. This in turn affected the rates of exchange, which were so much higher in London than in Lisbon that the former city became more important as a banking and trading centre.

During modern times economic factors have played an important part in the development of both countries. Portugal still retains many of her original possessions and has held a stable if insignificant position in world affairs. Spain has gradually lost almost all her possessions which once included half the known world, and has in consequence been forced to turn her attention to internal affairs. Here the separatist element in Catalonia, the industrialization of the north, and the agrarian problems of Castile and Andalusia still present certain problems.

Catalonia has been described as *infelix*, unfaithful to the common Spanish unit. From medieval times this province has considered itself an entity separate from the rest of Spain. The interests of the Catalans have always been commercial and originally lay eastwards in the trade of the Mediterranean. Under Aragonese kings Barcelona maintained consulates at such distant trading posts as Famagusta, Ragusa, Alexandria, Tripoli and Constantinople; Catalans compiled a series of maritime laws adopted widely along the main sea routes, and helped to maintain a brisk interchange of goods across the northern parts of the Mediterranean. The union of Aragón and Castile in 1469 diverted some of the coastal merchants' wealth into the treasury of a centralized government, thus helping to finance Atlantic expeditions which were to direct European attention away from the Levant coast and to cause the partial stagnation of Mediterranean trade. It is entirely in keeping with the paradoxical nature of the Spaniards that the colossal statue of Christopher Columbus should look out serenely over the harbour of Barcelona, the regional capital which benefited least from his discovery.

The struggles of Spain to maintain her possessions have offered Catalonia several chances of seceding from Castilian rule. In

1640 both the Catalans and the Portuguese were in revolt; Portugal gained her freedom but the Catalans were ruthlessly suppressed after appealing for French aid. Again in 1705 Catalonia proclaimed as king the Archduke Charles of Austria, and only in 1714, after fierce resistance and hideous carnage, was the province subdued. Modern Catalanism, however, dates from the end of the nineteenth century, with the founding of several political parties, such as the Centre Catala and the Unio Catalanista. After the first world war came a demand for regional autonomy, a demand repeated during ensuing decades. Barcelona was the last stronghold of the Republican government during the Spanish Civil War, and subsequent events, like the shooting of the Catalan president, Lluis Campanys, showed that, for a time at least, there were to be no concessions to regionalism.

The desire for autonomy exists, however; strikes, illegally printed circulars and semi-public anti-Franco meetings attract police attention in Catalonia. The fact that the province is one of the major industrial areas of Spain adds to the general feeling of discontent, since many Catalans consider that they are giving much to a government from which they can expect no reciprocal favours. Theoretically it is possible for a separate state of Catalonia to exist. Economically it could be self-sufficient by exporting the early vegetables, citrus fruits, wine, textiles, light metal goods and luxury goods produced within the province in exchange for foodstuffs and raw materials. Barcelona is already established as the major port and capital of such a hypothetical unit, and suitable markets might be found in France, Italy and other north European nations, though competition would be keen. Catalonia has an area of 31,968 sq. km, and is thus comparable in size with Belgium, 30,507 sq. km, and Switzerland, 41,288 sq. km. Well endowed by nature with natural resources such as potash salts, barytes, Pyrenean streams for hydro-electricity, and a climate ranging, according to altitude, from warm to cool temperate, Catalonia has been badly served by the course of historical events which, while allowing such anachronisms as Leichtenstein and Luxembourg to remain, has included this marginal and separatist element in Spain.

In north Spain there is another zone of discontent in Asturias and the Basque provinces, where autonomy is also desired.

Renowned for centuries as the spearhead of attack against the Moors, these north-west provinces retain much of their old spirit of independence, and the discovery and exploitation of Asturian coal led to the development of industry which only emphasized the already considerable differences between this coastal region and the centre. As with Catalonia, the economic and political secession of these provinces is theoretically possible. The total extent of the Asturian–Basque–Navarre provinces is 28,584 sq. km, and communications with France are easier and quicker than with Spain; there is, moreover, an historical and linguistic link with the occupants of Gascony north of the boundary. As a geographical unit the Biscayan coast is compact and complete, containing valuable coal and iron which could produce goods for export in order to pay for foodstuffs needed to augment the maize, green crops and cattle locally produced. Fishing and a small carrying trade would also help to support a state which has more geographical, though perhaps fewer historical reasons for separate development than Albania (28,748 sq. km) or the Netherlands (32,451 sq. km).

Although the north-east and north-west regions could function as units separate from Spain, their loss would deal a crippling blow to the economy of the parent country, and it seems extremely unlikely that even regional autonomy will be granted. Logically these provinces belong to the definite compact block of the Iberian peninsula, and are united in religion and language, since, though Basque and Catalan are still spoken, Castilian is the common language. The desire for independence is not restricted to Catalonia or Asturias; it so happens that in these two areas labour is well organized, the inhabitants perhaps more informed about world affairs and the economic factors involved greater than in south Spain, so that expressions of opinion are often more emphatic here than elsewhere. The blunt fact is that at heart the Iberian, Andalusian or Basque, is an anarchist, unwilling to merge his individuality into a regional or national unit. At the moment it seems that some sort of benevolent despotism is the type of government best suited to people who admire a 'strong man' even though they may dislike his methods. The political stability of the peninsula has been assured for the last twenty years by Dr Salazar,

Portuguese professor of economics, who came to power in 1928, and by Generalissimo Franco, who emerged victorious in April 1939, after almost three years of devastating Civil War.

The steady improvement both in standards of living and in health and medical services within the last two decades has resulted in a notable increase in population. Statistics for Spain are as follows:

Year	Population	Death rate per 1,000
1900	18,594,405	28·91
1910	19,927,150	22·95
1920	21,303,162	23·24
1930	23,563,867	17·33
1940	25,877,971	16·41
1950	27,976,755	10·80
1960 (estimated)	30,128,656	9·87 (1957)

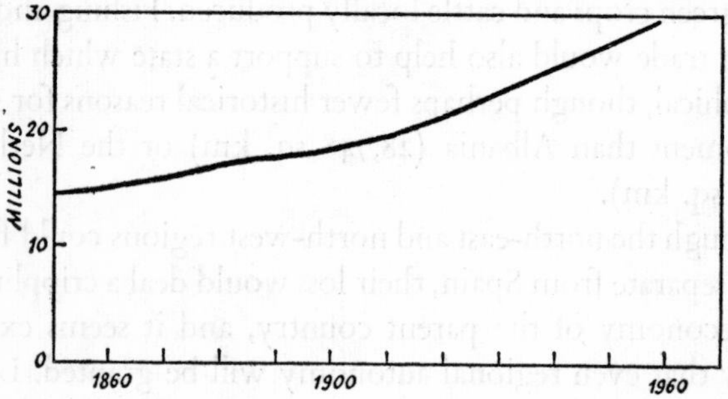

Fig. 21. The Growth of Spain's Population

According to the census of 1950 10,340,615 people lived in urban areas, 6,594,691 in intermediate zones, and 11,641,449 in rural areas. The rapid growth of urban areas can best be illustrated by comparing Barcelona and Madrid. In 1900 Madrid's population was 539,835, and Barcelona's 533,000; in 1930 Barcelona achieved the total of a million by the inclusion of several suburbs formerly counted separately. Madrid regained its numerical supremacy in 1940, and has maintained and increased the differential, containing 1,618,435 inhabitants in 1950 (1960 estimate 1,966,070), compared with Barcelona's 1,280,197 (1960 estimate 1,503,062).

The modern tendency of the population to aggregate in the towns has been responsible for a general exodus from the country-side, but this has been counterbalanced by the steady overall increase in population, so that only the provinces mentioned below show a numerical decline over pre-war years:

Province	1910	1950	Main direction of movement
Almería	380,388	366,550	Málaga and Madrid
Ávila	308,796	253,000	Madrid
Gerona	339,679	326,950	Barcelona
Guadalajara	209,352	206,200	Madrid
Teruel	255,491	239,800	Madrid, Barcelona

Otherwise there has been a slight increase of rural population within Spain which helps to maintain agricultural stability, whereas rapid urban growth leads to seasonal periods of unemployment, for example, during droughts which affect hydro-electric generation, or between harvests of crops destined for processing, for example sugar beet. Government schemes such as those of the Plan Badajoz have been adopted to avoid a continued steady drift from the countryside.

Although the rural population tends to seek work in the towns, in the wetter north-west regions, where systems of land tenure lead to fragmentation of property, many men turn towards the Americas rather than to the mother country for aid, and there is some emigration. Two-thirds of all Spanish emigrants leave from Atlantic ports, and the vast majority go from Galicia, Barcelona and Madrid to Venezuela, Argentina, Brazil and Uruguay. Immigration takes place on a smaller scale, and affects primarily Spaniards or nationals coming from the same South American countries. There is governmental control on emigration, and the numbers involved are small, as the following figures show[1]:

Quinquennial totals for	1941-5	1946-50	1951-5	1958 only
Emigration	3,663	29,530	60,388	54,496
Immigration	1,564	6,810	17,638	29,460

Density of population within Spain varies greatly from that of such barren provinces as Soria (15·8 per sq. km in 1950) to that of

---

[1] Compare these figures with those for Portugal, 1958, which, in the light of subsequent events, perhaps indicate slight economic or political discontent:

Emigrants to Brazil:	21,928
„ „ Canada:	1,938
„ „ Argentina:	764

rich agricultural provinces, for example Valencia (176 per sq. km in 1950), or to that of industrial provinces as typified by Guipúzcoa (197 per sq. km in 1950). All too frequently, however, such density figures are calculated simply by dividing the total population of the province by its area. In the case of provinces with large urban agglomerations this gives a misleading picture of rural density. Madrid province in 1950 had an average density of 240 per sq. km; by deducting the population of Madrid from the provincial total and using the result as a basis for calculations, the density is reduced to 55 per sq. km, a result which tallies with actual conditions, since Madrid lies in one of the more sparsely populated barren provinces of Spain. A map based on similar calculations is appended to show the distribution of population within the peninsula.

The growth of population in Portugal has been more gradual than in Spain, as the following figures reveal:

1920	6,032,991 (including Azores and Madeira)
1930	6,825,883 " " " "
1940	7,722,152 " " " "
1950	8,441,312 " " " "
1958 (estimated)	8,980,000 " " " "

The gradual drift of rural inhabitants to the towns or overseas has shown a trend similar to that of Spain, though on a smaller scale. There has been a slow but steady growth of population in the major urban centres, of which Lisbon and Oporto are cited as examples:

	1930	1940	1950	1958 (estimate)
Lisbon	594,390	709,179	790,434	783,226
Oporto	232,280	262,309	284,842	281,466

Of the two countries Portugal has the densest rural population, ranging from 150 to 200 per sq. km in 1950. Here there is a direct relationship between population and the wet, mild climate which permits the growing of a large variety of crops including grapes for the port wine industry. The lower densities of population correspond, as they do in Spain, with areas of barren waste or poor agricultural land. Portugal, with an average density of 247 people per sq. mile, is comparable with other temperate and agricultural countries such as Denmark (258 per sq. mile) or

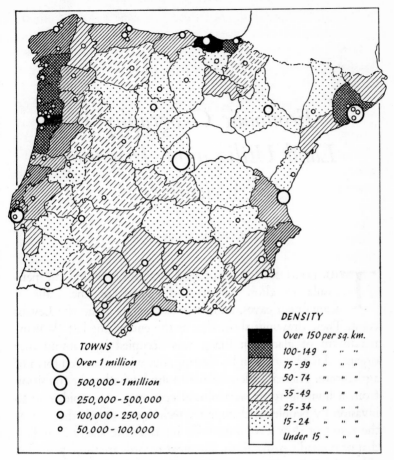

Fig. 22. Towns and Rural Density of Population

central European states such as Hungary (265 per sq. mile), or
Czechoslovakia (253 per sq. mile). Spain, on the other hand, with
an average density of 143 per sq. mile, more nearly resembles
Yugoslavia (159 per sq. mile), Greece (149 per sq. mile) and
Bulgaria (170 per sq. mile), all predominantly agricultural
countries suffering from such geographical disadvantages as
mountains, infertile soils, low temperatures and aridity.

CHAPTER VI

Economic Geography I: Land Utilization, Irrigation, Agriculture

I. LAND UTILIZATION

THE FIRST RECORDS of land utilization within the peninsula are those carved and painted on the walls of Cantabrian caves, and on rock shelters along the Levant coast. These drawings show that at the end of the last (Würm) maximum of glaciation Iberia was occupied by communities organized for hunting and collecting, but with no settled form of agriculture. There is little evidence to show whether the transition from a hunting to an agricultural economy was rapid, due to invasion by peoples with superior techniques, or whether it was the result of slow evolution with intermediate stages including that of nomadic pastoralism. The next records are those provided chiefly by Roman writers.

From Roman times until the present day there have been three periods of maximum land utilization within Iberia, alternating with two periods of economic uncertainty or chaos. Although irrigation and intensive farming or horticulture were practised during the Bronze Age (Tartessus could never have existed without a sound basis of local agriculture), the Romans brought improvements in method, new crops and, because of the demands of Rome, new incentives to the farmers of the peninsula. During this occupation there were three main types of land utilization; in the Guadalquivir valley and on the fertile coastal plains vast slave-worked estates, or *latifundia*, produced a great variety of crops including vines, cereals, olives and vegetables. (The word 'huerta' is derived from Latin *hortus*, a garden.) Systematic fertil-ization of the soil (using green crops, manure and a mixture of earths, for example clay combined with chalky soil) and irriga-tion were both practised extensively, pigs were reared in local forests and Cordoban wool, derived from sheep reared on the foothills of the Sierra Nevada, was highly prized in Rome. Records of very low prices for foodstuffs in Lusitania during the second century B.C. reflect the intensive and remunerative use of the land by the Romans. The rest of the peninsula was far less productive, however. In the dry Mesetas wild horses roamed under the lax supervision of semi-nomadic tribes who, as a subsidiary occupation, grew a few basic crops or tended goats or cattle. These herds provided horses for the superior Iberian cavalry and, later, for the Roman circus. Finally, in the cooler and wetter mountain zones, tribesmen of Celtic or Iberian origin practised subsistence agriculture among the forests and moorlands.

This stable agrarian pattern was disrupted by the invasions of barbarian hordes during the fifth century A.D. and was re-estab-lished only under Moslem rule, which reached its apogee during the tenth century. Of all the economic benefits bestowed on the peninsula by the conquering Moors, that of efficient irrigation ranks among the most important. Every flat piece of ground near a water course was eventually brought under intensive cultiva-tion, and some of the irrigation channels still exist. New crops, for example rice, pomegranates and oranges, were introduced and, since the Caliphs ranked agriculture as one of the most important occupations of the peninsula, estate owners regarded agrarian improvement as a sound financial investment not liable to ex-cessive taxation. The pattern of land utilization practised by the Moors had much in common with that of the Romans; the flat huertas formed rich oases separated by drier hills in the forests of which sheep, goats and some cattle were allowed to graze. (Pig production was unimportant, owing to the religious principles of the Moslems.) In the central Mesetas the wild horses had by now been replaced by flocks of sheep and goats. These roamed the grassy steppes, leaving the forested zones uncultivated. In the wetter north and west, regions less affected by the Moorish occupation, the highlanders continued to practise subsistence agriculture.

The protracted fighting of the reconquest gradually brought to a halt many of the agricultural enterprises so carefully nurtured by the Moors. The new Christian conquerors were soldiers, not farmers, and considered manual labour undignified, a sentiment still to be found in Spain. Only in those regions of adequate rainfall (north and west) or where local irrigation schemes survived (some areas of the east and south) was agriculture practised on an economic basis. Many areas were simply abandoned, to suffer the consequences of soil erosion, or allowed to revert to a degenerate type of scrub. Internal dissension and lack of capital hampered agrarian reform. Only within the last hundred years has any serious attempt been made to improve the agricultural situation, and the results of this effort are just beginning to be realized. What the Romans achieved with slaves has today to be achieved with machines, but capital for mechanization is difficult to obtain. Modern land utilization, though not yet as efficient as it could be, is, however, slowly being extended and improved. The present situation is summarized on the appended map and diagrams, and it is interesting to note that the tripartite division (corresponding with climatic regions) into south and east, central, and north-west zones, is the same as that of Moorish and Roman times.

Agriculture in both Spain and Portugal suffers from three serious disadvantages of a technical, socio-judicial and climatic nature. Techniques of farming in both countries are still primitive. This does not always mean that they are uneconomic; on the tiny terraced plots in the Sierra Nevada, for example, crops can only be grown by hand cultivation, but such methods become uneconomic when applied to the wide fields of *latifundia*, where extensive cultivation is normal. Many man-hours are wasted by using flails or oxen instead of threshing machines, or by ploughing with ox or ass instead of with tractors. Mechanization of agriculture in Spain is continuing steadily: there is both import and home production of tractors (10,000 tractors were in use in 1958), threshers and other similar machines, and recent improvements have been made in other branches of farming, for example vines in La Mancha are now sprayed with insecticide from the air. In

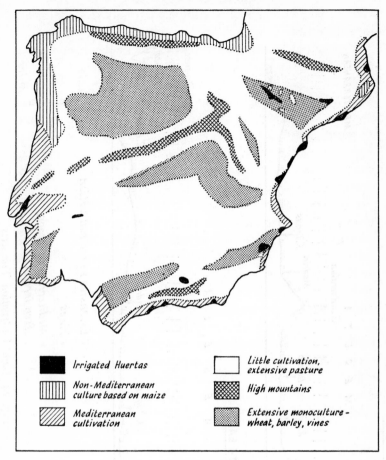

Fig. 23. Land Utilization

Portugal the change has been more gradual, but recent development plans will do much to further the use of modern methods.

Technical improvements create new problems of a social and, occasionally, of a judicial nature. There can be no general optimum farm size in a country with such varied geographical conditions, and when mechanization is introduced the need to increase the farm size becomes more urgent if full employment is to continue. For instance, where 75 acres are an economic family unit for a farmer using oxen or mules, 1,250 acres become necessary for the economic use of tractor and combine-harvester. Furthermore, the

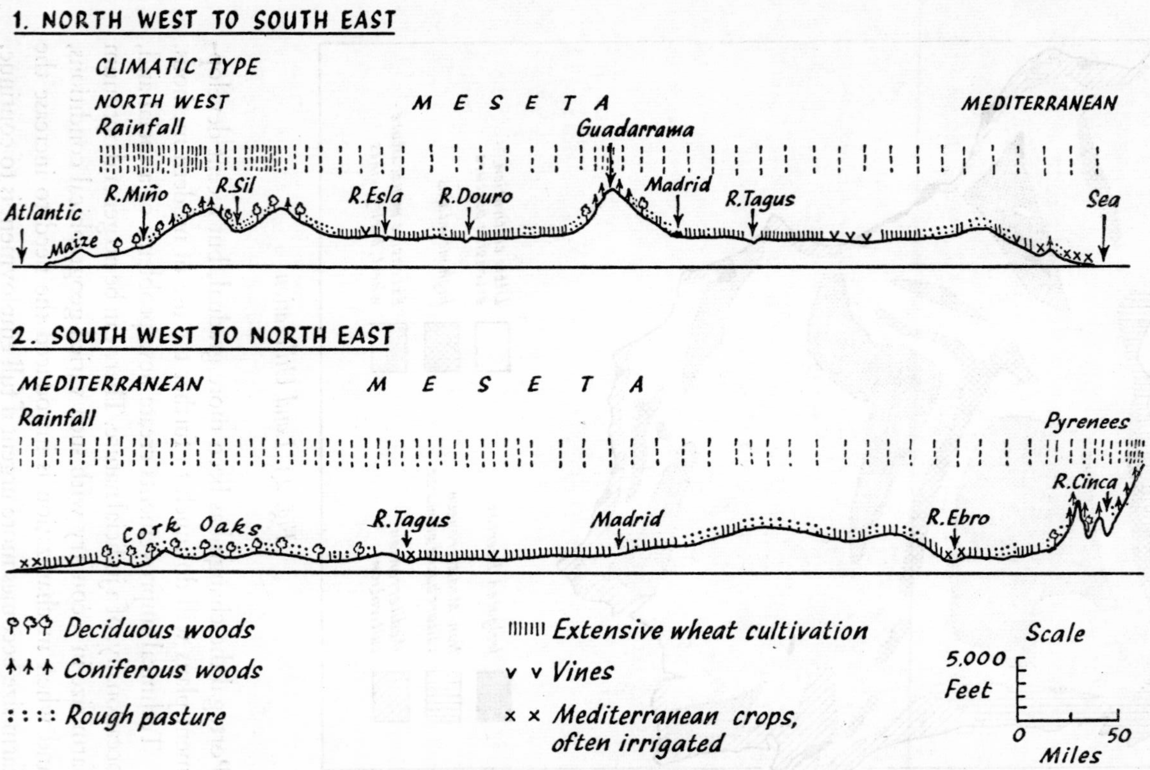

Fig. 24. Land Utilization Transects

issue is complicated by the very great diversity in size of holdings within the peninsula. In the fertile Valencian huertas, where the hoe and spade are as important as the plough, 5 to 10 acres is the normal family unit. In the north and west, where the ancient Celtic law of equal distribution of land to inheriting sons still applies, farms become minute ($\frac{3}{4}$ to 2 acres) as they are progressively split up, so much so that many men emigrate in order to provide land for the rest of the family. A census of 44 per cent of Spain, taken in 1930, showed that 77·6 per cent of the total number of farms were *minifundias* containing less than $2\frac{1}{2}$ acres. At the other end of the scale the greatest acreage was occupied by *latifundias*, large estates of over 12,500 acres, which occur especially in the centre and south of the peninsula.

There has been some controversy within recent years over the part played by *latifundias* in the Iberian economic system. Bearing in mind their size and the fact that the actual owner is often an absentee landlord letting some land to tenants and employing seasonal labour when required, the more socialist-minded Spaniards would like to see a reduction in the number and size of *latifundias*. On the other hand, in regions of sparse and irregular rainfall a large farming unit provides a greater measure of security in times of economic distress, whether occasioned by climatic vagaries or by price fluctuations. Jose Antonio Primo de Rivera voiced this opinion aptly when he declared '. . . agrarian reform is not a question of great estates or smallholdings, but of farming units'.

A far more pressing problem is that of redistribution of land. Much revenue is lost each year by the time wasted in farming widely scattered land, by the non-cultivation of land now used for boundaries and landmarks, and by the non-conversion of *secano* to irrigated land, because of the initial cost of such undertakings. An act passed in the Spanish Cortes in December 1952 aims to concentrate individual plots, improve means of transport and provide irrigation wherever possible. An act passed in July 1954 limits the subdivision of small farms, thus helping to stabilize the size of such holdings.

Further agrarian reforms have been carried out in Spain by the Instituto Nacional de Colonizacion, which was created in October

1939 and reorganized in November 1947. This Institute was empowered to buy land offered voluntarily, and to expropriate land (usually when the estate was suitable for irrigation) where definite social problems existed, for example where seasonal unemployment was excessive due to mismanagement of land. By 1955 the Institute had acquired 488,841 acres of *secano* and 953,552 acres of irrigated land, and had converted 76,242 acres from *secano* to irrigation and improved 29,776 acres of irrigated land. The increased productivity of these lands has permitted the settling of 27,758 additional workers in 26 new townships. These peasants are carefully chosen and loaned seeds, fertilizers and fodder, paying for it in instalments covering lengthy periods of from 25 to 40 years. Another type of land settlement is carried out by the Syndical Land Settlement Group which is composed of peasants who elect members to the governing board. The workers produce crops chosen annually by a central committee, but the syndicate pays the common expenses of cultivation (irrigation, fertilizers and machinery). Profits are shared on a percentage basis between peasant and syndicate. In addition the syndicate grants the peasant use for life of a family plot (usually irrigated) of approximately $\frac{1}{4}$ acre, which lessens the effect of seasonal employment, raises the standard of living and increases agricultural output. Some of these plots provide annual monetary returns of as much as 5,000 pesetas. Further incentives to good farming, especially on large private estates, were laid down by law in July 1952, when special benefits were promised to farms graded as 'qualified' or 'exemplary' by the Ministry of Agriculture.

State-sponsored agrarian improvements include the Plans for Badajoz and Jaén, both provinces of climatic difficulty where emigration was once rife. The Plan Badajoz involved government expenditure of 5,374 million pesetas, invested over a period of 14 years in the following:

2,413 million pesetas:	hydraulic works	
1,800 „ „	agricultural changes and land settlement	
1,008 „ „	communications	
153 „ „	re-afforestation	

Initiated in 1952, the Plan is already well under way and should be completed by 1966. Re-afforestation of treeless zones has been undertaken by the Forestry Service, established in 1939, and the mass-production of pre-fabricated concrete structures for irrigation has helped to reduce the costs of major irrigation schemes. The ricefields and marshlands of Spain have been drained and malaria is now rare. In 1942 there were 500,000 recorded cases, but by 1945 this number had dropped to 100,000 and by 1957 the disease was practically eradicated.

In Portugal agricultural aid is generally government-sponsored and controlled. During the last few years two Development Plans have been initiated, the first in 1958, and the second and more ambitious scheme in 1959. The latter plan devotes £1,825,000 to agriculture (including forestry) and, since forestry products occupy a significant place in Portuguese exports, high priority is given to re-afforestation of both State and private lands. In some zones crops such as wheat and rye will be replaced by eucalyptus, pine, cork and holm oak, which give higher returns per acre and prevent or reduce soil erosion. Irrigation schemes, particularly in the Alentejo province, are already under way, as is the reorganization of property. In the north small scattered holdings are being regrouped into more economic farming units, while in the south large estates are gradually being bought up and resold in smaller units to several smallholders, who pay for their land in annual instalments at a low government rate of interest of 2 per cent. In order to maintain stable prices the government is not only improving means of transport, but is also setting up storage plants to avoid seasonal fluctuations in such commodities as wheat, rice, potatoes, dried figs, wine and olive oil. With measures such as these both Spain and Portugal are trying to avert too great a drift from the country to the towns.

Climate is the greatest obstacle to agricultural improvement, and rainfall the greatest single controlling factor. It is an unfortunate fact that, in Iberia as elsewhere, paucity and unreliability of rainfall are synonymous, and greatly increase farming risks in the isohyetal 'fringe' areas. It is precisely these drier areas which are poverty-stricken, sparsely populated and therefore unable themselves to finance large-scale irrigation schemes. Some form of government aid is essential, and within the last decade both Spain and Portugal have given increasing priority to such schemes, aiming not only

at increased production, but also at repopulating some of the
deserted regions of the peninsula, generally those receiving under
24 inches of rain per year. A barrage system, when complete,
regulates the flow of the rivers, thus controlling flooding and
providing water not only for irrigation but also for hydro-electric
power. This power in turn is utilized for domestic and industrial
purposes, the new crops grown by irrigation supplying raw
material for industries. The correlation between irrigation and
population distribution is obvious when the relevant maps are
compared.

2. IRRIGATION

The two principal methods of agriculture practised in the peninsula
include that of the *secano*, on drier land, and that of the *regadio* in
irrigated areas. Crops grown by the *secano* method receive no
water other than that from rainfall; pluviose regions such as north
and west Iberia are agriculturally rich, but most parts of the peninsula have such scant rainfall that both the variety of crops
grown, and the yield, are necessarily meagre. The *regadio* areas
provide a complete contrast; although small, they produce crops
in such vast quantity and so great variety that they account for
more than half the total value of Spanish exports. The difference
in extent of *secano* and *regadio* areas is shown by the following
figures:

> 1,500,000 hectares of *secano* in humid Spain
> 18,000,000 hectares of *secano* in arid Spain
> 1,679,000 hectares of *regadio* in arid Spain

The main irrigated zones of the peninsula consist of flat, fairly
low-lying regions within easy reach of aqueducts; the water
supply comes from barrages erected across major rivers, or from
subterranean sources. Since the volume of water in the rivers depends on rainfall which is often irregular, the building of barrages
serves not only to provide a head of water for the generation of
hydro-electricity, but also to regulate the natural flow and prevent floods. Large irrigation schemes are still under construction,
and new schemes have been projected, though capital to finance
them is difficult to raise. Despite all these projects, however, the

fact still remains that of the cultivable land of the peninsula a little under 75 per cent can never be irrigated; either the land is too sloping, or too high, or reserves of water or capital are too small.

The methods of irrigation vary from region to region, but fall into two main groups; primitive methods of raising well-water,

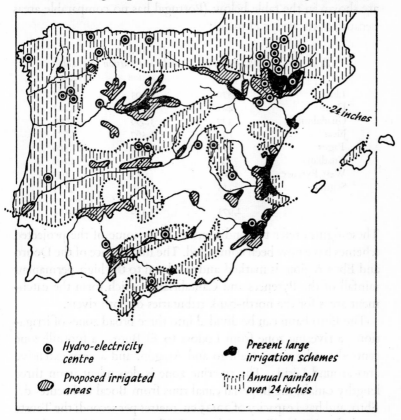

Fig. 25. Use of Water in Spain and Portugal

and modern methods of distributing water from reservoirs. Primitive methods are more conspicuous and picturesque; the *shaduf* is still used in Portugal and parts of central and southern Spain, but is of limited application, since it cannot tap water below about 15 feet. Donkeys or petrol engines are frequently used to turn a variety of water wheels; this method taps the deeper sources of water and is encountered throughout the peninsula, but is only practised on an extensive scale along the Levant coast. In mountainous areas such as the Sierra Nevada and in the drier parts of Galicia spring water is diverted into small runnels between the rows of crops.

The main Spanish areas of irrigation from barrages and canals are shown in the table below (Portugal has no comparable areas because of its wetter climate):

Zone	Present extent sq. km	Projected or under construction sq. km	Total sq. km
Ebro	1,870	6,003	7,873
Douro	403	9,818	10,221
Guadalquivir	377	3,299	3,676
Júcar	105	1,567	1,672
Tagus	45	1,481	1,526
Guadiana	22	2,180	2,202
West Pyrenees	16	643	659
Segura	15	1,540	1,555
	2,973	27,339	30,484

These figures refer to conditions in 1950; some of the projected schemes have now been completed. The importance of the Douro and Ebro regions is marked and is related to the high permanent rainfall of the Pyrenees and Cantabrians, which form the catchment areas for the north-bank tributaries of both rivers.

The Ebro basin can be divided into three broad zones of irrigation – a riverine zone from Lodosa to El Burgo, a foothill zone centred on the rivers Gallego and Aragón, and a very extensive area around Lérida. The riverine zone is dependent upon three lengthy canals; the Imperial canal runs from Bocal to Fuentes del Ebro, and has a capacity of 20·25 cu. metres per second; the Tauste canal, from Cabanillas to Cabañas de Ebro, has a capacity of 6 cu. metres per second; the Lodosa canal runs from Lodosa to Tudela, and links up thereafter with the Imperial canal. All these canals depend for regularity of supply on the great barrage, opened in 1949, at Reinosa; this has a capacity of 540 million cu. metres and provides irrigation water for the upper and central Ebro basin.

In the Huesca district the greatest barrage, not yet completed, will be that of Sotonera, with a maximum capacity of 140 million cu. metres. This barrage will provide a new canal, that of

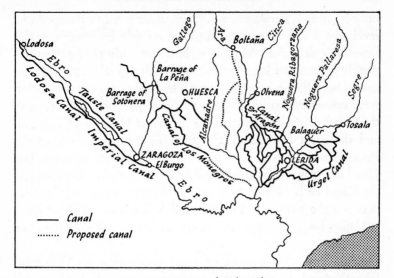

Fig. 26. Irrigation by the Ebro

Los Monegros, with water for irrigating nearly 70,000 acres. There are, in addition, other smaller canals to irrigate inter-fluvial strips. The Bárdenas canal, recently completed and 87 miles in length, runs almost parallel to the river Aragón from a point just north of Sos to the Ebro above Tudela, and when fully exploited will irrigate about 250,000 acres. The Yesa barrage, on the river Aragón, provides most of the water for this scheme.

In the Lérida region vast tracts of steppe-land, originally the Llanos de Urgel, are already irrigated. The great Urgel canal, 90 miles long, stretches from Tosal, on the Segre, through Agramunt, and Borjas Blancas to Serós, on the lower Segre, and a network of canals links this main canal to the river. To the east of Lérida the area between the rivers Cinca and Noguera Ribagorzana is extensively irrigated; the two most important canals are the Aragón canal, linking the Barasona barrage (70 million cu. metres in capacity) on the river Esera to Lérida, and the Zaidin canal, which links the Aragón canal to the river Cinca. The new Mediano barrage now under construction and the new Cinca canal, will add another 123,500 acres to those already irrigated.

In León and Old Castile irrigation schemes have been aided by surface topography. The typical meseta landscape is flat, broken only by steep scarp slopes, and when water is led or pumped to a level area a vast expanse of land can quickly be brought under intensive cultivation. At present, however, only the land immediately adjacent to large rivers is irrigated; capital for other more ambitious schemes is not yet available. Some canals in this region were constructed originally for transport purposes, for example, the Canal del Duero which links the rivers Douro and Esgueva, and the great Castilla canal, 129 miles long, which joins the Pisuerga and Carrión rivers and irrigates about 148,000 acres. The Canal de Campos links the Castilla canal to the river Sequillo, and the Canal de la Granja connects the rivers Pisuerga and Carrión, between the towns of Villalaco and Villamuriel. A short canal (12 miles long) irrigates land along the lower course of the river Arlanzón.

Apart from the network of canals converging on Valladolid from the north, there are extensive tracts of land irrigated by water from the river Esla and its tributaries. The Canal de Cerrajera, which utilizes the river Orbiga, irrigates about 30,500 acres, and the Canal de Esla brings water to about 24,700 acres of the riverine tract between Valencia de Don Juán and Benavente. The most ambitious project of this area is the construction of Los Barrios de Luna, a barrage which, with a capacity of 300 million cu. metres, will eventually irrigate about 103,500 acres. The new Santa de Teresa barrage on the river Tormes will, when completed, irrigate nearly 78,000 acres of land in the Salamanca region. The smaller Villameca barrage in the Astorga district waters about 12,000 acres. The eventual completion of new barrages and the resultant control of water will minimize the flooding to which this area is at present subject.

Irrigation in the Guadalquivir basin occurs on a smaller scale; a few of the stone barrages and canals constructed by the Moslems in medieval times are still in use. The vegas of Baza, Guadix, Motril, Granada and Málaga all utilize water systems originally devised by the Moors. The major barrages include the following, with capacity given in millions of cubic metres:

Tranco de Beas (500) on the upper Guadalquivir
Jándula (350) and Encinarejo (15) on the river Jándula

Rumblar (126), Guadalmellato (109) and Breña (115) on the
  Guadiato
Pintado (175) on the river Viar
Guadalcacín (77) and Chorro (86) on the river Turón

Canals are shorter and smaller in carrying capacity than those
further north; the two largest are connected with the river
Guadiaro, near Cádiz, and together they irrigate about 6,000 acres.
The most intensely irrigated area is around Granada, where the
Genil and its tributaries bring water to over 240,000 acres of
otherwise arid vega. Along the lower Guadalquivir, in the province of Seville, nearly 177,000 acres are now under irrigation.
The agricultural richness of the Guadalquivir basin is due to the
high rainfall of the Sierra Nevada, and to the continuity of
supply maintained during the long dry summer by water from
springs. Federico García Lorca has summed up the inter-depen-
dence of crops and river in his poem 'Baladilla de los tres ríos' (*vide*
Oxford Book of Spanish Verse):

> El río Guadalquivir
> va entre naranjas y olivos.
> Los dos ríos de Granada
> bajan de la nieve al trigo.

The basin of the Júcar forms the most important single unit in
the great network of canals and ditches which help to irrigate
lowlands along the Mediterranean coast. The river rises in arid
country beyond Cuenca but receives during the upper part of its
course some water from underground springs. There are several
barrages along its upper course, the most important being the
Alarcón which, when completed, will hold 700 million cu.
metres. Smaller barrages along this river and its tributary, the
Cabriel, include those of Enguldanos, Tous, Escalona and Carcagente. Rich alluvial plains some 123,500 acres in extent depend
on the Júcar for water, which is distributed by means of such
canals as the great Júcar canal (36 miles long) from which lead off
lesser canals, for example, those of Játiva, Enova, Meres and
Cuatro Pueblos. A new barrage, Forota, with an estimated
capacity of 30 million cu. metres, is now being built on the river
Magro, a tributary of the Júcar.

The river Turia contributes an appreciable amount of water to the irrigation schemes of the Valencian huertas. Three barrages, Generalísimo, Buseo and Blasco Ibáñez, conserve water which is fed by canals, in particular the Liria canal now under construction, to the lowland north of Valencia. Land immediately around Valencia draws on the waters of two streams, the Moncada and Cuarte, which together irrigate 37,000 acres by means of the canals Tormos, Mestalla, Rescaña, Mislata, Fabaro and Rovella.

An important aspect of irrigation in the Valencia district is the very strict control exercised over the rationing and usage of available water supplies – a control which is a necessity in an area subject to prolonged droughts and great irregularity of rainfall. The Water Tribunal meets every Thursday of the year at the main door of the cathedral in Valencia to judge cases of infringement of the water regulations. There is no court of appeal and the penalty is usually a fine; this has not always been the case, however, for in the early days of the Tribunal (it first started to meet in A.D. 1350) a man proved to be an habitual offender could be stoned off his land. Water rights are inseparable from land tenure, and each farmer using water from one of the main canals has the right to vote for a representative to the *junta de gobierno*, which in turn elects a *sindico*; the latter has special and absolute powers in times of emergency, and the combination of *sindicos* from each zone constitutes the Water Tribunal. Subordinate to the *sindicos* are the *atandadores*, men whose duties are vigilant rather than administrative.

North of Valencia the river Mijares is utilized in irrigation schemes around Castellón de la Plana. The María Cristina (27 million cu. metres) and Viuda barrages on the Mijares, and the Onda barrage on the Caballera, at present serve the region, but new barrages at Sichar, Bechí and Onda are being constructed. The Erbo delta, originally barren heath or marshland, is now an important rice-growing area, as a result of the construction of two canals, one on either side of the river, which bring the Ebro waters to some 61,000 acres of rich alluvium. This acreage may be increased fourfold in the next ten years if plans for extending the irrigation zones are put into operation.

South of Valencia the coastal lowlands become smaller in extent, rainfall decreases, supplies of water diminish, and irrigation areas are no longer continuous but limited to definite centres separated by arid highlands. The huerta of Gandía derives most of its water from the Beniarrés barrage on the river Serpis, and around Alicante a series of small irrigated zones is served by such barrages as Relleu, on the river Guadalest, Tibi, on the river Castalla, and Elda, on the river Vinalapo.

The river Segura and its tributaries provide a large number of barrages with water which is distributed lower downstream between Murcia and Alicante by a network of canals, for example, those of Segura and Espuña. The most important barrages are as follows (capacity is given in millions of cu. metres):

Talave (45) and Camarilla (39) on the river Mundo
Quipar (36) on the river of the same name ⎱ These serve the Lorca district
Corcovado (7) on the river Mula
Valdeinfierno and Puente (22) on the river Sangonera
Cenajo (400) and Fuensanta (233) on the river Segura

When all barrages and canals have been completed it is hoped that 123,000 acres in the Cartagena district will be irrigated by water from the newly constructed Cenajo barrage.

The importance of these Levant regions to Spanish economy is great. The total of irrigated land is 7,425,000 acres; 3,450,000 acres belong to the Valencian region, 2,200,000 to Alicante and 1,775,000 to Murcia. This total is exceeded only by that of the collective schemes along the river Ebro, which together irrigate about 10,200,000 acres.

The two central rivers of the peninsula, the Tagus and the Guadiana, have several disadvantages which limit their use for irrigation purposes. Their headstreams lie in arid mountains, where rainfall is sparse and irregular, giving rise to alternate droughts and floods. Each river is wide and shallow for much of its long course, providing a large surface for evaporation. Underground water supplies which augment rainfall are being increasingly tapped for well-irrigation, thus making it difficult to estimate the annual discharge. On the other hand, the existence of wide meanders and land below river level enables irrigation to be carried out close to the rivers without the construction of large barrages.

In the Tagus basin the huertas of Aranjuez, Añover del Tajo, Talavera de la Reina, San Fernando de Jarama, Morata de Tajuña, Plasencia, Sigüenza and Alcala are all irrigated by water coming directly from rivers, little attempt being made to control or conserve it. The largest canal is the Henares canal, which on its course from Humanes to Meco (23 miles) irrigates about 22,250 acres. One of the barrages of this area utilizes the rocky gorge of Gargüera as a suitable site for its dam; the waters irrigate the Plasencia region. The upper part of the Tagus basin receives water from the Bolarque barrage on the tributary Guadiela. New barrages will include those of Palmares and Varo on the Jarama, while in Portugal about 30,000 acres of land near Villa Franca will be irrigated if projected plans materialize.

The Guadiana basin has recently been transformed from a semi-arid area of *secano* farming to one of agricultural value. In 1956 several large irrigation schemes were inaugurated which, when completed, should bring 347,000 acres under *regadio* cultivation. Several barrages are now being constructed; the greatest is that of Cíjara, with a capacity of 1,670 cu. metres. Smaller barrages on the Guadiana and its tributaries include those of Puerto Peña, Orellana, Zújar and Alanje, which together will conserve 3,183 million cu. metres. New canals are also being built to distribute this water; the largest is that from the Orellana barrage (81 miles), followed by the Montijo canal (50 miles), the Zújar canal (45 miles) and the Lobón canal (36 miles). This scheme, when completed, will provide employment for 57,500 additional agricultural workers, who will live either in new buildings attached to already existing villages, or in one of the eight new villages to be built as soon as the land is ready to farm. In addition, 5,000 people will be employed in industries connected with the agricultural products, and the superphosphate and cotton factories at Badajoz, as well as the slaughterhouse at Mérida, will be reorganized and expanded. In Portugal certain areas of the Alentejo will eventually benefit from new irrigation projects. Unfortunately, these grandiose schemes apply only to Estremadura; in the upper course of the Guadiana

i

ii

iii

iv

VII   i Moorish legacy: the Patio de los Leones, Alhambra, Granada.

ii Memorial of the Christian reconquest: the walls of Ávila.

iii The influence of the Church: Tarragona Cathedral.

iv Memorial to Portuguese explorers: the Tower of Belem, near Lisbon.

i

ii

iii

VIII   i   Sakia method of irrigation in Minorca.

      ii   Irrigating an onion plot, Gerona.

     iii   Aerial view of the Esla barrage near Zamora. The field strips are typical of the Northern Meseta.

irrigation schemes are few in number and small in extent. The
barrage of Gasset (with a capacity of 22 million cu. metres)
irrigates a limited area around Ciudad Real.

The rest of the Iberian peninsula is, in general, devoid of large-
scale irrigation schemes, even though in certain areas they would
be beneficial. In the Bierzo district the barrage of San Cristobal

Fig. 27. The Major Reservoirs of Spain and Portugal

already serves the Sil valley, and a new barrage at Barcenas will
bring 29,600 acres under cultivation. At the opposite end of the
peninsula in Andalusia, a series of small dams and barrages, for
example the Chorro barrage on the river Guadalhorce, conserves
water for the irrigated lowlands of Estepona, Málaga, Vélez
Málaga and Almería.

Of all European countries Italy has the greatest area (1·82
million hectares) and greatest percentage (almost 6 per cent) of

E

irrigated land. Iberia comes second, with 1·68 million hectares and approximately 3·3 per cent of the total area under irrigation. When all projected schemes are completed, however, 6 per cent of Iberia will be irrigated; this small figure reflects the many geographical disadvantages which preclude any really extensive hydraulic schemes in the peninsula. Aridity is widespread, but even in the wetter north-west the non-porous crystalline rocks and general slope of the land combine to return much of the rainfall to the Atlantic, and there are few artesian basins in the Mesetas to provide large subterranean reserves. Difficulties of terrain often make it uneconomic to install canals and pumping stations, while lack of capital retards the general rate of progress.

3. AGRICULTURE

Iberia is often assumed to be a typically Mediterranean land, and as far as crops are concerned this assumption is justified. From prehistoric times the basic food of Mediterranean man has been wheat or barley loaves, olive oil, wine, with perhaps goats' milk, cheese, fish and game to supply valuable protein. This diet has never altered, although it has been augmented in recent years by imported goods, and it has the great advantage of providing all the human dietetic necessities in forms assimilated with ease and even with pleasure. Any Mediterranean country which is self-supporting in these three basic crops is capable of maintaining an adequate standard of health within its borders without recourse to excessive imports, more especially if stock-rearing and fishing are also practised.

For many centuries the peninsula was a great exporter of wheat; the Romans considered the country a granary, and even as late as 1850 wheat was still leaving Spanish ports. Today, however, Iberia is experiencing a deficiency in this product, due to the doubling of the population during the last hundred years. This deficiency is bound to increase if the population continues to multiply at its present rate; the land devoted to wheat cannot be appreciably extended, nor can the yield be increased to any marked degree. Furthermore, most of the wheat is produced on an extensive basis, and is subject to the vagaries of climate; Spain, in 1953, experienced a drought followed by storms which resulted in such a poor harvest that 1,400,000 metric tons of wheat had to be imported, the largest amount ever recorded.

Wheat growing in the peninsula is restricted generally to *secano* areas; in Portugal the dry plains of the Alentejo form the chief region, which extends across the border into the Tierra de Barros of Spanish Estremadura. About 2½ million acres are devoted to wheat in New Castile, the main regions being La Sagra, La

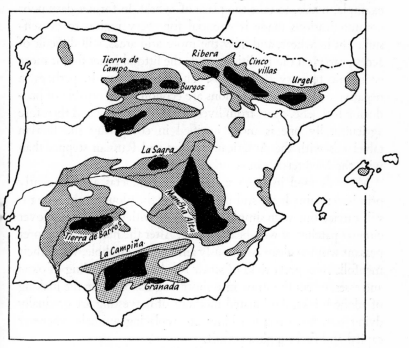

Fig. 28. Major Wheat-growing Areas

Mancha and La Alcarria. These localities have a yield varying from 10 quintals per hectare on the deep soils of the Tagus valley to 5 quintals per hectare on the thin soils of the *llanuras* of La Mancha. In Old Castile the Tierra de Campos, Tierra del Pan, Burgos highlands and the Salamanca district are all main production zones, with yields similar to those of Old Castile. Along the Ebro the north-bank regions of Ribera, Cinco Villas, Urgel and Monegros are important, and some wheatfields are irrigated, producing up to 15 quintals per hectare. In Andalusia the main areas are those of the Campiña, near the river Guadalquivir, and the vega of Granada, where the highest yields of Spain (20 to 30 quintals per hectare) are produced by means of irrigation.

There is a remarkable correlation between wheat-growing areas and the drier regions of the peninsula, and the reasons for this distribution are varied; irrigation or high rainfall of the coastlands enables cash crops, for example, oranges, or other cereals, for example, maize, to take the place of wheat. In former days poor communications made it essential for every region to be self-sufficient in wheat, and now the more arid areas, still difficult of access, carry on the tradition, while the littoral zones find it more economic to vary their crops. The basic reason is, perhaps, a negative one; the *secano* regions are economically capable of producing little else, apart from livestock. Climatically and therefore agriculturally one is more justified in comparing the Iberian tablelands with the American prairies and Russian steppes than with the Mediterranean coastlands.

Methods used in these vast unfenced mesetas are frequently primitive; animals are still used to draw the ploughs, threshing is still carried out with simple machines or with oxen treading over circular patches of well-beaten earth. After the harvest the poorer peasant women glean assiduously amongst the stubble, while their menfolk erect great ricks of straw for the winter feeding of oxen and asses, or cut the straw into short lengths for use in the making of adobe bricks. Antiquated methods of harvesting are gradually dying out, however; machines are replacing animals wherever capital and fuel supplies permit.

A hard type of wheat is generally grown in the peninsula, though the quality varies greatly from province to province; in a few select areas really good wheat is produced, but the bulk of the crop is of poor to average quality. In the La Sagra region, and in a few places in Old Castile, the 'Candeales Rojos' wheats are grown, of fine quality and good yield, while a Canadian variety, 'Northern Manitoba', is found in the Monegros zone. In Catalonia the high-quality 'Monte Catalán' crop is raised, and in Andalusia white wheats such as 'Bascuñana', 'Nano', 'Rubión', give good yields. In Catalonia, Castile and Aragón the hardy 'Jeja' varieties provide an average wheat and produce adequate yields even under poor conditions, as do the 'Lembrillas' and 'Chamorro' types.

The total amount of wheat produced in the peninsula annually approaches 5 million tons,[1] Spain providing slightly more than 4 million, and Portugal from $\frac{1}{2}$ to $\frac{3}{4}$ million tons. Both countries import wheat from abroad; Spain up to about $\frac{1}{4}$ million tons per year, and Portugal 100,000 tons. In both cases the amount imported depends on the harvest, which in turn depends on climate; a bad year can completely upset a nicely balanced budget. Within Iberia the movement of wheat is radial from the centre outwards; the old windmills, so typical a sight in Don Quixote's home province of La Mancha, have been replaced by large modern mills in towns situated, for the most part, in the peripheral regions. In recent years, however, this trend has been reversed; mills have been established in the main Meseta towns, and flour rather than wheat is sent coastwards.

Barley, a cereal more resistant to poor climatic conditions than wheat, grows quite well in the peninsula, and produces a yearly total of about $1\frac{3}{4}$ million tons (Spain over $1\frac{1}{2}$ million, Portugal 100,000). The distribution is generally coincident with wheat distribution, and it is therefore primarily a *secano* crop, although small quantities are grown on the irrigated huertas and vegas to the south. The yield is generally 50 per cent higher than that of wheat, and when irrigated one hectare of barley can produce 40 quintals of grain.

Rye, connotative of poor growing conditions, is found particularly on the wet highlands between the Douro and the Sil, and to a lesser extent on the high zones of the Mesetas and Galicia. It is frequently used as animal fodder, and less frequently for bread-making in outlying districts. The yearly total for Iberia seldom exceeds $\frac{3}{4}$ million tons; of this amount Spain provides about 530,000, Portugal 200,000, tons. In Spain hardy types of wheat are gradually replacing rye.

Oats, generally associated with cool wet conditions in more northerly countries, is in Iberia a *secano* crop, growing extensively in Spanish Estremadura, Old and New Castile and eastern Portugal, with areas of lesser importance in the Pyrenean foothills.

[1] Unless otherwise stated, all tons mentioned hereafter refer to metric tons.

It is used for animal fodder, and peninsular production seldom exceeds 700,000 tons, Spain providing about 75 per cent of this total.

Maize is a cereal requiring much water, and its Iberian distribution is limited to areas of high rainfall or to irrigated zones. The north and west coasts of the peninsula as far south as Coimbra receive adequate rainfall and are the major producing regions,

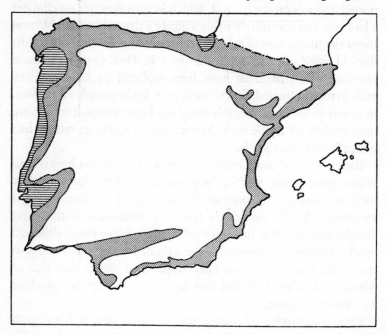

Fig. 29. Main Areas of Maize Production

followed by the wetter foothills of the Pyrenees, for example, the Gerona district. The irrigated lowlands of Valencia, Murcia and Andalusia also cultivate maize. The yield from well-watered fields is high – as much as 25 quintals of grain or 40 quintals of fodder from one hectare. The total production in Iberia is generally a little more than 1 million tons per year; Portugal contributes 35 per cent of this total.

Rice, a native of Asia, is primarily a tropical crop; nevertheless, its growing season is short (4 to 6 months), and if during this time it receives intense insolation and continuous supply of water, the plant will flourish in regions well away from its natural environment. The regions best suited to rice cultivation are flat irrigated lowlands; in Iberia these include the huertas of the Levant coast, especially the Ebro delta, and the Valencian and Castellón huertas, as well as small patches of land around the lower courses of the rivers Tagus and Guadalquivir. The main type is the Valencian 'Bomba', rich in protein and oils, and the 'Benlloch'. Both quality and yield are high; in a good year one hectare of fertile soil will produce 70 quintals of grain. A slight but steady decrease in Portuguese production is offset by a steady rise in Spanish production; the Iberian total per year remains fairly constant at about 600,000 tons, of which Spain provides 75 per cent. At the moment there is adequate labour for weeding and transplanting when required. Some plots are sown as for other cereals and then flooded to a depth of from 6 to 9 inches so that the need for transplanting is obviated and only weeding is necessary. Difficulties in cultivation include the levelling of each plot, and the production of a fine tilth for the seeds; both are overcome by alternate use of mattocks and heavy boards pulled by donkeys. Methods of harvesting vary from scything to cutting by tractor-drawn machines.

Viticulture in the peninsula is believed to have been introduced by the Phoenicians who brought the plant from the eastern Mediterranean between 600 and 500 B.C., and its production spread rapidly from the coast inland. Then, as now, cultivation was of the *secano* type; today only 3 per cent of the total Iberian acreage of vines is irrigated. A large section of La Mancha is planted with vineyards which provide one-eighth of the total amount of wine produced within the peninsula. The wines from this zone are mainly white (50 per cent), while red wines (36 per cent) and *rosados* (10 per cent) are less important. Varieties of grape include the 'Airén' and 'Cencibel' types; there is no well-known brand of wine. The methods of production are simple, with neither blending nor fortifying, and most of the wines are of average quality, being destined for ordinary domestic consumption.

Along the Catalan coast there are extensive vineyards of black grapes, concentrated in five districts; Panadés, famous for its sparkling wines; Vallés, Maresme, Bages and Martorell; further

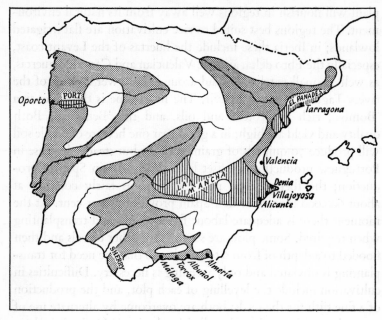

Fig. 30. Major Areas of Viticulture

south are the districts of Tarragona and Priorato, the latter important for the production of good red wine. Barcelona and Tarragona produce not only most of the sweet wines of Catalonia but also high-quality and sparkling red wines, while at Sitges a type of Malmsey wine is made from vines indigenous to Greece and brought to this coast by Mediterranean sailors. The main bulk of Catalan wine, however, is of good average quality and is used as an everyday table wine.

The best known grape of the Levant coast is the 'Morastrell', which gives a good red wine, the 'Bobal' and 'Tintorera', both black grapes for red wine, and the 'Marseguera' and 'Planta Nova' grapes for white wine. The quality of wine from these areas is average to good; one of the better wines is the *rosado* of Jamilla.

Andalusia, where there is a preponderance of white grapes, is noted for its high-quality wines of all kinds. Málaga is famous for its sweet and 'muscatel' wines, while Córdoba, Seville and Cádiz produce drier wines. The most celebrated of Andalusian wines is sherry, the name being a corruption of Jerez de la Frontera, the production centre. The two chief types of grape used in making this wine are 'Palomino' and 'Pedro Ximines' while oxidative fermentation and the Solera system of blending ensure a very high quality of wine. Sherry depends for its variety not only on processing methods, but on slight variations of aspect and climate, different stocks, and a variety of soils ranging from light sandy or limestone marls to richer clays. In 1957 the crop was partially spoilt by the Levant winds which scorched leaves and fruit; 1958, however, was a particularly good year for sherry. Although Andalusia is primarily viniferous, there is some cultivation of table grapes, particularly around Almería.

Estremadura and south-east Portugal produce large amounts of white table wines, and Badajoz is an important centre for the production of 'claret' types as well as white wines.

The river Douro forms the axis of another major production area which includes very varied geographical regions. In south Galicia red wines predominate, often light and aromatic, such as *ribero* and *caldetas*. High rainfall ensures a good yield, but cloudy weather in autumn sometimes prevents the grapes ripening fully. In the more arid interior of Old Castile and León large quantities of ordinary red wine are produced. In Portugal, however, the small area of the Paiz do Vinho, with the advantages of an infertile, shaly soil, intense insolation and infrequent rainstorms, grows vines believed to have originated as Burgundian stock, imported during the Middle Ages. These conditions are far from perfect, yet they provide the small black and white grapes, for example, 'Alvarelhao', 'Mourisco Prato', 'Tuita Madeira' and 'Touriga' varieties, which make an excellent port. Methods of production include fortifying and blending, to keep the quality uniformly high despite the effects of occasional climatic vagaries. There are few real vintage ports; after a good year (for example 1958 when the quality of grapes was excellent, though the quantity was small), a certain amount of must is retained for purely vintage ports. The good harvest of 1958 was followed by a poor one in 1959, despite the fact that almost every other vine-growing region in Europe benefited from a long, hot and dry summer; in the Paiz do Vinho August thunderstorms damaged some plants, while wet weather in autumn caused the grapes to rot on the stalks.

The Ebro basin is an important area of viticulture, the Rioja region near Logroño being especially noted for its red and sweet wines. The Rioja also produces the best table wines of Spain as well as large quantities of ordinary wine for everyday consumption.

Methods of cultivation vary only very slightly; propagation is by means of slips, grafted on suitable stock, some of it imported. Blight and mould are prevented, at least in part, by spraying with Bordeaux and other mixtures, pruning promotes healthy growth and better crops, and the harvest is gathered entirely by hand. Grape juice is expressed by treading with the bare feet, or specially nailed clogs which do not crush the pips, although in a few towns there exist presses for the production of *vino corriente*. Many vines grow unaided, but in some provinces, for example Galicia, stone, wooden or iron supports are provided. The total wine production of the peninsula fluctuates from year to year, but averages some 3 million tons, (cf. France 6 million, Italy $5\frac{1}{4}$ million), of which Portugal produces about 35 per cent. Portuguese production is, however, far more stable than that of Spain, owing to the greater regularity of rainfall.

The production of grapes for the table and also for sun-dried raisins is a speciality of southern Spain, where Málaga, Valencia, Alicante and Almería are the main centres, and the 'muscatel' grape a noted variety. Packing for export requires skill and care, and countries in western Europe, including Britain, are the chief importers.

The olive is a native of the Mediterranean, still to be found in its wild state in several areas. The Phoenicians introduced its culture into Iberia, and by Pliny's time it was well established. The oil was first valued exclusively for toilet purposes, but its use as an article of food rapidly spread, and even 2,500 years ago olive oil was a well-known commodity in Mediterranean trade. Today Iberia is the world's main producer of olive oil; Spain contributes a yearly average of about 28 per cent, and Portugal 8 per cent, of the average annual world total of 5 million tons of olives.

Propagation can be carried out in a variety of ways: cuttings are sometimes used, although these do not always bear fruit; some grafting is done, and knots and shoots are sprouted in nursery beds. The fruit is first harvested after four or five years' growth,

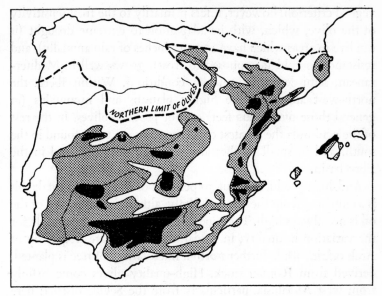

Fig. 31. Major Olive-growing Areas

and the trees come into full bearing after ten to fifteen years, continuing to bear for over half a century. Slight pruning is necessary, but in general the trees are seldom touched. On irrigated land catch crops grown between the olives may include wheat, maize and vegetables; on hillsides vines frequently utilize inter-arboreal space. The olives are frequently beaten off the trees with long sticks, and pressed as soon after the harvest as possible, to minimize the rancid flavour which deterioration usually promotes. Very high quality olives are frequently picked by women, and this is particularly the case where table olives are produced, since delicate handling is essential. The ripe fruit contains from 20 per cent to 60 per cent of oil, and there may be three pressings, each producing oil inferior in quality to that of the previous pressing.

The distribution of the olive in the peninsula is limited by climatic factors; frost (i.e. temperatures below 13° F.) will harm or even kill the trees, and excessively humid conditions cause deterioration in quality. The northern limit of the olive is often taken as the northern limit of the Mediterranean climate; this vegetal criterion, however, refers primarily to the frost sensitivity of the olive, which, with its adaptation to extreme drought (it can live in areas which have 10 to 12 inches of rain annually), and resistance to cold (as opposed to frost), grows well in Mediterranean, semi-desert and meseta conditions. Within Iberia the north-west areas and the higher plateaus and mountains (in general those over 4,000 feet) cannot produce olives. In the rest of the peninsula the greatest concentrations are to be found in the south, and in small patches along the Levant coast and in the Ebro basin.

Andalusia produces about 70 per cent of the Spanish total; this is as much as from the whole of Italy, although the quality of the oil is not always high. The type of tree is partially responsible for the variation in quality; in Andalusia the trees are frequently of Arab origin, while further north a finer variety of tree is planted, derived from Roman stock. High-quality olives come mainly from west Andalusia, particularly from the Seville district; here the 'Manzanilla' and 'Gordal Sevillano' varieties produce fine large olives for table use, while on limestone uplands the 'Aljarafe' type predominates. In the valleys of the Alpujarras the 'Léchin' olive produces a very high-quality oil. Other varieties, giving oil of good or average quality, include the 'Picudo', 'Nevadillo' and 'Carrasqueño'. In certain areas, notably those of Granada and Jaén, the olive groves are irrigated; in general, however, the olive is a markedly *secano* crop.

Catalonian olives are finer in quality than those of Andalusia, and are grown extensively between Barcelona and Tortosa. Here typical examples include 'Arbequin', 'Ovalis', 'Morrudo', 'Plateado' and 'Farga' olives. New groves have been planted recently in the Ampurdán district, while the Balearic Islands annually contribute some 250 hundredweight of olives, most from the north-west mountain range.

The Levant region produces olives on a *secano* basis often intermingled with vines and *algorrabas*, on the inland hills between 1,000 feet and 2,000 feet above sea level, but the lower irrigated zones of Valencia and Murcia produce very few olives. A wide variety is to be found here, partly as a result of the widely differing physical conditions. 'Manzanillo' and 'Morrudo' grow in well-favoured areas; the drought resistant 'Cornicabra' variety flourishes on the more arid hills, while in extremely dry districts where winters tend to be colder than usual the 'Léchin' type is grown.

The Ebro basin, though occasionally subject to frost in winter, has, in general, a warm enough climate for olives, which reach a maximum density on the hills between Tudela and Alcañiz and in the Llanos de Urgel. A small proportion of the crop is grown on irrigated land, and the type giving maximum quality oil is 'Empeltre', followed by 'Negral'; both flourish in the Alcañiz district, while around Lérida the predominant variety is 'Arbequin', which also produces very fine oil.

In New Castile there are two important centres of production; the first is around Plasencia, where aridity is accentuated by the rain-shadow effect of the Serra da Estrêla. The olive groves continue from Spain into Portugal, where they form a major zone of production on the right bank of the Tagus. The second centre, shared again between the two countries, is that of the mid-Guadiana district. The most prevalent type of olive is the 'Cornicabra', resistant to drought and capable of producing average yields even on poor soils. The 'Carrasqueño' variety, also hardy, has a wide distribution, and in the Guadalajara and Cuenca districts the 'Verdeja' type prevails.

Fluctuations in the olive harvests are great; this is partly due to the reliance on the *secano* type of farming in regions of sparse rainfall. Where grown near its isohyetal limits the olive is more likely to suffer from droughts, since it is here that irregularity of rainfall is most pronounced. On the other hand, some areas, notably the Levant, suffer occasional violent storms, accompanied by hail or even by frosts, which seriously damage both crop and tree. Andalusia is climatically more stable, and it is here that the bulk of Iberian olive groves are found, while about 65 per cent of the oil exported from the peninsula is Andalusian in origin.

The olive tree produces not only oil and table olives, but also oil expressed from the kernel and skin, which is used in soap making. In addition it supplies fodder for stock, and firewood from pruned branches, an important commodity in countries where coal, petroleum and wood are scarce.

The orange is a fruit popularly associated with Mediterranean coastlands; in fact, in its present form, it is Asiatic in origin, and a native of regions with a warm temperate eastern margin type of climate. The original bitter, or Seville, orange (*Citrus aurantium*) is thought to have been brought from Asia by the Arabs in the early ninth century, to have spread to Syria and thence to other Mediterranean lands. Today bitter orange trees form the stock on which are grafted the sweet orange scions; the origin of the sweet orange is obscure, but it first appeared in the Mediterranean a little before 1497, and may have been imported by the Portuguese. The semi-wild *Citrus medica*, or citron, was known to the Greeks, but appears to have had no connexion with the spread of the orange, although the Latin name for it is now used as a generic term for all similar fruits. The name orange, however, is Arab in origin, and in Spanish (*naranja*) is almost identical with the Arabic *naranj*. The trees prefer a warm climate, although they can withstand 4° F. of frost, but slight variations in summer temperatures are beneficial as they provide a balance between the formation of sweet and acid constituents in the fruit. Quick thaws, severe storms and particularly hail can damage or even kill the trees, as will late frosts such as those of February 1956, when fruit to the value of about £30 million was lost in the Valencia area. The trees rarely grow under *secano* conditions, and rainfall amounts are not critical. The plant prefers non-alkaline soils, and a certain amount of free drainage.

The Levant coastlands are the main orange producers within the peninsula, Valencia being of outstanding importance. Oranges are cultivated intensively throughout the irrigated huertas, but centres of maximum density occur around Burriana, Villareal, Sagunto, Játiva, Gandía, Catarroja, and in the lower valleys of the rivers Mijares and Palancia. In spring the coastal plain from Castellón de la Plana to Masamagrell appears to be one vast orange grove. The average yield for a mature tree in a good year is from 50 to 70 pounds, and varieties include the 'Cadanera' which gives a very high-quality pipless fruit, the 'Washington Navel' (individual fruits from this type of tree occasionally weigh seven pounds), 'blood' and 'mandarin' oranges, as well as smaller but good quality oranges of 'Comun' type for home consumption.

Further south orange production is important in the Murcia–Alicante region, where the main centres are Elche, Orihuela, Dolores, Calloso, Alcira and Carcagente. Here types of fruit similar to those of Valencia are grown, the 'Macetera Murciana', a sweet juicy fruit, being a local speciality.

Other orange-producing regions of Iberia are of much less importance; areas around Almería, Málaga, Ronda, Lora del Rio, Mairena, Viso de Alcor, Badajoz and Cáceres provide a few tons of average quality fruit per year, the actual yield in Andalusia being higher than that for most of the peninsula. In Portugal there are a few small patches devoted to orange cultivation near Lisbon, and in the valley of the Douro.

The average yearly production for the peninsula is a little over one million tons, of which Spain produces the greater part. One of the main problems facing Spanish growers today is the steady decrease in yield, which has not yet been counteracted. In 1926 one hectare of orange trees produced an average of 229 quintals of fruit; by 1936 the yield had dropped to 118 quintals per hectare, and in 1956 the yield was only 75 quintals per hectare. There has been, therefore, but a slight increase in the total amount produced, despite the fact that the total acreage now under oranges is almost double its 1926 figure. This discrepancy is accounted for in part by ignorance; many new groves are planted on soils unsuited to oranges, or in regions where climatic fluctuations are so great over a period of years that production decreases even from good stock. World prices for oranges remain high, and there seems little likelihood that yield can be improved to any great extent at present, while uneconomic areas are used for orange production.

Lemons and limes are in general restricted to the hotter regions of the Levant coast, where Murcia produces 40 per cent to 50 per cent of the total crop, followed by Valencia, Málaga, Alicante, Majorca and Barcelona. In the last-named province the yield is about 150 pounds per tree in a good year, and in Murcia about 130 pounds per tree. The total production is now slightly higher than that before the Civil War; about 70,000 tons are grown annually.

The prevalence of apples illustrates the variety of climates to be found within the peninsula. There are two types of climate suitable for apple cultivation; one in the humid cool northern regions, where Asturias and the Basque provinces are particularly important, and where cider rivals wine as a table drink. This kind of cultivation within the 40-inch isohyet is also found in Galicia, northern Portugal and the western Pyrenees. The other variety is a slightly more extreme climate where irrigation is practised; the huertas of Llobregat, the Rioja, Navarre and the valleys of the Jalón and Jiloca are all important centres. Approximately 2½ million tons of apples are produced annually, of which about 35 per cent are used for cider making.

The fig tree is well suited to the hotter and drier regions of Iberia, and much of the crop grows along the Levant coast, in Castellón, Murcia and in the Balearics. The Fraga plantations in the province of Huesca provide excellent quality figs, as do the plantations of Castile and Aragón, while many crops of average yield are produced in Andalusia. The average yearly amount of fruit is 200,000 tons.

Other fruits grown in Iberia include pomegranates, peaches and apricots, restricted by climatic requirements to the huertas of the Mediterranean coast and the south; dates which come primarily from Murcia and Alicante; melons and water melons which grow abundantly in the southern half of the peninsula; and bananas which flourish in sheltered spots in the Algarve and Málaga districts.

Although fruit farming is important (Spain exports significant amounts of oranges, grapes and melons every year) the lowlier vegetables are ubiquitous and form an essential part of Iberian diet. The potato thrives in both Portugal and Spain, where three-fifths of the crop is grown by *secano* methods. The influence of climate is revealed in the crop yields for each country; Spain, with drier conditions, produces an annual average of 3·5 million tons from 365,000 hectares; Portugal one million tons from only 89,000 hectares. Little, if any, of the crop is exported, since internal demands are so great.

The potato is a temperate crop requiring cool, fairly moist conditions, and thus grows best in the northern half of the peninsula. In north Portugal, Galicia and the Cantabrian region particularly good crops are produced, using such varieties as

'Gallega' and 'Asturiana'. The Pyrenean foothills, lower regions of Old Castile and irrigated huertas of the Mediterranean coast and Andalusia are also productive regions. All these areas are noted for their early potatoes, some of which are grown from English seed, and then exported to England in August. One aspect of potato cultivation common to both Portugal and Spain is the practice of growing kidney beans between the rows, which helps to conserve moisture and adds some nitrogen to the soil.

Apart from kidney beans several other varieties of pulses are grown within the peninsula, and provide some of the protein in which the diet of the poor is normally deficient. French beans grow well in the wetter districts of the north and west; Portugal annually produces about 30,000 tons, Spain almost 100,000 tons. Chick peas, a *secano* crop which grows throughout the southern half of the peninsula, and especially in Andalusia, provides approximately the same annual amounts. Lentils are another *secano* crop and thrive in the meseta lands and in the vega of Granada; Spain's annual total fluctuates between 20,000 and 25,000 tons.

Spain in particular is noted for its onion crop, some of which is exported, either in bulk or in strings hawked by itinerant individuals; the 'shoni (Johnny) onions' of the Welsh valleys, who worked his passage on a cargo boat bringing iron ore from Bilbao to Swansea is, however, seldom seen today. Nearly half a million tons of onions are produced annually, mainly in the Valencia region where the 'Valencia blanca' is a noted variety. Castellón and Alicante rank second in importance, followed by Murcia, and in all these regions the onion crop is irrigated. Tomatoes, grown especially in the Canaries and in the huertas of the Levant, now form Spain's fourth main export.

Forage crops occupy an important position in agricultural economy; their primary use is obvious, but apart from fattening stock the leguminous types also help to replenish the nitrogen content of the soil. In some areas they are grown simply to provide a vegetation cover and so help to prevent soil erosion. The main fodder crop is alfalfa, grown principally in the Ebro basin, and to a lesser extent, in the north-west and in the irrigated huertas along the Mediterranean coast, where five croppings in the same season from the same plot is not unusual. Clover is a characteristic crop of pluviose Iberia, as are kale and maize, while the *algorraba* which produces sweet edible beans is found in the meseta regions. Sugar beet and some cereals, such as wheat and barley, are also grown as fodder crops.

Cash crops, particularly those which provide a raw material for industry, are becoming increasingly important in the peninsula. Cotton is a typical example; it requires great heat, adequate but not excessive water, deep rich soils and a growing season of not less than six and a half months, during which period there must be no frost. Such conditions occur in Andalusia, the Mediterranean littoral and in south Portugal where, however, less importance is attached to cotton growing. 'Andalucia', 'Chirpan', 'U' (from Utrera) and other hybrids are of average quality and are all derived from American or Russian seed. 42 per cent of Spanish cotton is grown on irrigated lands, and the total, modest when compared with that of large-scale producers, reaches 100,000 metric tons a year, of which Andalusia produces 60 per cent. Production in Portugal is at present purely nominal.

Flax is grown for both seed and fibre, the latter being more important. Main production areas include the irrigated zones of the Guadalquivir valley and the northern half of Portugal. Total production is not great and in both countries is for local use only.

Esparto grass grows well in the arid steppe-lands of the Sierra Nevada foothills and in New Castile, and annual production fluctuates around 90,000 tons. Some is exported but most is absorbed in local industries.

The gradual loss of islands in the West Indies during the seventeenth and eighteenth centuries robbed Spain of her main source of sugar, and gave added impetus to sugar beet production. Portugal, with a smaller population and overseas territories in the Tropics, has no such problem and therefore grows very little sugar beet, preferring to import cane sugar from her African possessions.

Sugar beet is a crop requiring good soil and adequate moisture during the growing season; irrigated huertas in the northern half of Spain are well suited to its cultivation. The major production area is the Ebro basin, especially along the river itself between Haro and Caspe, while significant amounts are also grown in the Jiloca valley and in the irrigated zones of Urgel. Other subsidiary areas include Andalusia, the Tagus valley and the district around Valladolid. One of the main varieties is the 'Silesia Blanca', with a small root but a high sugar content, and the selling of both seed and crop is regulated, so that there is no delay in processing to cause deterioration. Refineries are widespread within each main area; in north Spain the largest are found in La Bañeza and Vegellina de Orbigo, just north of Benavente, in Baños de Cerrato on the river Pisuerga, and in Miranda del Ebro, Alfaro, Tudela, Luceni, Calatayud, Epila and Zaragoza in the Ebro basin. In the south the two main refineries are at Villarrubia and La Riconada on the Guadalquivir, while a large refinery at Málaga deals with sugar cane as well as sugar beet. Spain annually produces about 2 to $2\frac{1}{4}$ million tons of sugar beet, which yield about 225,000 tons of sugar.

Sugar cane requires tropical heat and moisture, and for this reason its growth is restricted to the sheltered lowlands of southern Iberia. Around Málaga, Granada and Almería small plantations provide Spain with an additional annual total of about 30,000 tons, so that, in general, importing is unnecessary.

A visitor to Iberia is frequently surprised to find that a large and luxurious building, with spacious lawns and gardens carefully tended, behind massive iron railings, is not a palace but a tobacco factory. Tobacco grows well in the peninsula, especially in Spain. Almost 90 per cent of the Spanish crop is grown on the irrigated vegas of Granada, which produce large quantities of average quality, and at Tiétar which produces lesser amounts of very high quality. A rotation of crops normally includes tobacco twice in four years, as follows: first year forage crops and tobacco; second year wheat and peanuts; third year tobacco and beans; fourth year wheat and maize. In some areas tobacco is grown in alternate rows with pimiento or barley. Varieties vary considerably, but those of higher quality include 'Mallorca', 'Cantabria' and 'Valencia Alto', all of which are used in rolling cigars. The total annual production is about 33,000 tons.

Nut trees thrive in Iberia, and their fruits are of greater importance in peninsular economy than is the case in more northerly countries. Almonds are widespread in the south and east, but the zone of maximum cultivation is limited to the south and east coasts and the Ebro basin. The most notable types are 'Marcona', a fine nut, regular in appearance and suitable for confectionery, 'Largueto', excellent either for confectionery or for roasting, and 'Mollar', a variety which easily sheds its skin. Catalonian almonds are of high quality, while those from Andalusia and the Balearics are of poor to average quality. The total Iberian crop seldom exceeds 150,000 tons per year, of which a small amount is exported.

Hazel nuts grow wild in the mountainous tracts of the peninsula, but intensive cultivation in plantations occurs primarily in the province of Tarragona, where 'Negreta' and 'Comun' types yield well. About 15,000 tons are produced annually, mainly for the home market.

The fruits of the sweet chestnut tree form a useful, if lowly, contribution to human food supplies in the remoter country districts, and are also used to feed stock. Chestnuts flourish in the wetter north-west; Asturias, León, Galicia and northern Portugal are important producers, while they also grow on the lower slopes of the Pyrenees and Sierra Nevada. There are few records of the total harvest; it seems unlikely that more than 200,000 tons are produced annually.

The woodlands of Iberia contribute other more valuable items to man, particularly cork, resin and timber. Cork is the bark of the cork oak, *Quercus suber*, a tree well adapted to the summer drought characteristic of a Mediterranean climate. The most important groves are found in the more arid tracts of Andalusia, Spanish Estremadura and central Portugal. Here the soil is often infertile, and there is no competition from other crops. Cork from this zone is of average quality; that from Catalonia, a secondary producer, is small in amount but of very high quality, and is used primarily for the manufacture of corks, while other inferior grades are destined for use, when granulated, in linoleum and in freezing apparatus. The peninsula is the world's greatest producer of cork; Portugal annually produces about 170,000 tons and exports about 144,000 tons, while Spain is extending her cork groves to meet the ever-increasing demand, and now produces about 100,000 tons per year, as compared with an annual average of about 50,000 to 60,000 tons in the previous decade.

The production of turpentine and resinous substances, such as colophony (a dark resin distilled from turpentine and water), is important in both Spain and Portugal. More than 20,000 pines in the central region of Spain help to provide annually from 30,000 to 40,000 tons of colophony and about 10,000 tons of turpentine. In Portugal the forests are likewise centrally placed and include those of the Serra da Estrêla and of the sandy coasts; the Portuguese annual exports of resin average 45,000 tons, while those of turpentine occasionally reach 10,000 tons. The influence of climate on tree growth is revealed in these statistics; the Portuguese pine forests cover approximately half the area devoted to pines in Spain, despite the greater size of the latter country, and predominate in the more pluviose regions of central and north Portugal. In general their distribution is contained within the 30-inch annual isohyet which excludes much of south and east Spain.

The natural forests of Iberia were once probably more extensive than they are today. Literary allusions to forests now nonexistent, as well as archaeological finds, all tend to support this theory. Their disappearance is due primarily to the destructive actions of mankind in his search for winter fuel, building timber and pasture for his goats. Even today re-afforestation is undertaken only in small selected tracts. According to some sources less than 10 per cent of Spain as compared with 25 per cent of Portugal is forested. Some Spanish textbooks increase the Spanish area to 15 per cent or even to 20 per cent, but normally include country which in Britain would be termed woodland, heath or copse rather than forest.

The chief timber-producing tree of the peninsula is the pine, which predominates in the wetter north-west and on mountain slopes elsewhere. The main varieties are the *Pinus silvestris*, which thrives in the higher regions, and the *Pinus pinaster* which grows well in more pluviose regions. Spanish pine forests are approximately twice as extensive as the Portuguese; on the other hand Portugal devotes more ground to cork oaks than does Spain. The common oak, *Quercus robur*, is found in both countries, but Spain has almost a monopoly of beech woods which are restricted to the cooler hills of the northern littoral and to the Pyrenees. Poplar trees are a common sight in the Pyrenean foothills, but are seen less frequently in Portugal, while chestnuts thrive in the north of Spain and Portugal as well as in the Central Sierras. Eucalyptus trees, which provide average quality timber in a short time, are becoming increasingly important, especially in Portugal, while many of the common European species such as birch, ash and elm are widely distributed in the north and west of Iberia.

Timber extraction is primitive in method and seasonal in character. In the Pyrenees, for example, working parties of some six to ten men maintain a base camp in some U-shaped valley throughout the summer, often climbing roughly 2,000 feet to fell selected trees growing on the steep valley sides. Mules are used to drag the trunks to the valley floor, and every week or fortnight a lorry removes the logs and brings provisions. The first snows of winter terminate all timber felling, and the men return to their homes and such alternative occupations as they can find. Saw mills are often driven by hydro-electricity, and are normally small in size, though they may serve an extensive area. Timber is scarce in Spain and wood has to be imported; Portugal, on the other hand, produces sufficient softwood and even exports pit-props, but imports small quantities of hardwoods from her tropical possessions.

In countries deficient in coal, iron and, at the moment, electrical energy, wood forms an important fuel. Portugal (27·7 per cent forest and woodland) is proportionally richer in forests than Spain (9·9 per cent forest and woodland), but in both countries it is no uncommon sight to see pine cones and fir branches offered for sale as fuel, while charcoal burning is still important in the forested areas, since charcoal lasts longer than wood and is light in weight (an important consideration when donkeys form the main means of transport). The average Iberian housewife uses a fan as much to kindle her charcoal embers to a blaze as to cool herself. Whole trees are seldom cut for firewood, except in mountainous districts; the lower branches only are stripped, leaving the pine umbrella-shaped.

The general picture of Iberian farming is one of isolated pockets of fertile, well-watered soils covered with a rich profusion of cereals, orange trees, sugar beet, vegetables and even tropical plants such as sugar cane, while the nearby rocky hillsides provide a somewhat insecure footing for vines and olives. Such a picture ignores the vast expanse of flat, arid country to be found in central Iberia. Here the heathlands and ilex groves provide the only vegetative cover and water supply is minimal. Yet this type of country forms the major part of Iberia; if area is taken into account pastureland constitutes the largest single element in Spanish land, utilization (38 per cent), followed by land devoted to *secano* cultivation (34 per cent). Irrigated zones, despite their wealth, cover only 3·3 per cent (1955) of Spanish territory, while useless land occupies 10·8 per cent of the whole. Iberia is, in fact, suited more to stock-rearing than to cultivation; it is only the constant demands of an ever-increasing population that have led to the development of what is virtually horticulture in selected zones of irrigation.

Stock-rearing in the peninsula was a Neolithic occupation. Sheep were of great importance and appear to have been derived from the 'urial' type of Turkestan; they were small of stature and had goat-like horns. In the Copper Age a 'mouflon' type of sheep, with long curved horns, made its appearance, only to become extinct at a later date. During the Roman occupation wheat growing for a time became more important than stock-rearing. After the unrest of Barbarian invasions the Moors introduced the methods of horticulture so well established today, but these affected only the south and east coasts. In the interior sheep-rearing continued, and, as numbers increased, local meetings of shepherds became necessary to deal with disputes arising from problems of strays and transhumance. The latter practice became firmly established, and the Mesta was instituted, originally to delimit transhumance routes and settle pastoral problems such as water and pasture rights *en route*. Transhumance increased, becoming national, not merely local; three main stock routes or *cañadas* across the central Mesetas were defined – the Leonesa, La Mancha and the Segoviana. The Mesta increased its hold on the organization of sheep-rearing and the sale of wool, and by the fifteenth century was an accredited and privileged Council. At this time wool was a highly profitable commodity; furthermore, the sedentary farmers of the Meseta, who stood literally and meta-phorically in the way of stock rearers, were decimated by plague, so that the Mesta was able to give increasing protection to its members, and became a model example of centralized control both of agriculture and trade, an example to be followed with less conspicuous success by later Spanish economic councils.

The Mesta has now ceased to function, although its influence is still apparent. Today the great *cañadas* are becoming less important as the pendulum swings away from stock-rearing to crop cultivation. The wide swathes cut every summer through the meseta scrub by thousands of migrant sheep coming from the parched tablelands to the cool grasses of the Cantabrians have been reduced to mere tracks; wheatfields cover all but the most important. Transhumance is still practised, however; the main movement is lateral, from the Mesetas to either the Cantabrian or the Sierra Morena slopes; from the Albacete and Teruel highlands to the coast. Vertical transhumance is practised in the Pyrenees and Serra da Estrêla, which form summer grazing grounds for sheep from the Ebro and lower Douro basins respectively. The sheep are often taken by train, and the sound of starved and thirst-mad animals in packed three-tier trucks is one which haunts the lonely meseta sidings.

Spain has over 16 million sheep, four times as many as Portugal. The main breeds include the 'Merino', of African origin, with short, curly and silky wool of fine quality, the 'Churro' of Old Castile, with long coarse wool, and the 'Manchegan' with medium length wool. Many Iberian sheep are kept for wool, meat and milk, but recent trends are towards an improved breed to provide both tender meat and good wool. Suffolk sheep which produce good meat and are resistant to disease, have been successfully crossed with Spanish breeds, but at the moment there has been no outstanding improvement in type. Meat is average in quality, the dead weight is less than in more northerly countries, while the average weight of fleece (in the grease) per animal is four to seven pounds compared with over seven pounds for New Zealand fleeces.

The most important sheep-rearing area is New Castile, followed by Old Castile and the Ebro basin; this distribution illustrates the importance of the arid heathlands of Iberia which can never be irrigated, but provide useful pasturage. A certain number of sheep

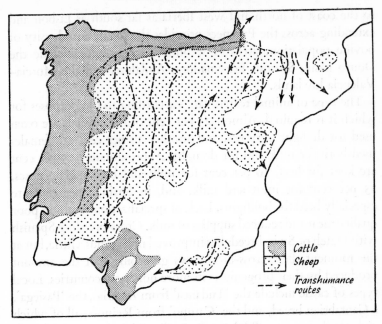

Fig. 32. Sheep and Cattle

are also kept in north Portugal and the Alentejo district, while in Spain areas of secondary importance include the hills along the Mediterranean coasts and the drier regions of Galicia and the Basque provinces.

The distribution of goats in Iberia is similar to that of sheep, but extends into higher areas and zones of poorer pasture, and the animal is particularly useful in the semi-arid steppes where goats' milk forms a valuable article of diet. Good milk-producing goats include the 'Murciana', 'Granadina', 'Costeña', 'Santanderina', 'Gallega' and 'Moncayo'; good meat is obtained from the 'Serranas' of the Sierra Morena, while the 'Manchega' and 'Pirenaica' breeds provide both meat and milk. Spain, with about 4 million goats, has almost four times as many as Portugal.

The distribution of cattle presents an entirely different picture; these animals require far more pasture of a lusher nature than that allotted to sheep, and such grassland is restricted either to the humid areas of the north-west or to the irrigated vegas and huertas generally devoted to other crops. A broad belt of land adjacent to the coast of north and west Iberia as far south as Lisbon and extending across the Pyrenees provides the maximum density of bovine population; areas of secondary importance include the Douro basin, Spanish Estremadura, Andalusia and the Murcia–Valencia lowlands.

The type of animal reared varies according to the purposes for which it is required. Almost 25 per cent of the animals are oxen used for draught purposes, and another 30 per cent are females used both for milk and for draught. Approximately 15 per cent are kept for beef, 10 per cent for milk and breeding purposes, 15 per cent for meat and milk, and, in Spain, 2 per cent are especially bred for bullfights. Lack of specialization results in poor quality meat and reduced supplies of milk. Cross-breeding Spanish with Dutch or Swiss breeds has improved milk yields a little, but at the moment these cross-bred cows give only half the amount produced by their progenitors in more northerly countries. Local types of cattle include the 'Tudanca' from Asturias, the 'Pasiega', a Cantabrian breed, and the 'Campo' from Reinosa, all of which give small amounts of high-quality milk, rich in cream. Beef cattle are also found in the north-west area, including the large black 'Lienia' and the smaller red 'Marela', both Galician. Bulls for bullfighting are bred specifically for strength of neck muscle, speed and pugnacious spirit; they are normally grazed on the extensive ranches of Andalusia and Estremadura. Large bullfights (*corridas*) average 100 to 300 a year and practice fights (*novillades*) for those aspiring to fame in the bull-ring occur in many large towns every Sunday; there is, therefore, a steady demand for this type of bull.

There are two basically different types of swine in the peninsula; that of the north, white, similar to the north European varieties and believed to have been introduced by the Celts; and that of the south, lean, black and of African origin. Portugal has a proportionally larger number than Spain – about 33 per cent of the peninsular total of almost 4 millions. In general pigs are allowed to wander over the arid central plains, and are fattened on acorns from the holm oak, but in the north-west regions of the peninsula maize, chestnuts, apples and roots are given to stall-fed animals. Apart from providing excellent leather and less excellent meat, these pigs also provide local regional delicacies such as the hams of Trévelez (cured by the process of sun-drying in the snow to prevent deterioration), the smoked hams of Chaves, and the sausages of Vich and Majorca.

Of all the domesticated mammals of the peninsula the donkey (or ass) is best known. In previous centuries the ass and its half-brother the mule (the offspring of a male ass and mare or less frequently of a female ass and stallion) were the only animals able to negotiate safely the miserable tracks which served as roads. Main lines of communication have improved, but there are still thousands of Spanish and Portuguese villages linked only by mule trails to the nearest large centre. This is particularly the case in mountainous regions, where gradient and dangerous rocky terrain put a great strain on bulkier animals.

Spain annually rears about three-quarters of a million asses and a million mules, while for Portugal the figures are a quarter of a million and an eighth of a million respectively. Though requiring more fodder, mules are stronger and hardier than asses, and better adapted to the harsh conditions of arid and mountainous Spain; asses require less fodder, and are better suited for lighter tasks and less difficult routes. The distribution of both animals is the same; they are widely scattered throughout the peninsula except in the extreme north and west (where they are replaced by oxen) and they predominate in the central regions, reaching a maximum density in Spanish Estremadura and Andalusia.

Horses are less numerous than either asses or mules; over half a million are reared in Spain, but only about 85,000 in Portugal. In the south, especially in Andalusia, Spanish Estremadura and south Portugal the descendants of Arab equine stock provide horses more suited for riding, while in the central areas lighter animals are reared for riding and farm work. In the north and west and around Gerona, Barcelona and Valencia heavier types including Breton and Norman imported stock have provided useful cross-bred horses such as the 'Breton-Ampurdanés' and 'Breton-Pamplonés', which are suitable for farm work and for transport.

The keeping of domestic fowls is widespread throughout the peninsula; there are no recent statistics available for Portugal, but Spain annually produces about 24 millions. Most chickens are kept for eggs since there is no great demand for table birds. The best layers are the 'White Leghorns' followed by black Spanish varieties such as 'Castellanas', 'Andaluzas' and 'Mallorquinas'. 'Rhode Island Reds', 'Prat Blancas' and 'Prat Perdiz' are kept for both eggs and table use. The north and west parts of the peninsula provide the majority of birds, since the maize crop, restricted to these zones, forms an important source of fodder, but chickens are also reared in Catalonia, Valencia and Andalusia, while turkeys are bred round Salamanca.

Bee-keeping is restricted to three main areas; the Mesetas where rosemary and lavender heathlands provide the high-quality 'Alcarria' honey; the Mediterranean coast where fruit trees encourage insect life; and the western heathlands of Spanish Estremadura and Portugal. About 7,000 tons of honey are produced annually and most is absorbed by the home market.

Silkworms are kept in the Murcia, Alicante and Valencia districts where mulberry trees are specially grown. The total amount produced has almost doubled in the last twenty years, now reaching nearly 600 tons per annum. This is partially due to the planting of more trees, especially the white variety which is ready before the black mulberry, and provides the silkworm with leaves early in the season. The main reason is the ready adaptability of the local populace to the continuous delicate-fingered skill necessary to successful sericulture.

Fishing is important off both the Mediterranean and Atlantic coasts. The fish from Mediterranean waters tend to be smaller in number and size than their Atlantic counterparts, due to the greater prevalence of plankton in the ocean. For this reason the major fishing centres are along the Atlantic coast – Setúbal, Matozinhos, Portimão and Olhão in Portugal; Ondárroa, Bermeo, Laredo, Santoña, Avilés, Ribadasella, Pontevedra, Villagarcia, Vigo, Corunna and Cádiz in Spain. In both countries most of the catch consists of pelagic and demersal fish; molluscs comprise 5 per cent of the total, and crustaceans 3 per cent.

In Spain 30 per cent of the total catch consists of sardines; in Portugal the percentage is much higher. Annual amounts vary slightly, but Portugal nets about 100,000 tons and Spain about 180,000 tons of sardines and anchovies in an average year. Almost half the Portuguese catch is tinned and exported, tinned fish ranking as the most important export. In Spain under half the catch is preserved, and there is little export. The main sardine-fishing zone of Spain is the Galician coast where the *trainera* type of boat uses a *traina*, or small-meshed wide net, while off Portugal similar apparatus is used. Many Spanish fishing boats are coal burning, but the Portuguese still use sailing boats, often with an 'eye' painted on the prow to ward off evil.

Tunny fishing is widespread in the Atlantic, but less so in the Mediterranean, where there are fewer of this species. The larger varieties are caught off the south-west coast of the peninsula by means of the *almadraba*, a labyrinthine system of deep nets which catch the fish as they move annually from one fishing ground to another. This system was introduced by the Moors and is similar to that practised off the west Sicilian and Sardinian coasts. Smaller varieties of tunny, particularly the striped tunny or bonito, are prevalent off the north and west coasts; these fish are less frequently seen off Portugal. In Spain an appreciable amount of tunny is tinned.

A very common type of fish, similar to hake or cod, is the *merluza*, obtained chiefly from the Atlantic, to be eaten fresh, salted or dried, but not tinned. Anchovies are caught in the Atlantic and Mediterranean, but their tinning takes place mainly in Atlantic ports. There are, in addition, numerous other varieties of fish, ranging from the *bacalhau* (cod) often served in Portugal, to the rarer mullet, *angulas* (minute eel), squid and octopus. There is also a small but thriving trade in molluscs and crustaceans such as clams, *percebes* (large barnacles), cockles, mussels, lobsters and the huge crabs (*centollas*), which lurk in dark niches along the Cantabrian coast. These have a limited and usually local market.

The small size of Portugal makes it easy to distribute fresh fish quickly to main centres; in Spain, however, longer distances and difficulties of terrain combine to limit internal distribution of fresh fish. Approximately 50 per cent of Spain's total catch comes from the Galician and Cantabrian coasts, 15 per cent from the Cádiz area, and 25 per cent from the Mediterranean coast. Fast main-line trains take at least eight hours and often twelve hours to travel from the coast to Madrid, and long-distance lorries are used. Transport difficulties are one of the main problems facing the Spanish fishing industry; the distribution of fresh fish is, in fact, limited to the coastal regions and to one or two inland centres, such as Pamplona and Córdoba, neither far from the sea. In the central regions the regular Friday meal consists of dried Newfoundland cod, served in a variety of ways. The import of dried cod is appreciable in both countries; Spain imports about 60,000 tons and Portugal about 45,000 tons a year.

Methods of fishing are still somewhat primitive; boats are small, often propelled by oar and sail, and able to travel only short distances. Spain, with just over 44,000 boats, has a fishing fleet three times the size of the Portuguese fleet, although in 1958 and 1959 new plans were promulgated for the building of additional Portuguese fishing boats, especially trawlers. Nets are used in preference to lines, and unloading is carried out either by small derricks or by hand (at Avilés bonito are thrown from man to man until they are finally deposited in a waiting cart). There are large tinning and preserving factories in all the major ports around the coast; in Portugal tinning in olive oil is the primary concern, while in Spain approximately 50 per cent of the factories are engaged in salting, 40 per cent in tinning and 5 per cent in drying the fish.

Spanish Agriculture

Total area of Spain – 503,486 sq. km, including Canaries and Balearics.

Land utilization – 1. Cultivated:

			thousands of hectares
Treeless	Secano	Sown	88,649
		Fallow	50,571
		Irrigated	14,280
Some trees		Secano	49,114
		Irrigated	323

2. Uncultivated:

Treeless	139,141
Forested	112,074
Not productive	47,523

N.B. 100 hectares = 1 sq. km

Production: provisional figures for 1958, in thousands of metric tons:

Wheat	4,540	Cork ('57)	77,476 tons
Barley	1,777	Resin	42,482 „
Maize	916	Esparto	96,770 „
Rye	515	Wine	19,833,833 hectolitres
Oats	519	Fish:	
Rice	375	Sardines	98,356 tons
Potatoes	4,292	Anchovy	79,328 „
Sugar beet	3,207	Small fry	57,360 „
Cotton ('57)	106	Codfish	42,320 „
Alfalfa	247	Bonito	34,637 „
Olives	1,644		
Olive oil	313		
Oranges	1,078		
Mandarins	97		
Lemons	69		
Peaches	82		
Apricots	25		

Re-afforestation: Aim: to replant 5,678,625 hectares in 100 years.

Work started in 1940: by 1951	440,000 hectares planted	
by 1953	540,000 „	„
by 1954	656,000 „	„
by 1955	860,000 „	„

Portuguese Agriculture

Land Utilization: Total area – 92,200 sq. km.

	%
Arable, orchard, pasture and permanent meadow	38
Forest and woodland	27·7
Waste, cities, etc.	34·3

Production for 1958, in thousands of metric tons:

Wheat	749	French beans	45 (1957)
Maize	405	Potatoes	1,196
Oats	140	Cork	139,586 (1957)
Barley	110	Resin	57,534 (1957)
Rye	211	Wine	8,580,000 hectolitres
Rice	157	Olive oil	1,100,571 „ (1957)

Forests:	Total extent	2,500,000 hectares	
	Pine	1,170,000 „	
	Cork oak	600,000 „	
	Other oak	500,000 „	
	Eucalyptus	100,000 „	
	Chestnut	70,000 „	

The World Position of Iberian Agriculture

The main crops and animals of Portugal and Spain, as compared with those of
Italy, other major producing countries and the world total.

All figures represent thousands of tons for 1958

	Wheat		Maize		Barley
Spain	4,430		1,770		950
Portugal	749		110		405
Italy	9,815		296		3,674
U.S.S.R.	75,300	China	20,000	U.S.A.	96,520
World	190,800		76,000		139,100

	Wine	Olives	Citrus Fruits
	thousands of hectolitres, 1959	thousands of metric tons, 1953–5 av.	thousands of metric tons, 1953–5 av.
Spain	16,800	1,423	1,299
Portugal	8,000	400	—
Italy	63,640	1,441	1,032
World	230,000	approx. 5 millions	U.S.A. 5,830

Livestock: numbers for 1957

	Portugal	Spain	Italy	World
Cattle	1,073,000	2,742,037	8,479,000	850,000,000
Pigs	1,516,000	2,792,630	3,545,000	380,000,000
Sheep	4,000,000	15,933,140	9,819,000	875,000,000
Goats	738,000	3,096,663	1,890,000	330,000,000
Horses	74,000	598,000	509,000	77,000,000
Donkeys	237,000	683,024	582,000	—
Mules	127,000	1,070,716	368,000	—

Wool: millions of pounds for 1958–9

Spain	82	
Portugal	2·5	(1953–5 average)
Italy	3·6	(,, ,,)
Australia	1,434	
World	5,020	

i

ii

iii

IX i Maize and haystack with distant meadows and woods, near Avilés, Asturias.

    ii Segovia Cathedral rising above the wheatfields, Northern Meseta.

   iii Flooded ricefields with shoots just showing, near Valencia.

X i Cork oak stripped of cork, showing dark trunk, Catalonia.

ii Collecting resin, near Guarda, North Portugal.

iii Oranges on frost-damaged tree, near Sagunto.

iv Selling water-melons, Huesca.

CHAPTER VII

Economic Geography II: Natural Resources, Electrical Energy, Industry, Trade, Communications

THE GREAT RANGE of geological strata in the Iberian peninsula is responsible for the rich variety of minerals found here. This fact was known to prehistoric man, who found copper in the south, to the Phoenicians who traded with the Bronze Age inhabitants, and later to successive occupants of the peninsula – Carthaginian, Roman and Moor. The diversity of minerals remains, but in the twentieth century quantity is of paramount importance, and in this respect there is a deficiency. Iberia has only a small mineral output, and is lacking in coal and petroleum, while scanty rainfall restricts the generation of hydro-electricity. In fact, natural resources in the peninsula do not encourage industrial expansion, though they have influenced industrial distribution. A high proportion of Iberian mineral wealth comes from the peripheral regions, and this fact has facilitated the export of minerals and determined the siting of such primary industries as iron and steel production and metal smelting.

I. SUBTERRANEAN RESOURCES

Non-metallic Minerals

Salt is of particular importance in countries where large amounts are needed, either in fish preserving or as a basis for the chemical industry. In Iberia great quantities are evaporated from sea water; approximately half the Spanish annual total of about $1\frac{3}{4}$ million metric tons and most of the Portuguese total of about 2,700 metric tons is derived from this natural source. The most important saltings are situated in the drier south and east where summer drought provides optimum conditions for intense evaporation; those of Aveiro and the Algarve are important in Portugal, while in Spain the largest saltings occur at San Fernando (Cádiz), followed by those of the Levant coast, for example Torrevieja, near Murcia. Rock salt, often associated with Tertiary sediments, is widespread in Spain; the primary producing region is Santander, where the mines of Palanco and Cabezón de la Sal are important. Lesser centres include Forcada (Huesca province), Belinchón (Cuenca province), Tierzo (Guadalajara province) and Laguna de Salinas (Alicante province). Potassium salts, found beneath a gypsum or limestone cap in silvinite (at a depth of 25–35 feet), and carnalite (between 100 and 170 feet) are mined almost exclusively at the Catalonian centres of Cardona, Suria, Sallent and Balsaremy, which together produce approximately $1\frac{1}{4}$ million metric tons per year. Near Cardona, at La Coromina, the 'Unión Española de Explosivos' refines the rock and sends it by an aerial ropeway, 8 miles long, to Suria, where it joins a narrow-gauge railway. Gypsum is another mineral associated with younger strata. Spain is the more important producer (1,055,000 metric tons in 1958, as opposed to Portugal's total of 65,000). Sarreal (Tarragona) produces high-quality alabaster, and other Spanish centres occur in the Ebro basin, Old Castile and Andalusia; the Portuguese gypsum is associated with the Tertiary limestones of the lower Tagus.

Kaolin is derived from granite rocks, so that production (Portuguese about 40,000 metric tons, and Spain about 20,000 metric tons, per year) is limited to north Portugal and north-west Spain, and the smaller granite outcrops of the Central Sierras, particularly the Toledo ranges.

Apatite, which provides phosphates, is mined in the Tagus valley around Cáceres, and, although the phosphate content is high, the rock is hard and difficult to dissolve in sulphuric acid. A factory at Villanueva de la Serena processes the rock, but annual amounts seldom exceed 20,000 metric tons.

Sulphuric acid forms an essential element in most branches of modern industry. In Spain there are two main sulphur deposits, at Hellín (upper Guadalquivir basin) and Libros (Teruel), while sulphur is also extracted as a by-product from the ferrous pyrites of the Sierra Morena, which contain from 47 per cent to 51 per cent of sulphur. The total amount of sulphur ore mined every year averages 60,000 metric tons.

Minerals of lesser importance include asphalt, extracted from the bituminous shales of the Alava–Logroño area; petroleum in very small amounts from petroliferous limestones near Puertollano; fluorspar (10,300 metric tons in 1958) from the Anglés and Papiol mines of Catalonia and those of Bielsa and Gistain in the Pyrenees; and mica from Martinamor (Salamanca) and Mijas (Málaga).

Non-ferrous Metals

Most of the subterranean resources of the peninsula appear in outcrops of older rocks in the north, west and central regions.

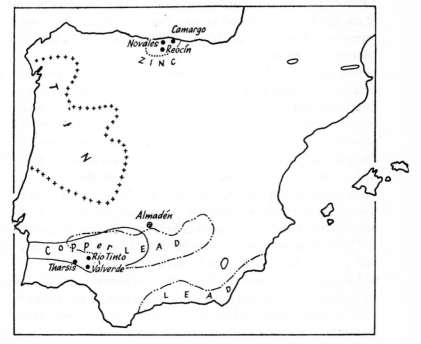

Fig. 33. Non-Ferrous Metals

Copper ores of a pyritic nature occur in the south-east highlands of Iberia, especially around Rio Tinto in Spain, associated with the partially metamorphosed Palaeozoic strata at the edge of the Hercynian block. These ores continue across the frontier zone and are mined in Portugal at such small centres as Beja, Aljustrel and Minas de São Domingos. Copper is also mined in the Aveiro and Feria (Badajoz) districts in the Muriano hills north of Córdoba, and at such small centres as Orsavinyá (near Barcelona), Almodóvar del Campo, Los Arcos and Bielsa; none of these produce more than 1,000 metric tons per year, and most produce considerably less. Lack of capital in both countries prohibits a more effective utilization of resources, and world demand for copper, once increasing, is now waning as American armament stockpiles are reduced. The average annual output of ore (including cupriferous pyrites) in Portugal is 600,000 metric tons, and in Spain $1\frac{3}{4}$ million metric tons. The Portuguese export much of the ore in a natural (i.e. unrefined) state, while in Spain the ore is refined and smelted at such centres as Rio Tinto, for production of electrical equipment and bronze, Lugo and Lejana for a wide variety of alloys, and at Palencia, Bilbao, Barcelona, Madrid, Burceña and Alsasua.

Zinc ore is mined primarily in Spain, which annually produces over 80,000 metric tons. In the province of Santander the 1,000-feet deep galleries of the mines on the Coto de Reocín, a rocky tract near the Picos de Europa, produce a blende containing 58 per cent to 60 per cent of zinc, and it is this area which provides the bulk of Spanish production. Other mines occur in the Sierra de Cartagena, the Sierra Morena, north of Córdoba, where the Peñarroya company operates, and the Val d'Aran, in the Pyrenees, worked by the previous company and also by the Belgian company 'Vieille Montagne'. Zinc ores have recently been discovered at Motril (Granada) and Solano de Pino (Ciudad Real). Both lead and zinc (frequently found together) are the results of thermal metamorphism and the flow of hydrothermal solutions; the distribution of both metals in Iberia is limited, in the main, to areas of Hercynian folding where such activity took place. Cadmium is occasionally found in association with these metals; Spain produced 8 metric tons in 1957, mainly from zinc smelted at

Arnao (Asturias). Zinc smelting is concentrated in northern Spain at Avilés in Asturias, and at Peñarroya, where in each case there are local supplies of coal. In the Val d'Aran the high-grade ores will be more effectively exploited when the Artiés waterfall has been harnessed for hydro-electricity. The problems of transport and adequate fuel for smelting are at the moment hindering the Iberian production.

Spain annually produces about 43,000 metric tons of lead ore, while the Portuguese contribution to world supplies is under one third of this amount, and comes chiefly from the Aveiro district. Lead associated with zinc is found in the Sierra Morena of Spain, where Linares is the centre of a mining district which contains 30 of the 53 lodes found in the province of Jaén. The most important mines here are La Carolina, La Cruz and Santa Elena; further west mining takes place at Peñarroya, Santa Barbara, el Hoya, and continues into Portugal, where smaller mines occur. Other Spanish regions include the south-east coast, where the Sierra Almagrave yields argentiferous lead ores, and the ports of Agua Amarga and Garrucha are exclusively engaged in exporting ore from such mining towns as Cuevas de Vera, Vélez Rubio and Níjar; and subsidiary centres in the Cantabrians such as Reocín, Reinosa, Santander, Guipúzcoa, and in Catalonia around Bellmunt and Molá. Lead is processed in Asturias and Peñarroya, but smelting also takes place on the spot near the larger mines, since galena is particularly heavy to transport.

For many years mercury has been extracted from the cinnabar of the Almadén district in Spain, which yields from 12 per cent to 40 per cent pure metal. The most important mines are those of San Diego, San Pedro, San Francisco and San Nicolás. There are, in addition, several less important mines, including Mieres and Muñón in Asturias, Castaras and Bérchules in the province of Granada, Chovar in Castellón, and several mines around Badajoz. Cinnabar is frequently associated with ancient solfataric or hot spring emanations, and the distribution of the mines coincides with regions subjected in previous geological epochs to intense earth movements, particularly during Hercynian times. The metal is smelted in modern installations in Almadén, and the annual production now exceeds 1,800 metric tons.

Iberian manganese comes primarily from the Soloviejo–Almonaster la Real nucleus in the Sierra Morena north of Huelva, where the ore is of good average quality, though somewhat siliceous. Small amounts of ore are also mined in south-east Portugal, in the Cangas de Onis, Covadonga and Cabrales mines in Asturias, in the Pozuelo de Calatrava and Almagro districts of Ciudad Real, where high-quality manganese oxide is found, in the Alfambra–Camañas zone in Teruel province and in the Cerdagne (Pyrenees). Spain annually produces about 38,000 metric tons of ore and Portugal about 5,000 metric tons. Much of the Spanish ore is smelted in the Cantabrian iron-smelting region.

Tin oxide, or cassiterite, occurs in a particular variety of granite; the oxide is frequently found in association with wolfram, and, nearer the edge of the intrusion or parent rock, with arsenical or copper pyrites. In Iberia, as in many other countries, tinstone is recovered from pebble concentrations in alluvial deposits washed down from the lodes of the neighbouring hills. The edge of the granite mass in the peninsula lies across the lower Douro, and it is within this broad region that the main extraction centres occur; Castello Branca, Guarda and Vizeu in Portugal, and Carbia, Silleda and Lousame in Spain. Portugal annually produces about 1,250 long tons and Spain about 240 long tons of ore.

Wolframite, the double tungstate of iron and manganese, is now in increasing demand owing to the use of tungsten carbide as the cutting agent in high-speed steels. The main reserves in Iberia correspond to those of tin, with the addition of a few less important centres in the Sierra de Gata, Badajoz and Salamanca districts. In 1958 Portugal produced 1,867 metric tons of tungsten concentrate, destined mainly for export, and Spain 923 metric tons; in addition Portugal produced 800 metric tons of arsenic, and Spain a smaller amount, from the complex Douro granites and the younger rocks of Asturias.

Bauxite is preponderantly a Spanish product; Spain annually extracts about 6,000 metric tons from the Catalonian mines of Santa Creus, Poblas, Mediona, La Llacuna, and from a few scattered mines in the hills round Teruel, where transport difficulties prevent a more intensive exploitation. The exceptionally high temperatures required for smelting the ore can only be obtained economically from hydro-electricity. In Spain the river Gallego provides the town of Sabiñánigo with sufficient hydro-electricity to smelt not only Spanish bauxite but also quantities imported from France; in 1957 Spain produced 14,900 metric tons of aluminium.

The precious metals of Iberia have attracted diggers from the Copper Age onwards, and the Romans exploited veins of gold in León and the Serra de Vilarelho, Portugal; today, however, although there are many deposits, for example the Sil gravels, where gold occurs in minute quantities, washing or mining for gold is generally uneconomic. There are several small mines, for example the Minas de Jales in north Portugal where the rock provides adequate returns, but in general both gold and silver are produced as by-products of the refining processes. In the Cape Gata and Huelva regions iron pyrites yields from 10 to 15 oz troy of silver per ton of rock, while in the same area from 15 to 40 oz troy of gold and from 80 to 150 oz troy of silver are derived from ore concentrates by the cyanide process. Silver is also obtained from the argentiferous galena of Galicia and the Sierra Morena, and from the slightly younger rocks of Hiendelaencina, Guadalajara province. Total amounts of gold are very small – in 1958 only 11,000 oz troy in Spain and 14,000 oz troy in Portugal, the latter coming mainly from Tres Minas and Évora. There is a higher production of silver – 1,645,000 oz troy in Spain and 50,000 oz troy in Portugal for the same year. There are very small amounts of other metals in the peninsula; nickel is found in association with lead in the Catalonian district between Vimbodí and Poblet, where a 10 per cent to 20 per cent nickel content occurs, and at Carratraca (Málaga), where both chrome and nickel are exploited. Molybdenum is found between Granada and Motril in Andalusia, and Spain annually produces about 95 metric tons of bismuth from the valley of Pedroches (Córdoba). Diatomite (11 metric tons in 1957) and vanadium are also produced in Spain, while in 1957 Portugal provided 169 metric tons of beryllium, and 300 metric tons of ilmenite, from which titanium is derived. Traces of uranium occur in the province of Córdoba, and Portugal has recently intensified the search for this valuable metallic element.

The Alentejo region of Portugal produces a small amount of asbestos.

Iron and Carbonaceous Fuels

Iron ores can be divided according to their origin into three main groups. One group is associated with sedimentary rocks and consists normally of deposits of hydrated oxide, carbonate or silicate, formed by precipitation, and with a low to average iron content. A second group consists of replacement ores, such as haematite, occurring in veins or masses which represent zones of transit either for ascending hot magmatic solutions or for descending meteoric waters. The third type, for example magnetite, is associated with gneissic metamorphic or igneous rocks, and, like the replacement ores, is rich in metal. Unfortunately most Iberian deposits are of the first group, and only a few areas produce really high-grade ores.

Iron ore production in the peninsula is peripheral and predominantly Spanish; of the total amount mined every year Spain contributes about 5 million metric tons, Portugal about $\frac{1}{4}$ million metric tons.

The Basque provinces rank as the major producers, and provide 70 per cent to 80 per cent of the Iberian total. Here the Biscayan *rubio*, a ferric oxide, contains up to 52 per cent of metal but this, unfortunately, has been exhausted in the most accessible areas; the remaining ores are less rich. The number of known deposits in Vizcaya is 1,500, but of these only 120 can be worked economically. Bilbao is the main centre, the actual mines being situated on the hillside to the west of the ria. The latter forms an excellent harbour and some of the ores are exported, but the trade between Bilbao and the South Welsh coalfield is now less important than formerly.

To the east of Bilbao there are small deposits at Lesaca–Irún, Oyarzún, Cerain and Matiloa, on either side of the river Bidasoa, while to the west is the subsidiary area of Santander, served by mines at Camargo, Mata and Solares. These deposits continue westwards where they are mined in the Picos de Europa, Sierra del Naranjo, and at Llumeres, La Picota and other small centres scattered over the Cantabrians in Asturias. The Galician mines include those of Silvarrosa and Villaodrid, linked by rail to the port of Ribadeo. The quality of ore in these western regions is inferior, containing high amounts of silica which consume more coal than do better quality ores.

Fig. 34. Iron Deposits

In the south of Spain there occurs a broad belt of country, containing a number of somewhat scattered iron mines, stretching parallel to the coast from Estepona to La Unión (Cartagena). Small amounts of high-quality ore come from Huenaja and Alquife; these ores continue eastwards and are mined at Gérgal, while additional centres occur in the Sierra de Filabres near Serón. Many of these mines are linked to the main line railway by aerial ropeway. Further west, the ores extracted from the Sierra de Ojén are exported via the port of Marbella. All these ores, like those of northern Spain, are associated with sedimentary rocks. Iron found in the interior is (when associated with pre-Cambrian strata) of haematite or magnetite type. Between Ponferrada and León occurs the 'Coto Wagner', a series of veins and lodes 14

miles long and parallel to the railway, ore from which produces up
to 55 per cent metal when smelted at Ponferrada. At Alborracín
small amounts of high-grade haematite are found, which yield
up to 70 per cent metal. Much of the ore, however, is of poorer
grade and associated with sedimentary rocks; that from the mines
of the Sierra Menera (Ojos Negros, Pardos and Cuculan) is sent
to Sagunto by a narrow-gauge railway almost parallel to the main
line run by the R.E.N.F.E. Other less important districts include
those of the Sierra de la Demanda and Monte Rubio which send
ore to Bilbao, the mines of the Sierra Morena (Jerez de los Caballeros, El Pedroso) which produce ore of inferior quality, the
Lumbrales and Barruecopardo mines of Badajoz, small centres in
north-east and south-east Portugal, and Vallferrara and Alp in the
Pyrenees. Iron mining in many of these areas is limited by difficulties of communication.

The distribution of carbonaceous fuels in the peninsula follows
the same broad pattern as that of iron; there is an important concentration of medium- to high-grade coal on the north coast, with
smaller deposits occurring centrally and in the south. Portugal,
with an annual average output of 720,000 metric tons of coal and
72,000 metric tons of lignite, fares badly by comparison with
Spain, which produces annually about 17,000,000 metric tons of
coal, about 2,000,000 metric tons of anthracite and about
2,000,000 metric tons of lignite.

In the fifteenth century the first coal mine to be worked in the
peninsula was at Castrillón in Spain. It was not until the Industrial
Revolution, however, that coal resources became of real importance. Unfortunately, Iberian geology is so varied that there
are very few areas of high-grade coal, and some of these are so inaccessible and so bleak in winter as to be virtually useless. Furthermore, the softness of the coal and the narrowness of the seams
(the average thickness seldom exceeds 30 inches), coupled with
irregularity of thickness and steep pitch due to folding, prevent
the use of machinery and make the coal difficult and costly to
work, even when the average Spanish miner's wage is taken into
account.

Asturias is the outstanding coal-mining region of the peninsula,
providing almost 70 per cent of the total output. Bituminous

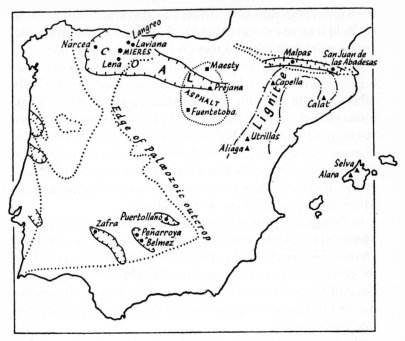

Fig. 35. Carbonaceous Deposits

coal predominates, but a very small amount of anthracite is also
extracted from seams bordering the main zone. Coal pits are
scattered over the hills on either side of the river Nalón, and the
coal is brought by narrow-gauge tracks or overhead cables to the
main R.E.N.F.E. railway lines which transport it to the ports of
Avilés or Gijón. Many pits also occur around the rivers Caudal,
Aller, Teverga and Noreña, each valley being served by narrow-
gauge railway or aerial ropeway. The Tineo and Cangas del
Narcea pits produce anthracite, while many such as Mieres,
Turón, Noreña and Villabona produce bituminous coal.

On the south side of the Cantabrians extends a long, narrow
belt of carboniferous strata, which yields high-quality anthracite
between Igueña and Vegacervera. These pits are due south of the
anthracite mines of Asturias and occur on the eastern flank of the
coalfield, having a distribution similar to that in the South Wales
coalfield, although in Spain there is no marked syncline. Bituminous coal comes from a long east–west line of pits extending

from Cabrillanes through Carrocera to Barruelo. This part of the coalfield is more extensive than the Asturian zone, but the mines are far more scattered, and transport difficulties are greater.

No other centres compare in size or output with the Cantabrian zone, but coal of local significance is mined in several subsidiary areas. In the south near Puertollano good thick (3 to 7 feet) seams of coal are mined at Santa María, San Hilarión and Don Rodrigo. Quality is not high, however, and the output is shared between the expanding industrial concerns of Peñarroya and local power stations. A useful, if small, amount of anthracite is mined at San Rafael, while a group of mines near Villanueva de las Minas provides coal for use on the railways.

In Portugal the two main centres are at Moncorvo and in the Mondego valley near Coimbra; the deposits of coal lie east of the Oporto–Abrantes fault-line, and are not extensive; the quality of the coal is poor or medium, and the difficulties of transport limit the exploitation of other known seams. The new thermal power station (opened July 1959) at Tapada do Outeiro, near Oporto, uses local anthracite.

Hercynian folds in the eastern Pyrenees have been eroded to reveal a few seams of inferior-quality coal. These are worked at San Juan de las Abadesas, Pla de San Tirs, Ortó and Arfa. Other deposits are so inaccessible that they cannot be worked economically – as, for example, the high-grade coal of Bisauri (Huesca province). Smaller centres include those of Juarros, Villasur and Pineda, on the eastern slopes of the Sierra de la Demanda, and the Estremaduran mines of Llerena and Zafra.

Lignite is concentrated in the north-east section of the peninsula, where it is associated generally with slightly folded Mesozoic strata. Teruel is the primary producer, the most important mines being those of Utrillas, Gargallo and Aliaga. The lignite of this area is, unfortunately, very rich in sulphur (about 10 per cent) which minimizes its extensive utilization. The seams continue north-eastwards and are worked in the broad belt of country extending between Velilla de Cinca and Mequinenza, in the lower Cinca and lower Ebro basins.

In the Pyrenean foothills there occurs a semi-circular zone of lignite, linking such tiny mining centres as Capella, Saldes and

Calat. These Catalonian seams are of high quality, light, rich in volatile material – up to 40 per cent. Some of this lignite is sent to the industrial towns of Catalonia, where it can be used efficiently in the lighter industries.

Less important producers are widely scattered; the younger rocks to the west of the Oporto–Abrantes fault-line, near Coimbra, contain some lignite, while small centres such as Selva, Sineu and Alara in Majorca have a slight but regular output (8 per cent of the Spanish total).

Mineral Production in Iberia

Production figures for Italy, the United Kingdom, the world's largest producer and the world total, all for 1958, are included for the purposes of comparison.

All figures refer to metric tons unless otherwise stated

m = million   th = thousand

	Bauxite th	Antimony	Arsenic	Barytes th	Coal m	Copper ore th	Felspar th
Portugal	—	10	800	—	0·72	1·1	1·2
Spain	6	215	—	26·8	17·09	7·5	6
Italy	299	118	1,000	93·2	1·54	·81	56·1
U.K.	—	—	—	64·3	219·29	—	—
	W. Indies	China	U.S.A.	U.S.A.	U.S.S.R.	U.S.A.	U.S.A.
	6,098	15,000?	10,440	441·2	496	888·4	477·3
Total	21,000	40,000	36,000	2,300	2,436	3,390	1,040

	Fluorspar th	Gold th oz	Graphite th	Gypsum th	Iron ore th	Lead ore th	Manganese ore th
Portugal	—	14	—	65	217	12	5
Spain	103	11	0·5	1,055	4,908	42·3	37·9
Italy	140	6	4	670	1,238	56	43·4
U.K.	78·6	—	—	4,055	14,848	4·1	—
	U.S.A.	S. Africa	Korea	U.S.A.	U.S.A.	Austr.	U.S.S.R.
	289·9	17,666	94	8,709	69,038	332	5,366
Total	1,600	40,400	305	33,435	403,453	2,280	11,843

	Pyrites th	Salt th	Silver th oz	Sulphur th long tons	Tin ore long tons	Tungsten	Zinc ore th
Portugal	598	—	50	—	1,245	1,867	—
Spain	1,765·9	1,829	1,645	3·7	240	923	82·9
Italy	1,513·9	1,610	1,334	158·7	—	—	136·8
U.K.	4·1	5,007	27	—	1,087	50	—
	Japan	U.S.A.	Mexico	U.S.A.	Malaya	China	Canada
	3,193·4	19,877	47,590	4,645·6	38,458	20,000?	384·8
Total	17,933	73,400	236,800	6,500	152,400	57,600	3,040

Spain produced 55,000 flasks of mercury in 1958, and is the second world producer after Italy (58,712). World total – 204,467 flasks (of 76 lb. each).

The table on page 161 gives some idea of the Iberian position with regard to world production of the basic minerals required in industry. Mercury alone is extracted in such quantities as to place Iberia high on the list of world producers; in all other minerals production is notably small. Coal is deficient not only in quantity but in quality, there is no petroleum, and power for industry from these sources is minimal. In this respect, however, Iberia follows a typically Mediterranean pattern, since there are no appreciable reserves of coal or petroleum around the Mediterranean sea. Spain produces more coal, and Italy more oil, than any other Mediterranean country, but in neither case are the figures in any way comparable with those of highly industrialized countries. The production of basic metals such as iron and copper is also slight when compared with world production, but even so there is an annual surplus which the industries of Spain and Portugal cannot absorb. Such natural resources form useful articles of trade, accounting annually for approximately 25 per cent (by value) of the exports of both countries.

The total number of people engaged in mining and quarrying is small; 173,808 out of a total Spanish labour force of 10,793,057 (1956) and 25,000 out of a total of 3,005,000 Portuguese workers (1956). These figures are small when compared with the numbers of people engaged in agriculture or in manufacturing, but the raw materials produced form an essential part of Iberian economy. Shortage of capital and few assets overseas make it imperative for both Spain and Portugal to increase home manufactures, since such goods as cars, textiles and tools are too expensive to import. For this reason both countries within the last decade have made increasing use of electricity, which after initial expense provides cheap, clean and continuous power.

2. ELECTRICAL ENERGY

Spain generates more electricity than Portugal – about 15,000 million kilowatts per year of the total annual peninsular production of about 16,900 million kilowatts. Only 25 per cent of this total is thermal in origin, the rest being hydro-electricity. There is a marked correlation between the 24-inch isohyet and the distribution of hydro-electric power stations, very few falling outside this line.

The north-west districts of Galicia and Asturias, and the higher parts of the Serra da Estrêla, have the highest rainfall of the peninsula, but the eastern foothills of the Pyrenees contain more power stations, in response to the demands of Catalonian industry. Thermal stations here are few – one at Figols utilizes local lignite, and two just outside Barcelona at San Adrián and Mata use imported fuels. The waters of the Noguera Pallaresa and Segre are intensively utilized, and hydro-electric stations occur in their upper courses at Escaldas and Camarasa (on the Segre), and Capdella, Molinos, Pobla de Segur, Tremp, Gavet and Terradets (on the Noguera Pallaresa). There are, in addition, further stations at Cledes on the upper Garonne (Val d'Aran), Gerona on the Ter, Urdiceto, Barrosa and La Fortunada on the upper Cinca, and Los Baños, Pueyo and Biescas on the upper Aragón. There are more stations on the lower Cinca and Ebro at Serós, Sastago and Flix. An extensive grid links these stations to each other, to the Catalan industrial towns and to Barcelona.

Electricity from the upper Aragón and upper Cinca is connected to an important system which supplies Pamplona and the Basque coast. The main stations occur at El Cortizo, Alloz, Puentefarre, Aranguren and Bilbao. High-tension cables link Bilbao to Valladolid, where an extension branches west to the hydro-electric power stations on the Esla, and to Madrid.

In the north and west coal is more widely used for generating electricity, and there are thermal stations at Burceña and Altos Hornos, near Bilbao, and at Felguera and Sama near Oviedo. Rivers are smaller than in the Pyrenees, and there are few hydro-electric stations; the main ones occur at Barceña on the river Torina, Peñarrubia on the river Urdón and Camerina (Santander), Somiedo and Navia (Oviedo), and Pindo and Tambre (Galicia).

Central Spain is characterized by summer drought, and slight annual rainfall, which seriously limit the generation of hydro-electricity. Only in the wetter Central Sierras is there adequate rainfall, and the main hydraulic plants are situated at Punte Nuovo, Burguillo, Marmeta, Torrelaguna and Bolarque. These, however, cannot satisfy the increasing industrial demands of

Madrid, and are supplemented by two thermal plants on the outskirts of the capital. Production, however, is still deficient, and power cuts occur every dry summer, sometimes causing temporary unemployment as factories are forced to restrict working hours. It is hoped that new stations associated with irrigation schemes in Guadalajara will eventually remedy this deficiency.

Along the Levant coast a localized grid centres on Valencia and towns beside the rivers Júcar and Cabriel. Hydro-electricity is generated at Villora, Molinar, Cortes, Millares and Albentosa; in addition, there are three thermal stations just outside Valencia. High-tension cables link this zone with Madrid and with the Murcia–Alicante network, which is provided with electricity by plants at Cañarerosa and Los Almadenes.

In Andalusia the coal resources of Puertollano, Peñarroya, Rio Tinto and Prado (near Seville) provide thermal electricity, while along the southern edge of the Sierra Morena hydro-electricity is generated at Jaudilla, El Encinarejo and Cala. Stations in the Sierra Nevada include those at Velez, Castillo, Choro and Buitreras. This forms only a local network not at present linked to the grid systems of the Levant coast or of Madrid.

In Portugal the great potentialities of the wet highlands in the centre and north are only just being realized. Small stations along the river Zêzere provide Lisbon with power, and much progress has been made in the last decade in the northern provinces; the names of the more ambitious projects and the date of their opening are as follows:

1951	Castelo do Bode, Venda Nova,* Belver
1953	Salamonde*
1954	Cabril
1955	Caniçada and Bouçã
1956–7	Paradela* – one of the largest stone-built dams in the world
1958	Picote, on the upper Douro

The stations marked with an asterisk are situated in the Cávado basin; when all projected schemes (for example, new stations at Miranda, Bemposta and Távora in north Portugal) are finished there will be a complete grid system covering the whole of the country; at the moment the annual production is about 2,200 million kilowatts.

The main consumers of electrical energy are the industrial towns of Catalonia (about 25 per cent of the Spanish total), the Basque provinces (about 12 per cent) and the Levant regions (about 12 per cent). Electricity is used primarily in industry (about 50 per cent of the total) and lighting (about 20 per cent), and almost 20 per cent is lost in transmission and in transformers, while transport uses about 5 per cent and agriculture about 2 per cent.

The production of electricity within the peninsula increases annually, as the following figures show:

Spain: Production for 1929/30/31 = 100

1952	1953	1954	1955	1956	Average yearly increase – 12%
362	380	395	471	492	

Average yearly increase for Europe – 8%

In Portugal there has been a similar increase, becoming more rapid during the last five years as projects in the Cávado and Douro basins have been completed. The total amounts generated are small when compared with those for other countries:

Spain	15,468 million kw	32% thermal	(1958)
Portugal	2,169 ,, ,,	25% ,,	(1957)
Italy	42,715 ,, ,,	25% ,,	(1957)
U.S.A.	544,645 ,, ,,		(1958)
World	1,360,400 ,, ,,		(1958)

They reflect the general aridity of the peninsula and the limited amount of industry.

3. INDUSTRY

Factors influencing the location of industry may be summarized as follows:

1. Adequate sources of energy, i.e. coal, petroleum or electricity.
2. Adequate provision of water.
3. Easily obtainable or local supplies of raw materials.
4. A local reserve of skilled workers who have not only a tradition of industrial service but also a progressive outlook.
5. Ready markets in which to sell the goods manufactured.

The first four of these conditions are realized only in the northern half of the peninsula, and in a few isolated places in the interior. The last condition is one which has, until recently, proved a major obstacle to industrial expansion in the peninsula. In general, Spaniards and Portuguese have a low standard of living, and can afford few luxuries; on the other hand, Iberian industries are small and techniques often uneconomic, so that neither Spain nor Portugal can compete with the mass-production methods of the U.S.A., Germany or Britain. Furthermore, in the past, political considerations have caused discrimination in world markets against goods produced under the dictatorial régime prevailing in Spain. Iberia, restricted in its overseas trade, has to depend on a home market to absorb most of the manufactured goods, and this market is limited by the low purchasing power of buyers. This vicious economic circle is steadily being overcome, however, as American dollars (in exchange for air bases) and tourists' foreign currency provide more money to spend, create a greater demand for consumer goods and stimulate industrial expansion.

The Iron and Steel Industry

The elder Pliny wrote of the famous Triano hills in the Basque country: 'Metallorum omnium vena ferri longissima est. Cantabriae maritimae parts, quam oceanus adhuit, mons praerupte altus, incredibile dictu totus ex ea materiae est, ut in ambitu Oceani diximus.' From pre-Roman times until the present day the Basque iron mines have provided the raw material for a flourishing industry. As early as the eleventh century the *olagizonak*, or organizations of metal workers, were well established, and in 1262, by order of Alphonso X, the town of Mondragon was released from payments of iron taxes. In these early days the iron was smelted by charcoal derived from local forests, and running streams were used to temper the blades of knives, axes and swords. Steel, from Bilbao, enjoyed a certain reputation beyond the Spanish border – in the Tower of London there are several sword blades stamped with the name 'Bilboes' – and the export of iron brought in a steady revenue, so much so that the seventeenth-century author Tirso de Molina was inspired to write of the Vizcayan mines 'por su hierro, España goza su oro'.

The deep-seated tradition of iron-working in this area has given rise to a remarkable economic situation. In most iron- and steel-producing countries the main movement is of iron ore, which is generally more valuable (bulk for bulk) than coal and therefore less costly to transport. The iron ore of the Vermilion and Mesabi ranges in the U.S.A., for example, are transported the full length of the Great Lakes, a distance of approximately 900 miles, to join, at Cleveland, the coal coming from the Pennsylvanian coalfield only 100 miles away. Similarly, the iron and steel industries along the south Welsh coast depend on local coal from the Welsh valleys, but on imported iron ore. In Spain, however, the progressive Basques quickly learnt the techniques of iron smelting which used coal and coke, and started to import coal, by sea, from Asturias. This unusual and somewhat uneconomic situation has only recently been reversed by the setting up of three new blast furnaces at Avilés. Nevertheless, the heavy iron and steel industry remains almost a monopoly of the Basque provinces.

This monopoly was originally challenged by metal workings in Catalonia and Andalusia; in 1846, however, the first Spanish blast furnace, the Santa Ana de Bolueta, was lit near Bilbao, and other regions succumbed to this better-provided and more highly organized northern region. The main centre is Bilbao; originally a sandbar across the ria necessitated the use of Portugalete as an outport, but the bar was dredged, the ria deepened, and ores exported to South Wales in return for coal. When the best lodes became exhausted, poorer ones were mined and treated on the spot; in this way a certain amount of industry arose, which now uses Asturian coal. The company 'Altos Hornos de Vizcaya' has six blast furnaces in Bilbao (as well as two in Sagunto on the Levant coast), and thus owns almost a third of the Spanish total. In addition it has administrative control of coal and iron mines, a small fleet of five coaling ships, several metallurgical installations and sheet metal factories, and produces most of the coke needed in the blast furnaces as well as by-products of coal such as gas and tar. The company produces pig iron, ingots, varieties of steel, including stainless and carbon steels, rails, sheet metal, axle bars, rifle and gun barrels, galvanized iron, coal-tar derivatives (benzole, creosote, naphthalene) and sulphate of ammonia.

Other companies in the vicinity include 'Echevarría', with two factories, one at Santa Agueda (Baracaldo) and the other at Recalde (Bilbao). The first possesses two blast furnaces, the second refines the metal proceeding from the first. The Recalde factory specializes in steels (high-speed, tungsten, stainless), while the Santa Agueda factory produces wire and rivets as well as pig iron. Sheet steel is used in the ship-building yards of Bilbao.

Basauri lies just outside Bilbao, at the intersection of four railway lines. The proximity of two waterfalls and a thermal electric station has facilitated the production of sheet steel, tinplate (using tin from west Spain), screws, rivets and bolts.

At the mouth of the river Nervión heavy railway, marine, and agricultural machinery is manufactured, while the 'Euskalduna' company produces all kinds of railway engines, rolling stock and signalling equipment in factories at Elorrieta and Olaveaga. Zorroza is a noted centre for the production of bridges, cranes, girders, rods and bars, and the Babcock and Wilcox works at Sestao and Salvador del Valle produce electric engines and motors, while small boats and rolling stock are built in Deusto.

Further east there is an important group of towns in Guipúzcoa – Legazpia manufactures a great variety of steels, Beasaín specializes in rolling stock, trams and buses, and Rentería and Lasarte produce cast iron and a variety of steel goods.

To the west of Bilbao lies the Santander region, where coke, coal-tar products, and, at Corrales de Huelva, sheet steel, metal cables and hawsers are produced. Inland, at Reinosa, steel plate is manufactured by the 'Sociedad Española de Construccion Naval', and used in ship-building at Sestao, Cádiz and El Ferrol.

In Asturias the main centres are Moreda, and Mieres where blast furnaces provide an appreciable amount of iron and steel, and Felguera which produces girders, bars and superstructures such as hangars and bridges. Avilés has recently become another important iron and steel centre; three blast furnaces have been lit within the last five years, the last in 1958, and this enables colliers taking coal from Asturias to return with iron ore from Bilbao, a more economic arrangement than that previously in operation.

Catalonia, like the Basque provinces, has a long tradition of iron-working. In the tenth century Catalan forges were well known for their high-quality workmanship, those around the upper Noguera Pallaresa being particularly important. Their significance continued as long as horse-shoes, tools and weapons were locally forged; in the nineteenth century, however, the rapid advance of heavy industry in the north, connected with the coalfields, and lack of adequate supplies of local fuel, caused a recession. More recently the provision of hydro-electric power and the demands of local textile mills have initiated new iron and steel industries, usually light and varied in type.

Barcelona is the main centre, and, although there is some production of heavy goods (for example, the manufacture of sheet steel for ship-building, diesel engines, girders and textile machinery at Barcelona and San Andrés), the emphasis is on lighter goods. Motor-cars (Ford Motor Ibérica and General Motors Peninsular), aeroplane engines and fitments, buses and taxis, typewriters, industrial and office safes, radiators – these are a few of the great variety of iron and steel goods made in the Catalan capital and its suburbs. Furthermore, in many textile towns, for example Sabadell, Tarrasa, Manresa and Ripoll, general engineering forms an ancillary industry, supplying and repairing textile machinery.

Apart from these centres the iron and steel industry of Iberia is widely dispersed, occurring wherever local supplies of fuel and raw material permit. The most important of these centres may be listed as follows:

Valencia	construction of merchant ships and oil-tankers as well as railway rolling stock.
Vigo	merchant ships and railway rolling stock.
Cádiz	merchant and naval vessels, railway rolling stock and armaments.
Málaga	railway rolling stock; originally contained a blast furnace, but this no longer functions.
Valladolid	all types of engineering, turbines, pumps.
Villaverde Bajo (Madrid)	Euskalduna Co. produces railway stock.
Cartagena	naval vessels.
Albacete	knives.
Seixas	a new Portuguese iron and steel centre, which will produce pig iron and rolled steel.

Fig. 36. Industry

Textile Industries

'... her mother, Teresa Panza, came out spinning a bunch of flax', wrote Cervantes (J. M. Cohen's translation of *Don Quixote*, Penguin Classics). Such cottage industry was ubiquitous in the peninsula from Neolithic times onwards; in Majorca and parts of Portugal peasant women still use a distaff for spinning, and at Guimarães in Portugal coarse linen is still hand-woven. A well-established textile industry first arose in the Middle Ages. The raw material was provided by the Meseta sheep, with fleeces ranking second only to those of English sheep. The organization of the Mesta was powerful enough to gain many privileges for wool traders, and production of the cloth occurred in many towns, both in the Meseta and along the Levant coast (especially in Catalonia). Furthermore, the processing and manufacturing of flax and cotton was also widespread, flax being more important in the north-west and cotton in the south, where it had been introduced by the Moors. Textiles were exported from Catalonia to England, Holland and Italy from the thirteenth century onwards. It was not until the introduction of new machinery in the nineteenth century, however, that the textile industry became more precisely localized. During this time Catalonia gradually increased the number of spindles and looms in use, and the energy and progressiveness of the Catalans enabled them to adopt new methods and try out new materials. When hydro-electricity was introduced Catalonia became the dominant textile centre of the peninsula.

The cotton industry today is of major importance in the peninsula, and almost 70 per cent of all Iberian cotton factories are concentrated in Catalonia, along the rivers Ter, Llobregat, Cardoner, Fresser, Fluvia, Noya, Tordera and Besós. Apart from this riparian alignment there is no further zoning of the industry, and specialization is rare, most of the large centres being engaged in both cotton spinning and weaving.

The valley of the river Ter is the most important, with the towns of San Juan de las Abadesas, Ripoll, Torello, Manlleu, Anglés and Gerona as the largest producers. Next comes the Llobregat valley, where Giranella, Puigreig, Sallent, Monistrol, Esmarraguera and Hospitalet are well-known centres. North of Barcelona, in the interior trench made by the river Congost, occur Sabadell and Granollers, and along the coast Badalona, Vilasar and Mataró – towns which are predominantly cotton-spinning nucleii. Other notable centres include Igualada on the Noya, Manresa on the Cardoner, and Bañolas near the Fluvia, while there are over seventy centres of lesser importance, contained within an area bounded by the rivers Ebro and Segre. Barcelona is the nucleus; as well as possessing more than 250,000 spindles, 12,000 looms and 156 factories for knitted goods, it also imports annually about 260 million lb of raw cotton from America, Egypt, India and some South American countries, and in addition is the main banking and marketing centre for the whole industry.

Small cotton-manufacturing towns include Oporto, where a wide variety of cotton goods is made, Lisbon, Braga, Vergera

(Basque province), Seville, Málaga, Murcia, Valencia, Castellón, Zaragoza and Alcoy.

The woollen industry of Iberia is similar in distribution to that of cotton, but less important. Nearly 100 million lb of wool (in the grease) are manufactured every year, of which only about 10 per cent is imported. Spanish wool, except from merino sheep, is generally coarser and harsher than imported varieties. The bulk of Iberian cloth is produced in the two Catalonian towns of Tarrasa and more especially Sabadell, which together contain about 82 per cent of the total number of wool spindles, and 67 per cent of the total number of looms. Barcelona comes third, with about half the number of machines found in Tarrasa, while other less important Catalan centres include Seo de Urgel, Puigcerda, Gerona and Ripoll. The Spanish Mesetas were originally important woollen-producing regions, but proximity to the sea, cheap and reliable power resources and an industrially minded population have helped Catalonia to capture much of the production of the interior. Nevertheless, such towns as Palencia, Medina del Campo, Salamanca, Zamora, León, Ponferrada, Astorga and Toledo are all minor centres, using mainly local wool, and producing cloth, shoddy and some articles of clothing such as berets and shawls. In Cantabria, Tolosa and Rentería, and, along the Levant coast, Alcoy and Morella are centres of local importance, while in Portugal, Castello Branca has a traditional woollen industry.

Pure silk production is confined principally to the Valencia–Murcia region, where local conditions permit the rearing of silkworms. A small amount of silk is imported from Italy, and about 80,000 lb are annually manufactured, mainly at Orihuela in Spain, and on a small scale at Braganza in Portugal.

Artificial silk and rayon are Catalan specialities – two towns concerned with their production are Prat de Llobregat and Blanes, while most of the material is woven in or near Barcelona, either as pure rayon or as a rayon/cotton mixture. Other centres include Burgos, Torrelavega, Valencia and Miranda del Ebro, while, in Portugal, Lisbon and Oporto are both now increasing their output. The basic raw material is wood cellulose from Scandinavia, but recently other materials, for example eucalyptus wood, esparto grass and rice straw, have been used with some measure of success. About 20 million lb of artificial fibre are manufactured yearly.

Manufacture of rope, canvas and sacking from sisal, hemp or jute takes place in Seville, the Basque provinces, Valencia and Catalonia.

A comparison of Spanish and Portuguese textile industries reveals several basic differences; the industry is more modern, progressive and better equipped in Spain, where 161,500 people are engaged in textile manufacture, as opposed to 45,000 in Portugal. Spain produces far more goods, with rayon fabrics now competing for second place with woollen cloth. It imports some wool and only a little more raw cotton than Portugal, and has a slight export trade. Portugal, on the other hand, not only imports wool and cotton in greater proportion than Spain, but also exports more manufactured textile goods, particularly to her colonies.

Chemical industries tend to be dispersed throughout the peninsula; the danger of transporting such goods as acids and explosives has partially influenced the location of factories, but in general the distribution of raw materials has been the most powerful factor. Sulphuric acid is obtained from iron pyrites at Peñarroya, Rio Tinto and Seville, from phosphates at Badalona and Mongat in Catalonia, and from zinc at Hinojedo and San Juan de Nieva (Asturias). Almost every regional capital of Iberia, but especially Barcelona, produces sulphuric acid from raw materials either of local origin or imported, and the resultant product is used in the manufacture of fertilizer, steel or other chemicals.

Phosphates are of particular importance to agricultural countries, since they are especially used in the manufacture of fertilizers. Iberia is markedly deficient in phosphate rock – there is a small deposit at Logrosán (Cáceres) – so that the bulk is imported from Tunisia and Morocco. Barcelona is the main producer, but many other towns, e.g. San Juan de Nieva, Bilbao, Valencia, Huelva, Málaga and Pamplona, produce superphosphates on a smaller scale.

Nitrogenous fertilizers are produced from Chilean nitrate or from varied chemical processes – for example, those used to obtain caustic soda (as at Flix), coke (as at La Felguera, Asturias), and sulphate of ammonia (as at Sabiñánigo).

Explosives are derived from local potash salts at Cardona, and at Cartagena, La Monjoya (Asturias), Villafeliche (Zaragoza), Elorrieta and Arrigorriaga (Basque provinces). These centres produce, in addition, agricultural insecticides and sprays, gun cotton, fumigants and picric acid. Additional varieties of chemicals (sodium sulphate, hyposulphate, ammonia, bleaches, diverse acids and gases) are made at centres such as Barcelona, Zaragoza, Flix and Sabiñánigo.

The manufacture of paper is dependent above all on a clean and reliable water supply; apart from this, suitable raw material should be easily accessible, and skilled operators are needed at all stages of production. In the Middle Ages the paper industry was dispersed throughout the peninsula, but today it is concentrated in three major regions – the Basque provinces, Catalonia and Valencia.

In the Basque provinces there is a marked concentration of paper factories along the river Oria, at Legazpia, Amezqueta, Tolosa, Belausa, Berrobi, Villabona and Irura. Further east near the frontier occur the centres of Rentería and Hernani, and further west, around the river Nervión, those of Zalla, Sopelana and Arrigorriaga. Conditions are good; there is abundant rainfall throughout the year, a local supply of wood (although little is now used), convenient ports for importing a variety of raw materials, a population used to skilled industrial activities, and a very good system of road and rail transport by which much of the production is sent to the rest of Spain. All types of paper are produced; wrapping paper, some writing paper, newsprint, cellophane, cardboard and sandpaper (a speciality of Cizurquil).

In Catalonia the largest aggregation of factories occurs in the lower basin of the Llobregat; some mills date from the seventeenth century and still maintain a tradition of supplying hand-made paper of excellent quality. The largest centre is that at Prat de Llobregat, where the 'Papelera Española' produces wood pulp and a wide variety of papers; other centres include Torrelavit, Barcelona, Martorell, San Adrián de Besós and Santa Coloma de Cervelló. Along the river Ter, Ribas de Fresser, Ripoll, Gerona and Sarriá de Ter are of importance, while other centres include Bañolas and Vall de Viaña along the river Fluvia, Vespella, and La Riba, north of Tarragona, and Rosello and Borjas Blancas near Lérida.

In Valencia province large quantities of fine-quality papers are made for orange wrappers and cigarettes. Along the river Serpis occur the towns of Alcoy, Muro de Alcoy and Lorcha; other centres are more widely scattered, and include Játiva, Buñol, Valencia and Burriana, as well as Elche further south. In Portugal, Grahams, the port wine shippers, own paper mills near Lisbon.

Much industry in the peninsula is devoted to the processing of agricultural and piscine products. In general industrial location is contiguous to regions of supply. In the north-west part of the peninsula milk products are particularly important; Santander, Galicia and Asturias all produce condensed milk, butter and cheese in quantities which make possible their distribution in other parts of Spain. Leather manufacture is distributed throughout the peninsula, although the largest factory, at Mollet de Vallés (Barcelona), occurs in Catalonia, the most important region.

Fish-preserving factories are important: tinning factories for sardines and tunny occur at every major port along the north and west coasts of the peninsula. Two-thirds of the fish-canning factories of Spain are found along the Atlantic coasts, notably at Vigo, Corunna, Pontevedra, Laredo, Santoña (Santander), Bermeo, Ondárroa (Vizcaya), Cádiz, Sanlúcar and Ayamonte. In Portugal Leixôes, Setúbal, Matozinhos, Olhão and Portimão are important centres. Fruit and vegetable preserving is widespread, particularly in the Ebro basin at Zaragoza and Logroño and along the Levant coast at Alicante, Murcia and Valencia, where the production of nougat and other sweetmeats made from almonds is a local speciality.

The wine-producing regions have already been mentioned, but occupations associated with the wine trade include barrel and bottle making and the production of corks and labels. Cider making is restricted to the north-west part of the peninsula, Asturias being the outstanding producer, but breweries exist in every main town. Spirits and liqueurs are distilled in Barcelona, Madrid, Valladolid, Zaragoza, Seville and Málaga, but smaller centres are also significant, as, for example, Tarragona where Grande Chartreuse is made, Cartagena for Cuarenta y Tres (a liqueur made from oranges), and Jerez de la Frontera for brandy.

Flour-milling and the making of pasta for soups is associated with the larger towns of the Mesetas and the Ebro basin, although large ports such as Lisbon and Barcelona are also important.

Factories for tobacco processing occur in Lisbon, Oporto, Granada, Málaga, Navalmoral de la Mata, Corunna and Barcelona; both home-grown and imported tobacco is used, and local reserves of cheap unskilled female labour help to reduce costs.

Housing problems in Iberia are acute, particularly so in towns to which there is a steady drift of rural population. Tenements and flats house most of the inhabitants of the peninsula, but frequently one family occupies only one or two rooms, while sanitation and water supply leave much to be desired. Spain has recently taken drastic measures to remedy the housing shortage, and production of all building materials has correspondingly increased. Although in some areas local stone is employed, cement is the most widely used material.

The cement industry, originally over-centralized, is now more widely dispersed throughout the peninsula. National demand is amply catered for in both Portugal and Spain, with the greatest concentrations of factories around Bilbao, Barcelona and Madrid, and subsidiary centres at Oporto, Lisbon, Seville, Córdoba, Málaga, Ponferrada, Oviedo and Zaragoza. In this way each major region is self-sufficient in cement and this obviates the costly necessity of importing such a bulky commodity.

The production of tiles and coarse earthenware is particularly important in Barcelona; fine porcelain is manufactured at Santander and Irún, tiles and all types of pottery are made at Madrid, Toledo, Seville, Alicante, San Vicente, Altosanto, Valencia and Lisbon. Azulejos, the highly coloured glazed tiles introduced by the Arabs, are naturally found in the southern part of the peninsula; in Spain the chief centres of production are Seville (where the Cartucha works are pre-eminent), Valencia and Castellón, while in Portugal, where they are particularly prized, manufacture takes place at Lisbon and Coimbra. Glass is manufactured on a large scale in Bilbao, Barcelona, Seville and Madrid.

4. TRADE

Spanish Imports and Exports for 1958

I. General, value in thousands of gold pesetas

Imports	Value	% of total	Exports	Value	% of total
Petroleum and other oils	597,555	22	Foodstuffs	911,505	61
Machinery	431,407	19	Mineral oils	130,073	9
Chemicals	431,407	16	Minerals	117,709	8
Metals	265,960	10	Metals	82,425	5·5
Foodstuffs	213,567	8	Chemicals	77,077	5
Raw cotton	192,997	7	Woods (including cork)	55,472	4
Animal products (especially meat)	39,108	1·5	Machinery	24,215	1·5

II. In detail, value in thousands of gold pesetas

Main imports		Main exports	
Petroleum	448,559	Oranges, mandarins	174,257
Machinery	280,807	Iron ores, pyrites	91,819
Raw cotton	190,633	Mineral oils	90,397
Vegetable oils	154,872	Tomatoes	70,652
Iron and steel	113,998	Ordinary wines	68,894
Electrical goods	95,583	Almonds	65,421
Sulphate of ammonia	79,271	Olives	64,958
Coals	77,769	Fine wines	60,411
Vehicles and parts	67,044	Fruit and vegetable preserves	39,562
Raw tobacco	64,573	Spanish books	35,390
Wood pulp	56,134	Rice	34,410
Rubber	54,204	Mercury	31,818
Sugar	48,357	Petrol and solid fuels	31,787
Phosphates	47,097	Bananas	29,296
Copper	40,680	Cork, worked	27,976
Mineral oils	38,377	Grapes	27,589
Synthetic nitrates	33,071	Tinned fish	27,337
Fresh and frozen meat	31,843	Potassium salts	24,089
Wood	31,189	Lemons	21,959
Scrap iron	30,996	Cork, baled	17,125
Wool	30,538	Potatoes	14,543

Iberian trade is summarized in the tables on pages 177–178. The outstanding importance of agriculture in both Spain and Portugal is revealed in the export lists; foodstuffs dominate Spain's export trade as forest and fish products dominate that of Portugal.

Portuguese Imports and Exports for 1959

Figures refer to millions of escudos. (1,000 escudos are worth approx. £12 10s.)

Imports		Exports	
Iron and steel	1,106	Fish, tinned	1,142
Cotton	881	Sardines	834
Mineral oils	793	Cork, processed	666
Vehicles	303	Cork, raw	660
Vegetable oils	295	Wood, processed	417
Petroleum	280	Cotton cloth	409
Tin-plate	188	Port wine	347
Synthetic resin	163	Resins	335
Coal	154	Ordinary wines	306
Artificial fibres	141	Barrel staves	284
		Combustible oils	167
		Embroidery (Madeira)	132
		Pyrites	118

Figures from the Boletim Mensal do Instituto Nacional de Estatistica

Direction of Iberian Trade, 1958

1. Spain

Imports %		Exports %
7	France	10
9	Germany	10
8	United Kingdom	16
22	U.S.A.	10
11	Latin America	10

2. Portugal

Imports %		Exports %
7	Belgium, Luxembourg	4
18	Western Germany	8
15	Colonies	27
13	United Kingdom	11
7	U.S.A.	8
2	Latin America	3

Petroleum, other raw materials and manufactured goods head the list of imports for both countries, though recently there has been a slight decline in the figures for manufactured goods. Almost 30 per cent of Portugal's exports go to her colonies, especially Angola and Mozambique, other important markets including U.K. and the U.S.A., while Spain sells most of her goods to U.K.,

Western Germany, U.S.A. and France. Portugal imports goods mainly from Western Germany, U.K., U.S.A. and France, while Spain's chief suppliers include U.S.A., France, U.K., Western Germany and Arabia. Once flourishing trade connexions with the Latin American countries have lapsed into insignificance, and are now limited to slight reciprocal trade between Spain and Brazil.

Spain and Portugal, faced with competition from highly organized, more efficient and better endowed countries in North America and North West Europe are forced to control imports by quotas and tariffs which protect their own industries, but recent experience has shown that they cannot hope to become entirely self-sufficient. The discrepancy between exports and imports is made up partly by foreign investments, tourist currency, emigrant remittances and a slight carrying trade, but despite these additions there is usually an adverse trade balance. An increase in the tourist industry, in agricultural production, and in the value of agricultural exports is helping to redress the balance, and recent generous aid from the U.S.A. and the Organization for European Economic Co-operation, which Spain joined on July 20th, 1958, has done much to alleviate economic hardship.

Like many Mediterranean countries neither Spain nor Portugal appears on world lists of iron and steel production, textile manufacture, ship-building, or the production of newsprint, vehicles, aircraft, tools and apparatus. Spain produces 2 per cent of the world's cement, 1 per cent of the boots and shoes and 2 per cent of the sulphuric acid. Against these meagre statistics must be set the small total population of the peninsula and the paucity of natural reserves. The deficiency of manufactured goods is supplemented by imports, as the relevant tables indicate, but both Spain and Portugal are tending to import fewer finished products, and more raw materials as home industries increase their output.

Señor Francisco Martin, in his booklet *Labour Changes the Countryside*, states 'the aim of Spanish industrialization is not a self-sufficing economy, but rather a worthy sufficiency'. Attempts to achieve this latter aim are proving successful. New factories at Avilés have doubled Spain's output of iron and steel within the last five years, while Portugal has tripled her iron and steel output by the installation of new works at Seixas (near Lisbon). Spain has so increased her output of chemical goods that there is now a surplus for export, and the 1959 Second Development Plan in Portugal envisages the increased production, and eventual export, of nitrogenous fertilizers. One industry for which there are few statistics, but which undoubtedly has increased within the last decade, is the tourist industry. Facilities for tourists in both countries are being improved and extended; the revenue from tourism in Portugal rose from 246 million escudos in 1949 to 736 million escudos in 1958, and in Spain there has been an even larger increase in revenue. Subsidiary industries such as the production of tourist souvenirs, provide convenient out-of-season work for peasants and hotel employees.

The total number of industrial workers is as follows:

	Manufacture	Construction	Commerce
Spain	1,904,016	574,279	697,674
Portugal	569,000	145,000	216,000

Although some of these are engaged in cottage industries the vast majority work for concerns either privately financed or State-controlled. Of necessity the State has a controlling interest in both Spanish and Portuguese industry, since large undertakings and new schemes often require wealth beyond the means of private owners. In Spain the National Institute of Industry, created by law in September 1941, is one of the most important State enterprises, influencing every branch of industry and controlling many undertakings, such as the new iron and steel factories at Avilés, the refining of liquid fuels from bituminous lignite and slate, the construction of barrages in the eastern Pyrenees for hydro-electricity, the manufacture of fertilizers and vehicles, the building of ships and aircraft, and the installation of a nation-wide network of refrigerators. In Portugal the Second Development Plan provides for the reorganization of the fish-canning, textile, glass, metal and paper industries under State direction, with some government aid, but private enterprise will be financially responsible for several of the changes. The proposed amount reserved by the government for fisheries, extractive and transforming industries for 1960 was 1,154.5 million escudos.

i

ii

XI   i Goats browsing on drought-resistant shrubs, Minorca.
    ii Bullfight, Granada.

i

ii

iii

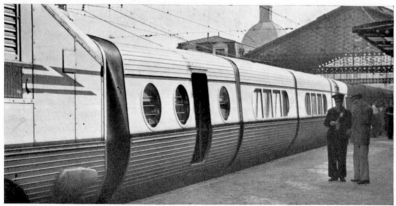

iv

XII   i Street scene in Oporto.

     ii Difficult terrain in Aragón; railway bridge and tunnel, road passing under tunnel.

    iii The mule is the usual means of transport in hill country; Peña de Oroel, near Jaca, in background.

    iv The luxury train 'Talgo'.

5. COMMUNICATIONS

The shortness of this section reflects the paucity of communications within Iberia; a paucity which, although common to all Mediterranean countries, is particularly noticeable within the peninsula. The total length of highways and roads is 149,550 km, of which a little over half are macadamized. (Italy and France, both smaller units, possess 171,202 and 649,900 km respectively.) A road map reveals four main road centres, all in Spain; first comes Madrid, which is linked to the north by roads crossing the Central Sierras via the Somosierra and Guadarrama passes, to the north-east by the Guadalajara road which runs via the Jalón valley to Zaragoza, to the south-east by the Utiel–Valencia and Albacete–Murcia roads, to the south by the Aranjuez–Manzanares road which leads to the Guadalquivir valley via Linares, to the west and Portugal by the Talavera–Badajoz road. The second focus, Valladolid, the only centrally situated town of size in the north Meseta, lies at the intersection of a cruciform pattern of roads – those from the north-west (Vigo, Corunna, Oviedo) continuing to Madrid, and those from the French frontier and Basque provinces continuing southwest to Salamanca and Portugal. A series of major connecting roads serves to link these four routes from Valladolid, for example the Palencia–Benavente road which shortens the journey from France to Galicia by by-passing Valladolid well to the north. The two other road centres of importance possess a road network that is more localized; in the Basque provinces the network is contained within a rough parallelogram between the towns of San Sebastián, Pamplona, Vitoria and Bilbao; in Catalonia, however, the valley-plan is such that routes are concentrated upon a single centre, Barcelona.

Apart from these internal road systems there is a comprehensive, though disconnected, coastal system. In Portugal the main road from Lisbon to Oporto, via Coimbra, continues north to Túy and Corunna, while along the east coast a main road extends from the French frontier through Barcelona and Valencia to Murcia, Cartagena, Almería and Málaga, and eventually reaches Cádiz, Seville and Córdoba. A continuous road system along the north coast links to France Corunna, Oviedo, Santander, Bilbao

G

and the Basque provinces. The surface and maintenance of roads within the peninsula in general is not up to north European standards. Lack of capital prevents extensive mechanization, but this deficiency is partially offset by the large amount of unskilled labour used in road-mending. The writer once saw a Pyrenean road being repaired by twenty-five people, comprising several families, where the women and children swept the road clear (lovingly clearing out potholes but making no attempt to fill them in), and the men followed behind with antiquated tar-sprayer and rough stone chips emptied out of baskets and raked over. The steamroller had been made in Rochester, U.S.A., in 1898.

Railways, particularly useful for the transport of bulky goods, such as coal and iron ore, have always maintained their relationship with industry; in any country the correlation between industrial sites and railway networks is obvious. In Spain the geographical necessity has been partially offset by an historical accident – the choosing of Madrid as the capital of Spain. The first Spanish railway line was built in 1848 from Barcelona to Mataró; but very soon the centralizing influence of the capital was extended to railway construction and in general railway lines in the peninsula now radiate from Madrid. The direction of the main lines has been very largely determined by relief. Linking the capital with the main peripheral regions has necessitated the crossing of transverse highland masses – difficult barriers for railway locomotives which, unlike lorries and cars, require an extremely gentle gradient.

Attempts to overcome these difficulties are of recent date; in Galicia, for example, there was but one major means of ingress for both road and rail – that via the pass at Brañuelas (3,444 feet) – until September 1958, when the new line from Orense to Zamora via the Puerta de Sanabria (3,132 feet) was opened. There is still only one route from Madrid to Asturias, through the pass of Pájares (Busdongo 4,077 feet), and one from Madrid to Santander via Reinosa (2,788 feet). The most important route in the peninsula is that from Madrid to the French frontier via the gap town of Burgos (2,863 feet); to reach the north Meseta the train has to climb from Madrid (2,149 feet) either to La Cañada (4,454 feet) on the Madrid–Ávila line, or to San Rafael (4,097 feet) on the Madrid–Segovia line; the former route, despite its height, is more generally used. Main routes eastwards include those via the Jalón valley to Zaragoza, and via Cuenca or Albacete to the Levant coast. There is only one trunk line to the south – an indication of the economic unimportance of New Castile and Andalusia – but this line branches at Linares into two, one route continuing south to divide at Moreda into the Granada and Almería lines and the other linking the main towns of the Guadalquivir valley and passing into south Portugal beyond Huelva at the town of Ayamonte, whence ferry and railway connexions lead to Lisbon. West of Madrid a line follows the Tagus valley as far as Cañaveral, and then runs south, to branch into two lines near Cáceres, one passing directly into Portugal via Valencia del Alcántara, the other taking a more southerly route via Badajoz, while a line north of the Sierra de Gredos, via Ávila and Salamanca, enters Portugal at Vilar Formosa. Lisbon, however approached, has no direct connexion with Madrid, due to constructional difficulties caused by the flood plain of the lower Tagus and the steep gradients of the Serra da Estrêla and its extensions.

Routeways in the peripheral regions are of great local importance, but often consist of isolated stretches of railway line joining industrial centres, rather than forming continuations of the main peninsular routes. The densest railway networks are found in the Basque provinces and Catalonia, where industrial demands require quick and easy transport both of factory personnel, and, more particularly, of incoming raw materials and outgoing manufactured goods. Barcelona has a great number of local and suburban services utilizing both main lines and narrow-gauge railways – for example, 35 trains a day to Mataró, 15 to San Juan de las Abadesas, 8 to Martorell – and in relation to the valleys served Barcelona is as much a local centre for valley routes as is Cardiff in South Wales. In the Basque provinces narrow-gauge lines predominate; Bilbao is the main centre and deals with more purely local traffic than does Barcelona; for example, 27 trains a day run between Bilbao and Plencia, 18 between Bilbao and Sondica, 14 between Bilbao and Lezama, while between Bilbao and Santurce-Puerto, at the mouth of the ria, there is a twenty-minute service from 5.30 to 23 hours. There are in addition frequent services by narrow-gauge lines from Irún to San Sebastián.

Another less important network links the tributary valleys to the Douro valley, in the Portuguese wine-producing region, and this network converges on Oporto, whence there is a good and rapid service, with at least five trains a day, to Lisbon. Apart from these regions the peninsula is not well served by rail traffic; the only other main line service of note is that from the French frontier to Valencia, Murcia and Granada.

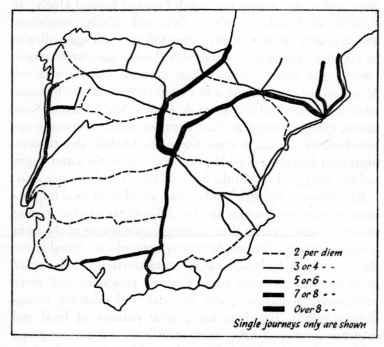

Fig. 37. Daily Rail Service

A detailed analysis of transport in Iberia reveals one important fact; the great amount of traffic in northern Spain, in particular the increasing use of the Ebro valley in linking the two major industrial regions. Whereas 30 trains leave Madrid either daily or more than four times a week, for destinations in the northern half of the peninsula, only 17 leave for destinations in the southern half. There are, in addition, many more local services in the northern regions, whereas in the south only really fertile agricultural areas, such as the vega of Granada and huerta of Málaga, maintain tram or local train services comparable with those of the north. Furthermore, through journeys from Barcelona to Bilbao, Vigo or Oviedo have been speeded up as far as possible and there are two services daily from Barcelona to Bilbao, taking approximately 14 hours at an average speed of about 35 m.p.h., and a thrice weekly service from Barcelona to Galicia. The only comparable journey in the south is that which runs daily from Valencia to Granada; the time taken is $13\frac{1}{2}$ hours, at an average speed of about 18 m.p.h., since the rocky foothills of the Sierra Nevada have made engineering construction extremely difficult, and tunnels, narrow curves and inclines abound.

The majority of railway engines in the peninsula still run on solid fuel – coal or briquettes. Diesel engines have been introduced gradually, since their running costs are high, but the results have proved their worth, particularly in regard to the Spanish 'Talgo', a luxury type of train now used three or four times weekly between Madrid and main regional centres. 'Taf' is another such train, with equivalent speeds but a little less luxury. The average speed for such trains between Madrid and Irún is 45 m.p.h.; this speed, high for Iberia, is equalled by the Portuguese in their express trains from Lisbon to Oporto, and a higher average could be achieved in both cases if, instead of stopping ten or more times, the trains ran direct. At the other end of the scale are mail trains, or *correos*; those between Madrid and Irún take 21 hours, stopping 100 times and averaging 19 m.p.h. over the whole journey; but it should be remembered that the high Central Sierras and dissected Basque hill country make tunnels and curves essential and almost double the length of the journey, as well as precluding any real burst of speed except over the Meseta. The difficulties of railway construction are perhaps best illustrated not by speeds but by such facts as that in the 31 miles between Pola de Lena and Busdongo (Puerto de Pájares zone of the Cantabrians) there are 80 tunnels.

In general the development of the railway system of Iberia appears to have lagged behind that of many other countries. Spain still retains three classes; both countries have only recently nationalized the railways, Spain in February 1941 (but only those of normal gauge) and Portugal in May 1954. The Companhia dos

Caminhos de Ferro Portugueses (C.P.) is responsible for 3,563 km of railway lines, while the Red Nacional de los Ferrocarriles Españoles (R.E.N.F.E.) deals with 19,098 km, of which 1,843 km are electrified. Electrification in Spain is, at the moment, progressing very slowly; large electricity plants, economically spaced over the country, are an impossibility so that only in the wetter north, where there are more hydro-electric power stations, is extensive electrification possible. The main electrified sections are shown on the appended map.

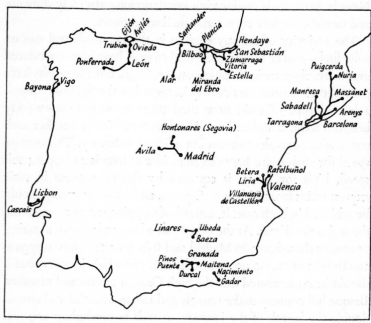

Fig. 38. Major Electrified Railway Lines

With regard to maritime transport Iberia occupies a somewhat paradoxical position. The peninsula lies just south of the zone of divergence of the world's two most important shipping routes (the North Atlantic and Mediterranean), acting as a barrier to be rounded rather than providing convenient ports of call. The reason is primarily economic; Iberia has nothing worth calling for. Furthermore, large modern ships tend to refuel within the Mediterranean basin and steam on to north-west Europe without pausing, so that, with the exception of strategically placed Gibraltar, there is no refuelling of large main-line ships at Iberian Atlantic ports, while the Mediterranean ports lie too far north of the Suez–Gibraltar route. Neither Spain nor Portugal has the resources for a large ship-building industry, and as a result marine commercial activity is necessarily limited in scope.

The merchant marine of both countries is small – 321 ships in Portugal, and 1,600 ships in Spain, the latter figure including petrol tankers and fruit ships. Visiting ships are generally of merchant or small passenger type; almost as many passengers enter Spain every year by aeroplane as by ship. Coastal shipping is important, especially from Cádiz to Barcelona, while good passenger links are maintained with the Balearics. The 'Compañia Transmediterranea' has almost a complete monopoly of regular maritime routes, maintaining thrice weekly services between the peninsula and the Canary Islands, a weekly service between Almería and Ceuta (taking in Melilla), an interinsular service in the Canaries and a two-monthly service to Spanish Guinea. The 'Naviera Pinillos' company also operates a circumpeninsular and a Levant–Canaries service on a smaller scale. The majority of ships entering Portuguese harbours are Portuguese, followed by British and Spanish, and Portugal maintains links with South America (Brazil), Madeira and the Azores, as well as controlling a very small coasting trade. Portugal and Britain are linked by the Royal Mail, Blue Star, Dodero, Booth and Yeoward and Ellerman lines, the latter sailing from Liverpool to Lisbon. American Export Lines link New York and Gibraltar, while Italian and Greek ships also sail from North America to Europe via Iberian ports.

In the field of aviation Iberia is regaining a little of its strategic importance as one of the most westerly points of Europe, and is therefore most convenient as a starting point for aeroplanes bound for Africa and South America. As might be expected, Lisbon, on the west coast, is an important transatlantic terminus and junction; P.A.A. and T.W.A. services link North America to Lisbon, Panair do Brasil links Lisbon to Rio de Janeiro, while B.O.A.C. and B.E.A. deal primarily with traffic from Lisbon to other European centres. In addition Lisbon maintains contact with

Africa, the Lisbon–Luanda–Lourenço Marques and Lisbon–Tangiers–Casablanca routes being the most widely used. Madrid not only maintains regular flights to Buenos Aires, Cuba and Venezuela but has several direct flights to such European capitals as Copenhagen (via Lufthansa lines), Amsterdam (K.L.M.), Rome (Alitalia) and Paris (Air France). At the same time weekly links are maintained by Iberia (Spanish Air Lines) with Bata, Kano, Accra and Lagos, thrice weekly services operate between Madrid and Melilla, Tetuan, Tangier, Casablanca, Sidi Ifni, Las Palmas and Villa Cisneros. Both capitals maintain services with their respective Atlantic islands, while Gibraltar is not only in daily contact by B.E.A. services with London and other European and African capitals, but maintains a regular air-mail service by Gibraltar Air Lines with Tangier.

Within the peninsula a network of air-routes radiates from Madrid, with Barcelona forming an important subsidiary centre. The highest daily flight-rate is between Barcelona and Palma, during the tourist season, with eight flights a day, followed by the Madrid–Barcelona route, with seven flights a day. There are three daily services between Madrid and Seville, two between Madrid and Valencia, Madrid and Lisbon, Valencia and Palma, Barcelona and Valencia, and a daily service between Madrid and Palma, Santiago da Compostella, San Sebastián, Córdoba, Málaga and Bilbao, and between Valencia and Iviza. Services three or four times a week are run between Barcelona and Bilbao, San Sebastián and Iviza, and between Valencia, Seville and Málaga. Portuguese Air Lines operate services between Lisbon and Oporto, while 'Iberia' provides the majority of aeroplanes for other internal traffic.

i

ii   iii

XIII i Haystack, chestnut tree and rough stone dwelling under a typically cloudy
         sky, near Gijón, Asturias.

     ii Oxen with sheepskin eye-guards, near Corunna.

    iii Collecting seaweed for manure from the shores of the ria, Pontevedra,

i

ii

iii

XIV i Typical farmhouse and 'horreo' – both made of rough stone and wood,
       with pantiled roofs – near pass of Pájares.

     ii The river Arga at Pamplona; Basque hills in the distance.

     iii Unloading Asturian coal at Bilbao.

CHAPTER VIII

The Natural Regions – the North West

STRUCTURE, RELIEF AND climate are the fundamental geographical criteria on which a division of Iberia may be based, and a map is appended showing the major natural regions of the peninsula. The regional chapters will deal more fully with the human aspects of each region, in many cases correlating facts given in previous chapters to illustrate the geographical bases for the distinctive characteristics of each region. Areas adjacent to the periphery will be studied first, and it is convenient to start with the North-West area, where three regions may be distinguished: Galicia, Asturias-Santander, and the Basque provinces.

GALICIA

Galicia has remained above sea level for such lengthy geological periods that it shows signs of peneplanation. However, successive faultings, founderings and risings of the whole block have caused rejuvenation of rivers, and constant erosion under very humid climatic conditions has given rise to bold, but rounded relief, while disintegration of the Archaean bedrock has resulted in the formation of large isolated masses of granite which litter the hillsides and are known locally as *panedos*, or *outeiros*. About 80 per cent of the region lies above the 1,000 foot contour line, and the highest ranges lie in the east where they form an effective barrier between Galicia and the rest of Spain. The mass of Rañadoiro, to the east of the Navia river, forms the boundary between Asturias and Galicia, and the Montes de León and ranges of Caurel and Picos form a double barrier between the north Meseta and Galicia. In the Sierra de Picos (which on some maps receives the name of

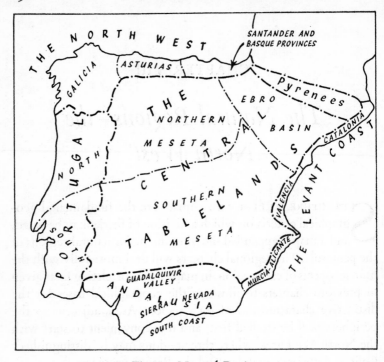

Fig. 39. Natural Regions

the Sierra de Ancares) the peak of Cuiña reaches 6,548 feet, and in the León ranges the peak of Teleño reaches 7,178 feet, and much of this highland exceeds a height of 6,000 feet. Between the Montes de León and the Picos and Caurel ranges occurs the depression of the Bierzo, once a lake but now drained by the river Sil. Around Lugo there is a small detached plateau about 1,000 feet high, but lower than the land around it, which averages 2,000 feet. These masses of highland extend to the sea, giving rise to steep slopes, cliffs and small sheltered bays, but to no continuous coastal plain. In fact, only around the mouths of rivers is there any appreciable area of lowland, and even this is often undulating rather than flat.

Galician rivers are short and swift-flowing owing to the excessive rainfall and steep gradient from the hills to the sea, but are of little use to man. The major rivers are the Navia, Eo, Tambre, Ulla, Sil and Miño, only the latter being large enough to reveal in its middle section the meanders typical of most graded rivers in their later stages.

Galicia has a mild climate and is one of the wettest regions of the peninsula. Depressions from the Atlantic bring frequent rain, drizzle and the *bretama*, which closely resembles a Scotch mist, while the average number of rainy days per year is 150, a figure rivalled only by the Basque provinces. Aspect is of importance

Fig. 40. Galicia

when considering annual rainfall; the large number of hill masses considerably complicates the distribution of rain, but average figures for the region as a whole range from 60 inches on exposed coasts to 30 inches in rain-shadow areas, and reach over 80 inches on the higher west-facing mountain slopes. Pontevedra annually receives 58 inches and Santiago 65 inches. Snow covers the highland in winter but skiing is not a popular pastime, as it is in the mountains of Asturias. Proximity to the sea helps to stabilize temperatures; at Santiago the average temperature in January is 45° F., and in August, the hottest month, 66° F., the time-lag between maximum insolation and maximum temperature being due to marine influence. Winter temperatures, on the coast, are generally mild, although frosts occur infrequently; the absolute minimum at Santiago is 23° F. Further inland, particularly on the higher areas, temperatures may remain below freezing point for several days; on the other hand the interior regions do not experience the full force of Atlantic gales, which along the coast are strong enough to prohibit tree growth in exposed places.

In the mild remote valleys of Galicia farming is different in scale, pattern and crops from that of other regions of Iberia. The custom of dividing estates equally among male successors has led to minute subdivision of land, giving rise to *minifundias*, or tiny farms of from two to six acres, and has encouraged dispersion of settlement. High rainfall is conducive to good yields of green crops, and potatoes, maize and beans are ubiquitous, irrigation on a small scale being necessary in the rain-shadow areas of Orense and Pontevedra. Cereals do not ripen well, and are restricted to oats, rye on the cooler uplands, and a small amount of wheat grown in the Limia district around Lake Antela. Vines do not produce high-quality wine under such humid conditions; the most important area is along the lower course of the river Miño, in the Ribera zone, while the valleys of the Sil and Cabe are other production centres. Hay forms an important subsidiary crop, since it is used to feed the numerous cattle of 'Liena' or 'Marela' type. Thirty per cent of Spain's cattle are reared in Galicia, and are used primarily for meat and draught purposes; one of the most common sights in country districts is that of a pair of oxen, their sheepskin eye-guards (a protection against flies) dripping in the rain, slowly pulling a creaking, solid-wheeled cart along the sodden, rutted lanes. Any surplus milk is taken to market, often in large wooden pails balanced on the heads of peasant women.

Trees thrive in the damp climate and help to emphasize the natural greenness of the province. Deciduous trees such as oaks (here called *carballos*, and not *roble*, as in Castilian) and beech (the Galician dialect converts the Castilian *hayas* into *fayas*) form the basic natural vegetation; the hillsides, however, have been re-planted with pines, sweet chestnuts have taken the place of many indigenous deciduous trees, and apple trees provide fruit for cider which often forms a local substitute for wine. Where forest cover has been removed and not replanted, poor heath and scrub have taken its place; such areas of moorland are frequently given the name of *dehesas* or *eriales*. Both crops and natural vegetation illustrate the transitional nature of Galicia; here Mediterranean and north European plants are found in close proximity. The vine flourishes beside the apple, Mediterranean and north European pines grow equally well, and wild flowers include primroses as well as lavender. In Santiago and Corunna parks a touch of colour is provided by the planting of pansies under palm trees.

Fishing forms an important occupation for the coastal population. Cod, bonito, sardines, anchovies and tunny are the main species caught, and the annual amounts fluctuate between a third and a quarter of the Spanish total. Fish preserving is carried on in all the coastal towns, Vigo possessing one-fifth of the salting and tinning factories of Galicia. Olive oil and tomato purée are easily imported from other regions of Spain, tin-plate is produced in the Basque region and normally brought by sea, while there is a steady supply of semi-skilled labour (especially female labour, which is cheap). Machines in most cases are modern and swift working, methods are efficient, and it is not surprising that Galicia annually produces almost half of all the preserved fish of Spain.

The natural resources of Galicia are limited; there is no coal, but a small amount of lignite is mined near Puentes de Garcia Rodriguez. The Sociedad Mineral de Villaodrid exploits the iron mines of the Ribadeo area, and iron ore mined under their auspices at Silvarrosa, Villaodrid and Castropol is sent by a small narrow-gauge railway to Ribadeo, whence it is shipped to the Basque provinces, along with the insignificant amounts of copper mined at Caudín, Palacios, Villafranca, Barquera and Freijo, gold at Carballino, antimony from Cervantes and Villarbacú, and tin from such centres as Carbia, Silleda, Villadeciervos, Ribadavia and Lausame. Seventy-four per cent of Spain's wolfram is mined in Galicia, at Muiños Blancos, La Vega del Bollo, Arnaoya, Noya, Santa Comba, and at several smaller centres in the Orense and Corunna districts. The superabundance of water in the province could provide hydro-electricity for much of northern Spain; lack of capital and local disinterest, based on the fact that Galicia is not highly industrialized, have prevented this, and there are few hydro-electric stations, that at Noya on the river Tambre being the largest.

The population of Galicia is fundamentally Celtic in origin, having settled in the region from about 500 B.C., after the Celtic invasion of Iberia. Rude stone forts, now known as *castros*, crown many hilltops, and lower more sheltered areas form the sites of *citanias*, or small villages of stoutly built circular stone huts. In the wilder country districts, especially in the Ancares (or Picos) mountains, the modern *palloza*, or primitive farmhouse, reveals how the Celts lived. Built on a circular plan, the *palloza* has a diameter ranging from 15 to 30 feet, with solid stone walls up to 7 feet high, surmounted by thick furze, heather or reed thatch carefully fastened to a massive wooden framework. There are few windows, often unglazed, one doorway and the building houses both animals and human beings in noisy and somewhat noisome proximity. Some *pallozas* have been 'modernized', and have two storeys, the upper one being reached by an outside flight of stone steps. Four or five *pallozas* constitute a hamlet, and are generally surrounded by sheds and barns. Of these the *horreo*, a word probably of Iberian origin now meaning storage shed, is characteristic of the whole region. Generally made of granite slabs, it is raised from 2 to 4 feet above the ground on four pillars, each surmounted by a flat circular stone called a *tornarato* (rat-guard). A space is left between each narrow upright slab forming the walls, and the wind, blowing through the narrow interstices, appears to dry the contents (normally maize cobs) more effectually than if the *horreo* had solid walls.

Celtic influence apart from that seen in the *castros* and *pallozas* is little in evidence. Bagpipes (*Zampognas*), typical of countries occupied by Celtic-speaking peoples, are still played at festival times, though their use is now waning; some moonlight fiestas are Celtic in origin, and belief in witches and both white and black magic still exists in country districts. Much emigration from this over-populated area has occurred, particularly to South America, but the Galician abroad suffers from *morriño*, a word not translatable into English, but expressed by the Welsh *hiraeth*, and signifying a deep yearning for one's own hearth and home. The language is purely Romance, being more akin to Portuguese than to Castilian, and contains few Celtic words.

Racial type in Galicia, cut off though it is from the rest of the peninsula, has also suffered change. During the Barbarian invasions Sueves settled here, to be followed after A.D. 575 by Berbers brought from North Africa in the train of the conquering Arabs. Today the population is predominantly rural and dispersed. A little over 2½ million people live in the region; on the rich lowlands near the coast population density reaches nearly 400 per sq. km, while on the bleak interior moorlands it drops to 50 per sq. km. Towns absorb the following numbers: Vigo – 155,319 (1950); Corunna – 161,750; El Ferrol del Caudillo – 79,725 (1950); Santiago de Compostella – 54,448 (1950); Orense – 80,336; Lugo – 66,712; Pontevedra – 46,232. (N.B. All population figures in the regional chapters are for 1960 unless otherwise stated.)

In 1800 Vigo was an insignificant fishing village with a population of 2,000; today it ranks as the second town, after Bilbao, in the whole of north-west Spain. The reason for this phenomenal growth is the rapid development of trade with South America and the expansion of the fishing industry. Situated on the south side of the ria which bears its name, Vigo has an excellent natural harbour, large and well sheltered, an important consideration along this extremely dangerous and stormy coast. It is the most important fish-preserving town in Spain, annually producing about a sixth of the Galician total, twice as much as any other fish-preserving centre. Since it derives much of its prosperity from the sea, it is only natural that it also contains ship-repairing yards and ship-building yards, where fishing smacks and merchant ships are constructed. Land communications have recently been improved by the completion of the new railway line to Madrid via Zamora and Orense, 132 miles shorter than the Orense–Ponferrada–León route which, until recently, was the only means of egress by rail from Galicia. Ships entering Vigo harbour mainly comprise cargo boats, coming from South America with fertilizers, tropical products and sometimes a few passengers, as well as smaller coastal steamers, mainly of Spanish nationality.

Corunna, the Roman Brigantium, still retains the Tower of Hercules, reputedly a Roman lighthouse, now enclosed within a modern tower. Characteristic of the old part of the town are the glazed balconies, or *miradores*, features also found in other towns in north Spain, for example Elgoibar and Vitoria; observation of the street crowds is thus possible even in cold, windy or rainy weather. Corunna has an active and well-sheltered harbour, on the western side of the ria caused by the drowning of the river Mero, and, unlike Vigo, contains many small industries; these include the manufacturing of glass, paper, cotton goods and the preserving of fish and other foods, especially those derived from milk. There is ship-building on a small scale, nothing larger than fishing vessels being constructed, and there is also an armaments factory. There is some export of fish and manufactured goods, and communications with the rest of Spain have recently been improved by the opening of the new railway line already described in connexion with Vigo.

Ferrol, situated on the north side of the ria of the same name, is the birth-place of Generalissimo Franco, and for this reason an official decree of September 30th, 1938, gave to the town the name of El Ferrol del Caudillo. Its population has doubled in the last fifteen years due to the expansion of industries connected with the arsenal, which was established here in the middle of the sixteenth century. Ferrol is an important naval base, and possesses large dockyards for the construction of smaller types of naval vessels and oil tankers. Foundries, engineering works and timber yards are all to be found near the focal point, the arsenal. As a naval base Ferrol has much to commend it; the ria is well sheltered, there is a long tradition of ship-building, and the stormy Atlantic provides a suitable training ground for every branch of sea-manship.

Orense is situated on the left bank of the river Miño, and still retains its Roman bridge. It is an important agricultural centre; chocolate factories utilize local milk and chocolate from Spanish Guinea. The hot springs called Las Burgas occur near the centre of the town and produce waters at a temperature of 153° F.

Santiago de Compostella, ancient capital of Galicia, rose to importance in the Middle Ages after the supposed discovery of the body of St James, a discovery aided by the shining of a star over the fields. This gave rise to the name 'campus stellae' from which the modern name is derived. Today Santiago is still important as a pilgrim centre, although it has lost some of its lustre; Lourdes, in particular, diverts many tourists who would otherwise tread the well-worn path over the Pyrenees, through the Basque country and on to León, Astorga and Santiago, one of the rainiest towns in the peninsula.

Lugo lies at a height of 1,526 feet on the banks of the Miño, and was an important town in Roman times, when it was known as Lucus Augusti. Parts of the Roman walls and bridge still remain. Lugo is an important road centre for north Galicia, and lies on the main railway from Ponferrada to Corunna. It is also a market centre and manufactures felt and woollen cloth.

Pontevedra, at the head of the ria formed by the drowning of the valley of the river Lerez, is gradually being silted up, and losing its importance as a port. Surrounding woods provide the timber needed for its wood-pulp factory, and there are some salting works which deal with meat as well as with fish.

Other towns in Galicia, far less important, reveal two of the interesting characteristics of the province. In the first place, there are many hot or sulphurous springs, some of them utilized since Roman times, and all owing their existence to subterranean masses of hot rock, not yet cooled. Carballo, La Cañiza and Sarria may be quoted as examples, and at Caldas de Reyes the two streams Dávila and Acuña provide medicinal waters at $112°$ F. and $98°$ F. respectively. The second characteristic is only of recent origin, and concerns the growth of the tourist industry. For those Spaniards with adequate money, particularly if they live in the hotter areas of Spain, Galicia forms a pleasant retreat in summer. There is an exciting coast, well stocked with fish and provided with sandy beaches, and temperatures are moderate. Communications are now easier, both by rail and air, and it is not surprising to find that many erstwhile fishing ports now accommodate tourists during the summer. Apart from such towns as Corunna, there are smaller centres like Marín and Vivero, while La Estrada, an inland town in a pleasant valley, provides adequate attractions for a country holiday. Tourists from wetter north European countries are just beginning to discover Galicia, and in ten years' time the Galician coast will probably rival other European coasts along the Atlantic seaboard.

ASTURIAS–SANTANDER

The structure and relief of Asturias-Santander have a degree of variety not found in Galicia. The boundary between the province of Lugo and Oviedo closely coincides with that of the Archaean and Palaeozoic rocks of the western section of the Cantabrian mountain range, while that between Oviedo and Santander corresponds roughly with the junction of Palaeozoic and Mesozoic rocks. The natural (as opposed to the cartographic) boundary of Asturias, however, is found in the Rañadoiro range to the west and, to the east, in the triple limestone peaks of the Picos (or Peños) de Europa, the highest of which reaches 8,786 feet. Asturian topography is complex and its scenery varied and even spectacular in parts. A coastal platform of rolling, down-like country gives way to an interior trench running to the east of Oviedo, floored by rocks deposited by relatively recent marine invasions, and forming a belt of fertile and sheltered land, well populated and used for communications within Asturias. To the south-east lie the highest summits of the Cantabrians, the Picos de Europa, dissected by deep limestone cañons on the lower slopes, while to the south rise the high Cantabrian crests, showing such signs of glaciation as hanging valleys, U-shaped valleys and cwms, the latter often occupied by a lake, as for example, lakes Andara, Enol, Somoyedo and del Valle. This southern range of peaks is almost continuous, and includes the Peña Rubia (8,167 feet), Mampodre (7,206 feet), Peña Espiguete (8,045 feet) and Peña Labra (6,566 feet), all of which combine to present an almost impenetrable barrier to communications. There is only one major pass – that of Pájares (4,513 feet) – and the steep gradient has necessitated the construction of a railway line with six wide subterranean loops, near Sotiella. This is in marked contrast to the Manzanal pass between Astorga and Ponferrada in Galicia; here the height is similar (4,034 feet) but the gradient is more gentle, and only one large loop is required at the Túnel de Lazo.

Rivers are short, turbulent and powerful; in the east they often reach the sea through deeply carved gashes, locally known as *focos*

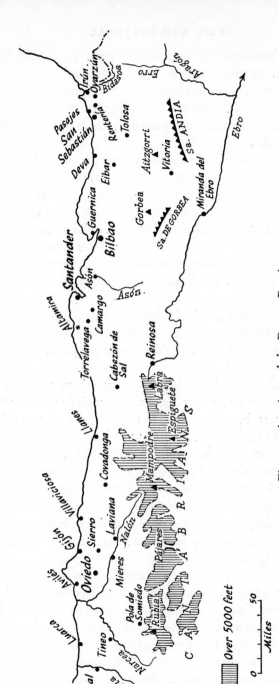

Fig. 41. Asturias and the Basque Provinces

or *escobios*, but in the west small rias occur. The Nalón is the largest river; 84 miles long, it discharges annually more water than the Guadiana, 510 miles long, and reaches the sea in the long, narrow ria Pravia. Of all the rias along this coast, that of Santander is the largest; no others are comparable in size or importance with the Galician rias.

Climatically Asturias–Santander shares the general climatic characteristics of north-west Spain, but has a little less rain – from 40 inches to 60 inches per year (Oviedo 38, Santander 50 inches per year) – and rather cooler temperatures owing to the greater height of much of the land. Snow abounds in winter, and there is skiing for the richer Spaniards on some of the mountain slopes near to main lines of communication, for example near the pass of Pájares, although hotel accommodation at the moment is limited.

Agriculture in this area is similar to that of Galicia; the major crops include maize, potatoes and beans, with some sugar beet and forage crops (hay, clover and alfalfa) near the coast. Cereals do not ripen well, but in higher areas, where farming is practised almost at subsistence level, inferior crops of rye and oats are grown. In many places steep gradients necessitate the construction of terraces, in order to utilize as much ground as possible. Grapes are not suited to this climate and are seldom seen, but apples are grown both for table use and for cider. Cattle are the most important animals of the region, and provide milk for widespread dairy industries. In the mountains transhumance of cattle, sheep and goats is practised extensively. Sometimes the herds are kept within daily reach of the farmstead; often, however, there is wholesale migration via recognized trails to the *brañas* and *alzadas*, the high summer pastures.

The importance of coal makes itself felt even in León, where one sees the newspaper *Carbón*, its title printed in thick black, smudgy letters. Once over the pass of Pájares the railway line links up the larger mining and industrial towns, and coal blackens the rivers and streams. There are slag heaps, furnaces and factories, and black-faced workers reminiscent of the Welsh mining valleys crowd on to the evening trains. Cloud and heavy rain add to the general murkiness. Enormous piles of coal awaiting shipment lie on the quaysides of Gijón and Avilés, and this is the only region of Spain with the appearance of a black country. The major coal areas have been mentioned in detail in Chapter VII. Generally speaking there is a descending scale of hardness of coal from north to south; near Arnas and Ferrones the coal is soft, while at Tineo anthracite occurs. The seams are usually thin, irregular, faulted and with a steep angle of dip. These disadvantages, coupled with the fact that transport is difficult and expensive, make production costs high, and though the area is important, prosperity is not apparent. There is a middle class, especially near the industrial areas, but the presence of coal has not given the Asturians a much higher standard of living than that found in the rest of Spain. Its value in the economy of Spain is, however, unquestionable; of the 600 important coal mines in Spain, 500 are found in Oviedo province.

In addition to coal, there are smaller quantities of other minerals. Iron, often containing a high proportion of silica, is mined at Quiros, Proaza, Sobrescabio, Laviana, Luarca, Luanco, Llanes and Camargo, while zinc occurs at Castrillón, Navales, Suances, Udias, Reocín and Camargo. Insignificant amounts of other minerals occur as follows: lead at San Martin de Oscos and Cabrales; manganese at Buferrera; wolfram at Degana; and rock salt at Cabezón de la Sal. As in Galicia, heavy and continuous rainfall, here coupled with steep gradient, presents ideal conditions for the generation of hydro-electricity. Coal, however, is the predominant fuel, and the number of hydro-electric power stations is more limited than might be expected; the most important are those of Boal, on the river Navia, Camarmena, on the river Caves, Pola de Somiedo, on a small tributary of the Pigüeña, and Bárcena de Concha, on the river Torina.

Settlement is dispersed on the more fertile lowlands and nucleated, for mutual protection and convenience, on the bleak highlands, which are frequently snowed up for a fortnight in winter. Roofing materials illustrate the diversity of geological strata, and range from thin grey slates to thicker limestone or sandstone slabs; newer buildings, however, are almost always pantiled. Farmhouses in outlying districts are often one-storeyed, built of local rock, with one end used for human activities and the other for animals (compare the 'old black houses' of the western isles of Scotland). The *horreo*, used here as granary, tool shed and, by the sea, as fish-drying rack, is quadrilateral and not rectangular as in Galicia, and made almost entirely of wood, since there are still extensive forests of oak, beech and pine on the lower mountain slopes. The roofs of both farmhouse and *horreo* may be pantiled, in which case the red roof forms an attractive foil to the predominant green of this rugged, well-watered countryside.

The population is at least partially Celtic in origin, but the area has retained few of its distinctive regional characteristics, since the advent of industrialization introduced new customs and different people from other parts of the peninsula. A few Celtic traces remain; the place name *pola*, seldom encountered elsewhere in the peninsula, is similar to the *pol* of Cornwall, and the *plou* of Brittany, both meaning a village; bagpipes are still played at rural festivals; there are several country dances possibly of Celtic origin, while a somewhat mild and amateur form of witchcraft, seldom acknowledged by the Roman Catholic church, is reputed to be practised sporadically in the remoter districts. Density of population is high, particularly in the fertile lowlands and mineral zones (average 200 to 300 per sq. km), but naturally decreases at higher levels. Approximately $1\frac{1}{4}$ million people live in this area, and population figures for the main towns are as follows: Oviedo – 134,000; Gijón – 115,877 (1950); Santander – 103,108; Mieres – 65,008 (1950); Siero – 32,700 (1950); Torrelavega – 23,728 (1950); Avilés – 21,070.

Oviedo, the provincial capital, stands 748 feet above the sea, between (and not on) the rivers Nalón and Nora. It is an important route centre, commanding the north–south route taken by railway and road from the pass of Pájares to the coast, and the east–west route which follows the interior trench from Cangas de Onis to Oviedo, and continues via more rugged country to Espina and the coast. It is also an educational centre, containing a University founded in 1598, and an important market centre for products from the surrounding countryside. Articles manufactured include arms, other metal goods, explosives, especially those used in mining operations, chemicals, china, furniture (there are good local supplies of timber), leather (particularly calfskin and oxhide, as a by-product of the dairy industry), cider and milk products.

Gijón has been a port since pre-Roman times, and was taken by the Moors in A.D. 715, to be recaptured by the Christians seven years later. The harbour facilities were improved in the sixteenth century, and after 1778, when trade was started with America, the port grew in size and importance. In 1884 the railway link with the rest of Spain was completed, and this further encouraged trade since Gijón's hinterland, once limited to Asturias, was extended to include much of Spain. Today Gijón utilizes the outport of Musel, 7 miles away, for export of fruits, cider, iron and coal. The town itself is highly industrialized, and contains many food-preserving plants (especially those connected with milk), iron foundries, engineering shops and ship-building yards. Less important products manufactured include cartridges, wire, nails, glass, cigars, beer and chocolate.

Santander is situated on the spacious ria which bears its name, and despite the terrible damage caused when the steamship *Cabo Machichaco* blew up in 1893, and the devastating fire of the night of February 15/16th, 1941, has steadily grown in size and importance. The port is one of the best along the north Iberian coast, being sheltered by the narrow opening (a half mile wide) of the bay, which opens out to a width of $2\frac{1}{2}$ miles inside this bottleneck. The hinterland of Santander extends to the tablelands of Spain, and exports include fish, milk, chemical and metallurgical products, while coal and foodstuffs are imported. The city (it was granted this status in 1775) is an important industrial centre, importing coal from Asturias for its blast furnaces, utilizing nearby deposits of rock salt as the basis of its chemical industries, and the facilities afforded by its sheltered ria for ship-building, in which local supplies of wood are also used. Food-preserving is important and there are several fish-salting and tinning factories. The Penilla de Cayón factories have an annual capacity of 30,000 tons and utilize the dairy products of the rich pastures around Santander in the manufacture of condensed milk. Other less important goods produced in the city include beer, soap, cigarettes and perfume.

Mieres is the most important mining centre in Asturias,

surrounded by collieries, and containing technical schools of mining and engineering, as well as factories for the production of iron, steel and cider. The main railway line and others of narrow gauge lead direct from Mieres to Gijón or Avilés, thus facilitating the export of coal.

Torrelavega lies at the confluence of the rivers Saja and Besaya, and the nearby waterfalls have been utilized by the Central Hidroelectrico de Viesgo to supply valuable power for both industrial and domestic use. The proximity of lead and zinc mines has given rise to metal smelting, and the Buelna smelting works are particularly important. Other goods produced include cotton textiles, chemicals and condensed milk, and transport is facilitated by the railway which runs direct to the outport of Raquena.

Avilés has a good harbour with an active trade in coal, which has recently been put to good use in three blast furnaces in Avilés itself, now smelting iron ore from the Basque provinces. Apart from iron smelting, Avilés is a metallurgical centre, dealing with local supplies of lead and zinc, and manufacturing iron and steel goods such as boilers, as well as chemicals, glass and textiles.

Apart from these larger towns there are others, each of individual significance; Pola de Siero is the third coal-mining centre of Spain, Luarca (24,730) is noted as a fishing port, Villaviciosa (20,348) is renowned for its cider, while Reinosa is the 'mountain' centre of the interior, with important markets. The area deals with a small tourist trade in the summer, and apart from the beaches at the larger ports already mentioned, there are two unique attractions – one, the rocky grotto at Covadonga, where the elected king Pelayo (A.D. 718–737) won a victory over the Moslems in 718, thus initiating the series of Christian victories which culminated in the expulsion of the Moors, and the other, the cave of Altamira, discovered by the Marquis of Sautola in 1879, in which may be seen some of the finest paintings of the upper Palaeolithic period.

THE BASQUE PROVINCES

Although Basque-speaking peoples once occupied much more extensive territory, the Basque region today covers an area of land shaped like a bull's horns pointing towards the Bay of Biscay,

i

ii   iii

XV   i Gullied Tertiary deposits of the Gallego valley at Sabiñánigo, with rugged
        crests of Tendeñera ranges in the distance.

     ii A corner of old Panticosa.

     iii The peak and glacier of Cylindro (10,670 ft.) with Mt. Perdito to the left.

i

ii

XVI i The Costa Brava near Port Bou.

    ii London-registered ship in dock at Barcelona; statue of Christopher Columbus dominates the harbour, and the Tibidabo range of hills can be seen in the distance.

one tip coinciding roughly with the Lascaux caves of the Dordogne, the other with the Altamira caves of Santander. Basque is spoken on both sides of the Pyrenees, in France more as a dialect, in Spain as a definite language. This linguistic unit is geographically divisible into several regions, only two, lying in Spain, being applicable to a study of Iberia. The collective name 'Basque provinces' is taken to cover land bounded in the west by the Asón river, in the south by the Bureba and Andia ranges, in the east by the river Erro, and in the north by the Bay of Biscay, which in Basque means the bay of headlands.

Structurally the area constitutes a zone of transition where the main east–west trend line of the folded Cantabrian mountains meets the north-north-west – south-south-east trend line of the more complex Pyrenean folds. A diversity of generally Mesozoic rock types, eroded under very humid conditions, has given rise to accidented topography of great complexity. There is here no definite alignment of hills, no obvious drainage pattern; the swift north-flowing streams, such as the Bidasoa, Oria, Urola and Nervión, have fairly direct courses culminating in a ria coastline with good harbours, but those which eventually join the Ebro follow the dictates of local geology and flow sometimes at right-angles, sometimes parallel to the Ebro. Much of the Basque countryside lies under 1,500 feet, and the two highest points of the region are Peña Gorbea, 5,054 feet, and Aitzgorri, 5,024 feet. The hills merge in the east into the higher ranges of the Pyrenees, and in the west into the Cantabrian mountain range proper.

The climate of the Basque provinces, like the topography, is transitional; along the coast oceanic conditions prevail, although the storms, for which the Bay of Biscay is notorious, provide slightly higher rainfall than in Asturias, while in the lower area the indraught of marine air which blows to the low-pressure system of the Mesetas tends to augment summer and particularly autumn rainfall amounts. Bilbao has 46 inches of rain a year, San Sebastián has 65 inches a year, with a maximum in the winter season; its average minimum temperature in winter is 37·2° F., and the average maximum summer temperature is 89° F. Cloud and mist are common, Bilbao having 68 fine days a year, San Sebastián 55, but the clouds are sometimes cleared by the *brisa*, a summer wind blowing from the north-east, and the *terral*, a winter wind blowing from the south-east. Further inland annual range of temperature increases while rainfall decreases, and 25 to 30 miles inland the climate is more continental than oceanic. Around Vitoria winters are often frosty, and snow lies on the higher ground, while on the other hand, summers are much hotter than at the coast, and midday temperatures rise well into the nineties. Rainfall in this interior region is less than at the coast, averaging 30 to 50 inches annually, and, although there is slightly more in the winter half of the year, there is a double maximum in spring and autumn.

Agriculture in this area is influenced by climate. Along the coast the only important cereal crop is maize, used locally to make types of bread known as *artua* or *talo*. In the drier inland districts wheat and barley flourish, and a few grapes are grown south of Vitoria, while sugar beet is cultivated along the Ega valley and around Alsasua. Cattle-rearing predominates along the coast, the local hardy Basque type being used for meat and draught purposes, and, when crossed with Swiss varieties, for dairy use. In the drier interior region sheep become more important, and there is transhumance on a somewhat limited scale, especially in the Pyrenean foothills; pig-breeding is ubiquitous, the major provinces being Vitoria and Navarre.

The Basque provinces are particularly well endowed with minerals, the most important being the iron deposits of the Bilbao region at Oyarzún, Cerain, Betelú, and the area around the river Bidasoa. Lead is obtained from Oyarzún (where zinc is also extracted from the ore), Irún, Vera, Oñate and Ezcurra, and zinc is mined at Barambio. Kaolin is found near Oyarzún and Legarreta, pure white marble at Mañaria, and a little asphalt is extracted from bituminous limestones in Alava province. Electricity is a necessary requirement in this highly industrialized region, and the constantly high rainfall is utilized, as well as coal transported from Asturias. There are 523 hydro-electric power stations, the two largest being Yaci and Oiz, while of the 83 thermal power stations, the most important is Burceña.

The Basques belong to an ethnic group of great antiquity, and the population today is composed of fairly tall individuals (average

5 feet 5 inches), with skins of a whiter colour than those of Spaniards to the south, medium brown hair which is wavy but never curly, elongated faces and long narrow noses, and heads ranging from dolichocephalic to mesocephalic. Their average proportion of rhesus-negative blood is much higher than in most Europeans, definitely linking them to the Berber tribes of North Africa, who also belong to this blood-group. Their existence as a unit antedates the Romans; many theories have been propounded as to their origin, but the one most generally accepted classes them as invaders from Africa during or before Neolithic times, who occupied much of Spain, and probably brought with them the language later called Iberian. Recent discoveries of Iberian vases at Liria, covered with writing which may be deciphered by means of the Basque language, will perhaps clarify the situation.

The language itself is unique, and, like some of the customs of the Basques, points to a very remote origin. Sentence construction is agglutinative, and, while collective nouns are few (for example there is no single word for sister, but two words signifying 'a man's sister', and 'a woman's sister'), there is a plethora of nouns dealing with every aspect of nature, and many nouns of a purely onomatopoeic character, for example, the word *triski-traska* signifies the noise made by sawing. The first to speak this language seem to have been simple, homely people, devoted to a life of primitive farming or hunting. Through the centuries they have adopted several new words from other languages: *pake* (peace) from Latin, *kai* (dock or quay) possibly from the French *quai*, and several Spanish words such as *arazión* from *ración*, or ration. In return the Spanish language acquired *nava*, a plain, *páramo*, a high barren plain, *izquierdo*, left, from Basque *ezker*; but very little else.

Few of the original customs remain. The practice of the *couvade* (when the father takes to his bed at the birth of a child) has died out, and so have many of the dances for which the Basques have been noted throughout the centuries. The *aurresku*, however, is still danced, and so is the *mutil dantza* in the valley of Baztán, often accompanied by a primitive flute, the *txistu*. Pelota is the favourite and characteristic game, whether played by small boys against a church wall, or by contestants in a well-equipped court, while in the western Pyrenees, pigeons are shot or netted as they migrate through the lower passes, clay discs being thrown above them at high speed, to simulate hawks and force the flocks to earth. Traditional costumes are seldom worn today; however, the *boina* (beret) is ubiquitous, and shepherds still wear the *kapusai*, or thick hooded cloak, and in the valley of Roncal the women wear loose red or multi-coloured skirts.

In this transit region it is surprising that the continuity of the Basque's existence has been maintained. Other invaders were deterred from settling here by the dissected topography, damp climate and the tenacious resistance of the Basques. Population tends to be dispersed in the countryside, nucleated in industrial areas. The basic unit of rural settlement is the *baserri* or tiny hamlet of 10 to 20 houses, which collectively form the *auzo*, or district, which in turn forms part of a larger unit grouped around a *kalea* or village. Further inland settlement is slightly more nucleated; the hamlets are larger, containing up to 100 houses, separated from each other by long narrow corridors called *arteak* (literally 'betweens'). Country houses are usually two-storeyed, built predominantly of wood with stone foundations, and often have carved over the door the date of construction and name of original occupant. The total population of the Basque provinces is approximately 1½ millions, and population density is high in the industrial areas (up to 720 per sq. mile in Vizcaya province). The towns absorb a large proportion of the population as follows (those marked with an asterisk form part of the Bilbao urban group along the ria Nervión and will be mentioned in conjunction with Bilbao): Bilbao – 267,293; San Sebastián – 123,935; Vitoria – 57,357 (1950); Baracaldo* – 42,240 (1950); Sestao* – 19,969 (1950); Irún – 19,956 (1950); Guecho* – 19,309 (1950); Miranda del Ebro – 18,094 (1950).

The modern town of Bilbao was founded in 1300 by Diego Lopez de Haro, and its growth in the last century has been rapid; in 1800 its population was 8,000; in 1820 the figure rose to 12,000; in 1877 it reached 50,000, and today it has nearly ½ million inhabitants (including suburbs). Built on the banks of the ria Nervión, which affords considerable shelter for shipping, it is surrounded by the Archanda, Arnotegui Miravilla and Santo Domingo hills.

Much of the high-grade iron ore from these hills has been exhausted. Bilbao is the maritime and industrial capital of the Basque provinces; its port, which ranks first in Spain for commercial activities, is modern and well equipped to deal with both passengers and a large amount of goods traffic. As far as industry is concerned Bilbao, with its satellite towns of Sestao, Beasaín and Baracaldo, is the most important iron and steel centre in Spain. The banks of the ria are covered with factories, workshops and shipyards; iron and steel bars, sheet metal, all varieties of steel, marine and agricultural machinery, locomotives and all classes of engines are some of the more important types of goods produced. Bilbao contains the largest number of shipyards in Spain, concentrating mainly on the building of merchant ships, while subsidiary industries include the manufacture of cement, glass, chemicals and fertilizers, paints and varnishes.

Baracaldo, largest of the Bilbao group of towns, with two blast furnaces and many engineering workshops, is engaged primarily in iron and steel production. Sestao contains four blast furnaces owned by the 'Altos Hornos de Vizcaya' firm, many engineering workshops and shipyards belonging to the 'Sociedad Española de Construciones Navales'. Guecho, on the right bank of the ria, has a good beach, Las Arenas, which provides a playground for nearby residents. Portugalete, the outport for Bilbao, has extensive docks well fitted to deal with continuous heavy traffic. Half a mile away lies Santurce Antiguo, a noted sardine centre.

San Sebastián, a large and popular resort, dates only from 1816, as much of its architecture reveals, since the original town was almost completely destroyed in 1813 by Anglo-Portuguese troops in their attempt to dislodge the French. The town is a thriving commercial centre, and the beach of La Concha, the many good hotels, and the rugged headlands at the foot of Monte Urgull and Monte Igueldo provide attractions for tourists. Pasajes, its outport, lies 3 miles away.

Vitoria, built on the banks of the Zadorra, is the capital of the province of Alava. An agricultural and route centre, it is also noted for the construction of furniture and other wooden objects.

Irún is a market centre and frontier town lying on the Paris–Madrid railway line. The Franco-Spanish boundary just north of the town is indicated by the river Bidasoa which is spanned by the International Bridge.

The position of Miranda del Ebro is similar to that of Pamplona, since it lies at the junction of three major natural regions, the north-west, the north Meseta and the Ebro basin. It is nearer the Basque provinces, however, and has important railway links with the north-west coast, acting as a main railway centre at the intersection of the Paris–Madrid and Barcelona–Bilbao routes. It specializes in the production of artificial fibres from wheat straw and other materials, the annual output of artificial silk being approximately 9,000 metric tons.

A large number of smaller towns and villages in this thickly populated and highly industrialized area specialize in particular commodities, as the following list shows:

Eibar	16,318	Firearms and bicycles
Tolosa	14,971	Most important paper centre of Spain
Rentería	12,784	Paper
Bermeo	12,517	Fish preserving, once a whaling centre
Pasajes	11,773	Most important fishing port of Cantabrian coast
Mondragón	10,014	Metallurgy and saw mills
Azpeitia	8,991	Iron foundries and jasper quarries
Galdacano	8,000	Explosives
Azcoitia	7,714	Berets
Elgóibar	6,913	Arms
Zarauz	6,729 ⎫	
Guernica	6,441 ⎬	Tourist centres
Deva	4,613 ⎭	
Guetaría	2,045	Nets

In north-west Spain the link between land and sea has always been strong; Palaeolithic men fished along the Cantabrian shores and hunted game further inland; Celtic tribesmen built their *castros* on the hilltops, but also traded around the coasts of western Europe; Garay, the Basque farmer, did much to settle Argentina, while Elcano, born in the fishing hamlet of Guetaría, was the first man to circumnavigate the world. Creaking ox-carts and small stoutly built fishing boats are equally characteristic of a region which combines a mild, humid climate suitable for the growth of temperate crops, with a rugged coastline facing an ocean well stocked with fish. Recently the growth of the iron and steel industry has produced a grimy urban area like the 'Black Country', which superimposes a bustling activity on the peaceful rural pursuits of this green countryside, and rocky gale-swept coastline.

CHAPTER IX

The Pyrenees

THE PYRENEES ARE high mountain ranges in the north of Spain, which extend for a distance of a little under 270 miles, forming the boundary between France and Spain, from the Basque coast in the west to the Mediterranean sea in the east, where they culminate in the promontory known as Cap Cerbère. Apart from the small republic of Andorra perched high up in the east of the central Pyrenees, the mountains are divided, though not equally, between France and Spain. On the French side the land is high and the scenery dramatic, with a very steep descent to the lowlands of Gascony, the rapidity of this descent (on the average a drop of 9,000 feet in 30 miles) giving rise to sudden changes of vegetation and land utilization within a very short distance. On the Spanish side, the scenery is as wild and spectacular as much of that in France though the slope is more gradual; from the high crests (11,000 feet) to the Ebro basin (1,000 feet) is a distance of 70 miles. This more gradual descent is interrupted at irregular intervals by successive ridges, or sierras, lying parallel to the main mountains, and forming barriers difficult to cross.

The inaccessibility of the Spanish side of the Pyrenees, the clannishness of the inhabitants and their suspicion of foreigners (anyone living further away than the next valley) have not been conducive to excessive exploration. It is therefore not surprising that little is known of the area, particularly of its detailed geology; and, although the Spanish government has employed specialists from other countries to map the rock formation of several areas, it will be a very long time before the geological history of the whole area is revealed. Comments on structure are, therefore, based on information restricted in scope.

The history of the Pyrenees earlier than Hercynian times is a matter of conjecture; it seems possible that there was a depression extending roughly from west-north-west to east-south-east which was filled with successive sediments, elevated and later depressed. During Hercynian times these deposits were probably folded to form a mountain range which was subsequently eroded. The sediments derived from this proto-Pyrenean mountain range were apparently deposited in a large syncline corresponding to the Ebro basin today, and during the Alpine orogenesis they were thrust northwards against and over the original mountain 'core'. There are many granite intrusions in the high Pyrenees which reveal the typical 'aureole' of metamorphosed rocks, and although dating them is by no means easy, it appears that some, at least, are Hercynian in origin. Associated with such intrusions are spas where the waters, often hot, have a high mineral content. These waters are generally found in the high Pyrenees, and the word *caldas* (for example Escaldas, Andorra) is sometimes used to denote them. In the east of the Pyrenees occur several diminutive volcanoes of Tertiary age, the lava of which is predominately acid and gives rise to the ropy formation, pitted with vesicules, which is associated with more viscous lavas. The volcanoes exhibit the usual layered formation, ash containing lava bombs alternating with lava.

The succession of rocks from the Tertiary formations of the Ebro basin to the highest peaks of the Pyrenees is from young to old, the sequence being broken by a line of Triassic formations which form the foothill sierras, and which intrude into an area of Cretaceous and younger rocks thus forming the syncline of Aragón. In the lower zones occur limestones and marls, with occasional sandstones, all of which show some measure of folding. Higher up can be found older rocks of the Devonian period, but of similar constituents; hard sandstones, carboniferous limestones and conglomerates, all folded, faulted and fractured to a marked degree. Granites and gneiss are found at high altitudes. Differential erosion has occurred to a marked extent; alternating hard and soft rocks form respectively sierras and valleys, while the drainage pattern is of the grid type, conforming in many places to the parallel rock formations. Subsequent streams often follow the

H

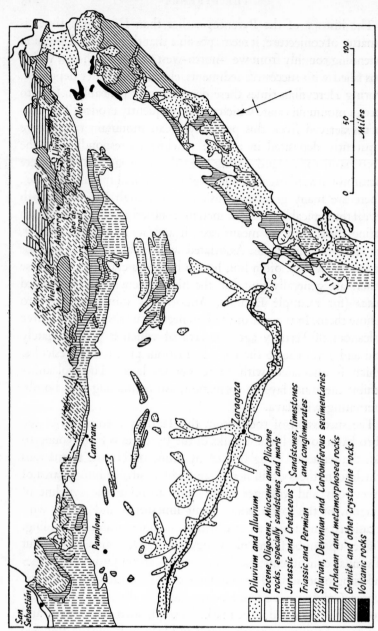

	Diluvium and alluvium
	Eocene, Oligocene, Miocene and Pliocene rocks, especially sandstones and marls
	Jurassic and Cretaceous } Sandstones, limestones
	Triassic and Permian } and conglomerates
	Silurian, Devonian and Carboniferous sedimentaries
	Archaean and metamorphosed rocks
	Granite and other crystalline rocks
	Volcanic rocks

Fig. 42. The Geology of the Pyrenees and Catalonia

lines of softer strata, their confluences with the consequent streams forming right-angled bends. One main fact emerges from a morphological study of the area; whereas the main trend of the Pyrenees as a complete mountain range is roughly from west-north-west to east-south-east, the individual ranges often follow another trend. The first runs from the Sierra de San Pedro, through the Sierra de Guara, which reaches nearly 6,500 feet, to the Sierra Monsech. The second extends through the Sierra de Leyre and the Peña de Oroel to Cabello. The third includes the beautifully coloured sandstone heights of the Peña Collorada, Tendeñera (in the national park of Ordesa). The fourth, more difficult to detect on the ground, passes from Cotiella to Turbón. The old highly complex strata of the central zone approximately follows these lines to the east, and then, in Catalonia, occurs another trend line formed primarily of Palaeozoic schists, this time running from east-north-east to west-south-west, through the Puig Mal range and the Sierra de Cadi.

This complexity of structure has led to great variety of relief. In the foothill zone flat dry plains, irrigated wherever possible, alternate with rugged sierras where rocks, if of a limestone or sandstone nature, weather to give fantastically shaped peaks. Many parts of the foothills are very sparsely populated because of extreme aridity, accentuated by the porous nature of the rocks and the steep slopes, which encourage soil erosion and give rise to rapid run-off of such rain as does fall. The lower plains stand some 1,000 feet above sea level, with the accompanying sierras rising abruptly to about 3,500 feet. As one progresses northwards these figures change gradually from 3,000 to 6,000 feet, and some of the highest sierras exceed 9,000 feet (Cotiella, 9,564 feet). The sierras make a gradual and graduated descent to the west, until at Irún the hills backing the coast are only about 1,000 feet high. In the east the Pyrenees form a more definite line of highland as the coast is reached, and the easterly extension, the Monts d'Albères, is quite a narrow belt of highland, coming to the sea as a promontory, and dividing the tectonic basin of Rousillon in France from that of Ampurdán on the Spanish side. On the western side the ascent from the sea to the mountains is more gradual, although steep slopes are characteristic, since the area has been greatly dissected by small streams with steep gradients, fed from high and regular rainfall, with correspondingly great powers of vertical corrasion. To the east, however, the ascent is scarp-like. The high region of the Pyrenees, centrally situated, is the zone of the main peaks, and below is appended a table of the major ones:

Name	Height (feet)	Type of Rock	Extent of glaciers
Pic d'Aneto	11,168	Granite	c. 3 sq. miles
Posets	11,047	Schists and granite	c. 1 sq. mile
Perdito (Mt Perdu)	10,998	Limestone	c. 2–3 sq.miles
Vignemale	10,820	Schists	c. 1 sq. mile (one flowing with crevasses and séracs)
Munia	10,332	?	None
Balaitous	10,319	Schists and granite	c. 2 sq. miles
Pic d'Enfer	10,112	?	Nivation hollows with permanent ice

This list is by no means exhaustive, but serves to show that the heights of the main peaks are comparable with some Alpine heights, for example the Jungfrau 13,671 feet and Wild Spitze 12,382 feet.

The presence of glaciers, small though they may be, is interesting. They are the sole surviving remnants of much more extensive masses of ice which covered the highland during the Quaternary Ice Age. There is one flowing glacier, the East Glacier of Vignemale (a peak first climbed, astonishingly enough, by an English lady, accompanied by a guide, in 1834), where good examples of séracs and crevasses can be found. There is much evidence of previous ice action. All major rivers flow in U-shaped valleys, which vary in width from one to half a mile, or less in the case of tributary valleys, and their sides occasionally rise to over 1,000 feet. There are many examples of truncated spurs and hanging valleys. Most of the streams start from large corries; the best examples occur to the south side of the Val d'Aran where there is a long line of tributaries of the Garona (Garonne in France),[1] which start in large corries sometimes occupied by lakes up to

[1] Garona: headstreams in the central and western Pyrenees are locally known as *garonas*, probably from the Basque *garai*, high or upper, and *-un*, a suffix expressing 'end' or 'extremity'.

half a mile in diameter, for example, Lake Bargadera. There are many patches of permanent ice, some in well-shaped nivation hollows, and the effect of a northerly aspect is well illustrated by the greater abundance of snow and ice on these slopes. Lower down each valley there is always a huge fan of pebbles, the result of snow and ice melt. All the river profiles show several breaks of slope, suggesting temporary halts of the glaciers due to fluctuations in melt rate. Barriers to glacial movement caused the temporary formation of lakes; for example, at the little village of Esterri there is a sudden widening of the valley floor, now covered with rich alluvium, where there may once have been a lake until the water cut its way through the rocky gorge which lies immediately to the south of the village. Sporadic humps of boulder clay are obvious morainic remains, but most of the glacial deposits were obliterated during the Quaternary interglacial periods by intensive river erosion. In many parts of the Pyrenees the effects of glacial and fluvial action are practically indistinguishable.

Most Pyrenean rivers are tributaries of the Ebro, with the exception of those of the Basque provinces and the Catalonian littoral. Many of them have pronounced right-angled bends, which, taken in conjunction with the tributaries, have enabled communications to be carried out parallel to the mountains, but only rarely across them. Inhabitable areas occur in elongated strips of comparatively fertile land, around a river, but they are separated from the next strip by arid sierras, which even mules find difficulty in crossing. A primitive standard of living as well as intense clannishness, and conservatism in outlook, is the result. The rivers of the region, though of little benefit to the people of the Pyrenees, are of immense value to the inhabitants of neighbouring districts of Spain, in fact, without them, the large towns of the Ebro basin and Catalonia would have no industry. These rivers all start in a land of perennial, and sometimes torrential, rainfall, and they are extensively used in their lower reaches for both irrigation and the generation of hydro-electricity. The irrigated zones in the Urgel district of Lérida are of great agricultural importance, while Catalonia is the area with the greatest consumption of electricity in Spain.

The climate of the Pyrenees is, like that of the British Isles, non-existent: there is only weather. As in most mountain areas, the Pyrenees experience weather that is extreme, variable from hour to hour, and quite unpredictable. There are, however, certain basic features of this weather which seem to occur more or less regularly. Summers are hot; in the foothill zones temperatures at midday occasionally reach the nineties, while higher up in the valleys a midday temperature of 75° F. is by no means rare. On the peaks it is naturally cooler, and, although there is no record, summer temperatures of 50° F. to 60° F. are likely, though they vary because strong winds, aspect, proximity to a lake and exposure on bare rock have marked effects on temperatures at high altitudes. In the months of August and September, and continuing into October, occur violent thunderstorms, of exceptional intensity, on roughly one day in four. It is possible that they have their origin in the passage into Spain, via the Basque areas, of warm moist air from the Atlantic, which is forced to condense rapidly over the high, and therefore cooler, mountains. Apart from such storms summers are generally dry and it is not surprising that even in the higher zones irrigation is essential, whether it be a mere ditch running from a stream, or a canal running from a barrage. In winter, however, it is a different story. Snowfall is heavy, and many villages are cut off from the outside world for weeks at a time, and houses are fitted with high steps to avoid flooding by melt-water in spring. All fuel has to be cut in summer, since it is impossible to go far in the winter, and the huge wood-pile is as prominent a feature in the Pyrenees as in the Austrian Tyrol. There is no official record of winter temperatures but a few isolated readings taken by private individuals give the impression that winter temperatures drop well below 0° F., even in the foothills. Such low temperatures are, however, continuous only in the highest areas. Apart from a few places near railway lines, where skiing is carried on, the winter is a time of hardship for the inhabitants, and even of danger, for, although there are no avalanches as in the Alps, floods sometimes do enormous damage.

There are two types of natural vegetation in this area; a steppe type in the lower zones and a mountain type at higher levels. Aromatic plants such as lavender, thyme or rosemary, thistles, coarse grass, low shrubs and stunted trees, particularly conifers, cover the foothills. Most of these plants are adapted to withstand drought. Higher up, however, the length of growing season coupled with the ability to withstand winter cold are the main criteria for plant distribution. Here, therefore, different belts of vegetation occur, varying with height. Where the trees have not been cleared for agriculture the lower areas are covered with deciduous forest; then follow the coniferous forests, where pine trees are abundant and undergrowth restricted; then, at 7,000 feet, the trees give way to the typical Pyrenean meadows, which correspond to the 'alps' of the Alps. In some places the meadows start lower down, their growth aided by the timber-felling of the local farmers who use the vegetation of the meadows for hay. The profusion of vegetation, the variety of plants, and the rich growth are of unique interest to a botanist; here abound many types of grass and innumerable flowers; harebells, rockroses, anemones and wild pinks, with others, like the *Cochlearia pyrenaica*, *Ramonda pyrenaica* and *Merendera pyrenaica* endemic in the Pyrenees. In addition, there are several wild fruits such as red currants, whortleberries, strawberries and raspberries. Amongst this vegetation, and rather more widely scattered, occur plants of true alpine character, such as the smaller gentian, alpine crocus, and, in a few restricted parts, the eidelweiss. This meadow zone ends abruptly when the slope changes, and is seldom found in large patches above 8,500 feet; above this level is a waste land of rock and ice. There are very few indigenous animals in the Pyrenees; the izart, a type of native sheep or goat, like the chamois, is hunted in the remoter parts, and bears used to be seen, but the writer has not heard even a hunter's tale about them during recent years. Eagles are occasionally seen and buzzards are more common.

For the inhabitants of this area life is hard, and mostly concerned with subsistence agriculture. The pattern and tempo of life is similar in foothills and mountains, but the higher temperatures of the lower zones allow more variety in cultivation. Throughout the area small plots of land are carefully tended and irrigated where necessary. In the mountains, from 4,000 feet to 5,000 feet, there are only three main crops; cereals (wheat or barley, with very small yields and seldom of good quality), potatoes and green vegetables, such as onions, cabbages and beans. In Andorra tobacco flourishes at these heights, but its cultivation in Spain is neglected. In the foothills, from 2,000 feet to 3,000 feet, maize and vines can be added to this list, and even olives. The mountains have a resource not found in the foothills – their meadows. Each meadow belongs to a farmer, who makes the long journey up to the mountain pastures (6,000 feet to 7,000 feet) by mule in late August or September, and with a scythe cuts out great swathes of hay, which will be stacked in his barn for winter use. The meadows are also used for the daily pasturing of cattle, but local fears of bandits (now almost completely groundless) demand that the animals be driven to the safety of the valley each night; this diurnal ascent and descent perhaps accounts for the toughness of steaks in such places. In the lower areas sheep and goats are allowed to roam over the poor vegetation, but special crops have to be grown for winter food. In the higher parts oxen are used for ploughing as much as mules, although the latter are used for transport since they alone can manage the steep, rocky mule-trails. In the drier foothills there is less pasture so that only mules are used for draught purposes. Chickens and pigs run indiscriminately around any Pyrenean village, and the entrance of a stranger is generally heralded by a chorus of howls from snarling dogs of the wolf-hound type, usually of uncertain and often of nasty temper. Since there are still a few lawless men in the high mountains it is perhaps as well that the inhabitants keep such animals.

The people of the Pyrenees are industrious and thrifty, and lose no opportunity of utilizing their natural resources to the full. Mention has been made of the meadows; in addition crops are often grown on south-facing slopes (*Solanas*), which receive the maximum sunshine. The pine forests are systematically exploited and some of them are being taken over by the State. Wood and charcoal are the only fuels, and wood is also used for constructional purposes. At the moment replanting of trees is not extensive, but neither is deforestation excessive as the removal of the trees is a slow, heavy job in which men and mules are the only sources of power, and rough trails the only transport routes. In remote villages water is used for domestic purposes by the simple means of conveying stream water through the middle of a village along runnels made of hollowed tree trunks. Its motive power is used either directly, by a water wheel for grinding corn, or indirectly as hydro-electricity, each tiny village receiving its power from a hillside station. Further downstream the water is ponded back behind huge barrages, or *pántanos*, and used for irrigation. As far as is known at present, there are numerous though scattered mineral deposits in the Pyrenees. Coal of Hercynian age is found in the east, at Malpas and at San Juan de las Abadesas. Lignite occurs to the south-east in Catalonia. Iron deposits are worked in the valley of the Noguera Pallaresa, close to Andorra, and Llavorsi is the collecting centre; transport difficulties and winter cold are problems likely to delay exploitation on a large scale. More iron is known to exist in Alp, near Puigcerda. Copper is found in the eastern half of the mountains, at Bielsa, and antimony at San Juan de las Abadesas. Lead occurs near Bielsa and Gistain, manganese at Alp, and a small number of oil wells, for example those just north of Boltaña have so far yielded little petroleum.

Many of the villagers are naturally resourceful. Smuggling over the high dangerous passes is a lucrative though risky pastime which tempts the ingenuity of many a Pyrenean man, with perhaps only a small farm or seasonal work to provide his livelihood. The risk of being caught is not great, although each pass is manned by a group of Guardia Civil, and in the past each person moving in the mountain zone had to have a special pass, renewed monthly. Smuggling would seem to be the *métier* of the Pyrenean; catering for tourists is another matter. The scenery is a great attraction, and, in addition, in some of the remoter villages such as Ansó and Plan the people still wear their local costume. This consists of a short waistcoat or jacket of black corduroy, white shirt of coarse wool, short corduroy knickerbockers, slashed down the outside of the leg and tied with coloured material on fiesta days, tough woollen stockings, canvas-topped sandals fastened with tapes, and a waistband of dark blue or black. Some years ago a shallow, flat hat completed the outfit, but hats have recently given place to the ubiquitous black beret. The women are not so conservative in dress as the men, and are seen less frequently in local costume; this consists of a long all-enveloping gown of dark material, gaily embroidered, black woollen stockings, canvas sandals like the men, and a large white head-covering rather like a wimple. These costumes, now dying out, vary greatly in detail from village to village. As well as such picturesque scenes, there is always winter skiing on the slopes of the Candanchu, for example, above Canfranc. However, the provision of adequate accommodation for tourists and the construction of good motor roads are very slow processes. For the latter some of the army surplus of unskilled labour is used, but the former is left to local enterprise. Only in those areas where rail communications with France are good has a real effort been made to foster the tourist industry, and as a result the population and prosperity of Jaca and Puigcerda have increased since the war. Apart from these two towns there are no other tourist centres of equivalent size, though the villages of Bielsa, Venasque, Viella and Panticosa cater for occasional visitors. Away from the railways there are few good means of communication; Pyrenean buses are few in number and sometimes unreliable in action, and only powerfully built cars can successfully negotiate Pyrenean roads. This attitude to the tourist trade is in marked contrast to that found in Andorra, where in the past nine or ten years hotels have been built in all the villages of the valley, and in Andorra la Vieille even the slogan 'Ices served here' may be seen—out of character, but good for trade. Since the encouragement of tourists is an important item of General Franco's economic programme, expansion in the Pyrenean zone seems likely. The creation of more national parks like that of Ordesa would be a step in the right direction.

Pyrenean people are all similar in appearance, but the common speech varies from east to west. In the west Basque is sometimes the only tongue known in the outlying villages, while in the centre a rough type of Castilian is used, which gives place to Catalan on the eastern side. In addition the people in the high villages often have a smattering of French as a result of proximity to France and contact with tourists. For the most part the inhabitants live in small villages, with populations rarely exceeding a thousand, isolated from one another, and continually at grips with nature. Their outlook is frequently narrow, and inter-marriage is almost inevitable. A man often states that he comes from a valley rather than from a village, an indication of the influence of the steep-sided valleys, and lack of inter-valley communications on the habits of the local people. The most important valleys on the Spanish side of the watershed are those of the Cerdaña (in French, Cerdagne) near Puigcerda, which leads via the little town of Seo de Urgel into Andorra; and Ansó, Roncal and Roncesvalles in the west which are attractive from a tourist's point of view. The Val d'Aran lies to the north of the watershed and is drained by the Garona, headstream of the Garonne; here traffic into the rest of Spain is so difficult in winter months that francs as well as pesetas are legal currency, so long as a transaction is completed in only one currency. (The exchange of currency by local shop- and inn-keepers is a lucrative 'under the counter' business.)

There are several towns, or large villages, all of which are to be found in inter-sierra plains, at places where the transmontane routes meet the main valley routes running parallel with the sierras. In the west, in the province of Navarre, is the great town of Pamplona; but this is strictly a town of the Ebro basin, not of the Pyrenees, and is mentioned on page 293. Apart from this major centre there are few towns of note. Jaca, backed by the picturesque Peña de Oroel, on the main railway line from France, is a flourishing tourist centre, and also serves as a market for local crops and animals. Barbastro, a foothill town, lies on the river Vero, and is a farming centre, with some manufacture of coarse woollen goods. Canfranc is little more than a village, and soldiers of the frontier guard still constitute an element in its population. Sabiñanigo, another foothill town, is at the junction of the railway and bus services that serve the mountain zone, and its industries include aluminium production. In the province of Lérida, Balaguer (6,469) (1950) with several flour mills, is the largest Pyrenean 'town', followed by Solsoña (6,500), and Seo de Urgel (6,543) (1950). The Bishop of Seo proffers religious aid to the people of Andorra, and from this town leads the only road to Andorra passable for most of the winter. Another town of note is Tremp, to which the railway from Lérida has at last been completed. This line will eventually connect with Sort, and the tunnels have already been constructed. In the province of Gerona there is Olot, surrounded by extinct volcanoes, with a population of 14,387 (1950), and several textile factories, Ripoll (7,451) (1950) where the people are similarly employed, and San Juan de las Abadesas, a small picturesque mountain town, with a population of 3,905, mostly engaged in agricultural pursuits. The density of population over the whole area is small as are the town populations, except where industry increases available employment.

The Pyrenees mark the end of Spain and the beginning of France, and the question of the boundary is an interesting one. As a physical barrier the mountains serve admirably; the passes are high, most over 5,000 feet, the area of high land is extensive, and the descent is neither easy nor continuous as it is broken up by the sierras. To a limited extent the mountains also act as a climatic barrier, much of the rain falling on the French side, while parts of the Spanish side suffer extreme drought. Different routes are used to cross the mountains; in general Frenchmen prefer the easier, more civilized route around the flanks of the mountains via the coast, while the few Spaniards desirous of leaving Spain with the maximum of safety and the minimum of police inter-rogation have been known to choose the highest and bleakest passes for their exit. That such passes are small in number is illustrated by the list below.

Name of pass	Height (feet)	Other information
Roncesvalles	3,470 – this is height of Col d'Ibañeta	Near the picturesque setting of *Le Chanson de Roland*, road only, no bus
Canfranc	5,349	Road and railway via Somport tunnel
Sallent or Portalet	5,877	Road only
Bonaigua	6,796	Road only, leading from Viella into Spain
Road tunnel of Viella	3 miles long	Only recently lit by electricity, links up Garona and Noguera Ribagorzana valleys
Road to Andorra, reaching France via Col d'Envalira	7,895	Snowbound in winter, Spanish side often snow-free
Puymorens	6,281	Pass before Puigcerda which lies in a depression, road and rail-way
Perthus	951	In eastern Pyrenees, road only

The boundary line follows the main peaks with great fidelity, except for a few interesting anomalies. The first of these occurs at Valcarlos, or the valley of Roncesvalles, where part of what by virtue of relief should be in France belongs instead to Spain; the western side of the valley is in Spain, and the eastern side in France, and there is a good deal of local traffic across the frontier. The real divide is the Col d'Ibañeta, mentioned above. From Valcarlos the line continues across the high crests, until it reaches the Val d'Aran, where, again, part of 'France' is included in the Spanish side, the real divide being the Puerto de Bonaigua. Finally, close to the little republic of Andorra, there is a levelling up; here the boundary approaches the town of Puigcerda situated in the valley of the Segre, thus giving to France the whole of the mountain divide near Latour de Carol; the divide is in fact before the town, in France, at the Col de Puymorens. In addition there is, in this area, the strange little enclave of Llivia, a fragment of Spain isolated by a few miles from Spain itself, and containing a small and characteristically Pyrenean town, Llivia, and a handful of tiny hamlets. The boundary finally continues along the watershed of the Monts d'Albères, and comes to the sea athwart the promontory Cap Cerbère, a rocky windswept headland.

CHAPTER X

The Catalonian and Levant Coasts

THE CATALONIAN COAST

THIS AREA IS not typically Spanish. There is adequate rainfall, a good deal of industry, a different language (Catalan), and a middle class. Here people are often better informed about national and world affairs than those further south, and throughout Catalonia's rather troubled history the desire for secession from the rest of Spain has been apparent.

The region consists of the eastern end of the Pyrenees and contains a variety of rocks, from Archaean granite to Quaternary alluvium. Many of the rocks are porous, while some areas show evidence of vulcanicity, for example the igneous rocks which appear along the coast north of Barcelona. Such complex structure gives rise to very irregular and dissected country, there being a series of alternating valleys and ridges that, at first, appear to have little plan. The narrow coastal plains, composed of late Tertiary and Quaternary deposits, are backed by a line of hills; Montseny and Guilleries are formed of Palaeozoic limestones and shales, while the strangely weathered peaks of Montserrat reveal Tertiary sandstone and conglomerate formations. These hills fall abruptly to a long narrow valley containing such towns as Sabadell and Tarrasa. This valley is thought to be a type of rift valley, and continues northwards to the basin of Ampurdán, which is probably a faulted depression. Both these large earth hollows are floored with alluvium, and rivers crossing them break through the littoral hills to the sea.

Rivers in this area include the Muga which, like the Fluvia, comes to the sea in the Gulf of Rosas, the Besós and the Llobregat which together have formed a large coastal alluvial plain, the Ter, and to the south of the area, the Ebro. The Ter, Llobregat

Fig. 43. Catalonia

and the Ebro alone rise on the landward side of the coastal hills and are the three longest rivers of Catalonia; the Ter has a length of 104 miles, the Llobregat of 100 miles, and the Ebro, 465 miles long, annually carries 7,500 million cubic metres of water towards the Mediterranean, losing much on the way through evaporation and irrigation. The other rivers are shorter, and in their upper courses have a large volume of water throughout the year. Downstream they are used for irrigation or hydro-electricity to such an extent that very little water ever reaches the sea.

Catalonia as a whole has a typically Mediterranean climate, with more than average amounts of rain and snow on the highland areas. The coast and interior valleys receive a moderate rainfall (Tarragona 20 inches a year, Barcelona 21 inches a year and Manresa 20·5 inches a year), while the hills are wetter (Viladran 33·6 inches per year and Berga 33 inches per year). Heavy storms are liable to occur in autumn, the wettest season, and sometimes in spring, but generally sunshine prevails. Precipitation is adequate for agriculture, especially where the land is flat enough for irrigation to be practised. Winters are mild (the average temperature of the coldest month at Barcelona is 47° F.), though subject to the *tramontana*, a cold north wind, similar to the *mistral*. Summers are not excessively hot (the average temperature of the hottest month at Barcelona is 74° F.), and are occasionally tempered by the *garbi*, a marine breeze which at times reaches the Ebro basin.

Agriculturally the region is rich, the climate, the fertility of much of the soil, and the patient hard work of the Catalans, all helping to improve conditions year by year. Many types of vegetables and fruits are grown, especially close to the large towns and cities, to supply the needs of the inhabitants. Olives and vines grow in profusion, often up to unusual heights in sheltered spots, while cereals are important, and sheep and goats as well as cattle are reared.

Irrigation is practised to increase the yields of many crops. In some parts the surface water tends to disappear as it reaches limestone rocks, a feature well illustrated by the river Francoli. In this case wells or *norias* are sunk, and the water pumped up, the underground reservoir being less liable to evaporation. In several areas, as for example near Riudecanos (hard by Reus) and around the Besós, there are extensive underground streams or *minas* up to 4 miles long. These are tapped at intervals. In some places *puarancas*, which resemble primitive *shadufs*, are used for raising water, when it is only a few feet below the surface.

The small coastal plains and interior valleys, where soils are fertile and local small-scale methods of irrigation can be used, are intensively cultivated. Maize is the predominant cereal in such areas, while wheat, barley and oats are of less importance. Rice is grown primarily in the Ebro delta and in other less noted regions such as the coastal strip between Pals and Castellón de Ampurias, the valley of the lower Llobregat, the irrigated zones of the

Maresme near Barcelona, and the vega of Cubelles. The same areas produce good crops of potatoes.

Well-known wines of several types come from Catalonia, although the phylloxera crisis of previous years has seriously reduced the number of vineyards. The Panadés is the main region, and can be subdivided into three zones; the first, the lowest zone, centres around Vendrell, and produces a dark red wine from the 'Sumoll' variety of grape. The central zone, further inland, and a little higher, is noted for its sparkling white wines made from 'Xarel-lo' and 'Macabeo' varieties of grape. The most important centre in Spain for sparkling wines is San Sadurní de Noia. The third, highest area of the Panadés produces a medium quality of white wine. Other noted centres include: Alella (table wines), Sitges (Malmsey), Tarragona (both white and muscatel wines) and Priorato (very high-quality red wines). Some wine is exported but most is retained for home consumption.

The olive flourishes along the Catalan seaboard, and the quality of oil produced is extremely high. The major centres are Tortosa, Borjas del Campo, Reus and Figueras. Other tree crops include almonds, which predominate in the districts of Vallés, Panadés and Tarragona, and hazel nuts, grown mainly in the districts of Priorato, Barberá and lower Panadés, with minor centres in Vallés and the Ter valley. Of the total production of hazel nuts in Spain 85 per cent is supplied by Catalonia.

Floriculture, which was introduced from the Italian Riviera by Benjamin Farina in 1922, is important in the Maresme, and has prospered because of its proximity to the large market of Barcelona. Thousands of carnations are produced each year, some of them for export.

On Catalonian lowlands cattle are reared primarily for dairy purposes; some Dutch bulls have been imported in order to increase the milk-producing capacity of local stock. Mules and donkeys are still widely used for draught purposes, and pigs are kept for both pork and bacon. The number of sheep and goats appears to be declining, and the custom of transhumance, whereby sheep winter along the coast and are taken up into the hills in summer, is slowly dying out.

Fishing is only a local concern; the main centres are Barcelona,

Tarragona, San Carlos de la Rápita and Villanueva y Geltru. The catch includes sardines, anchovies, squid, octopus, hake and crabs.

There is little mineral wealth in Catalonia. Some inferior coal is mined at Ogassa–Suroca (Gerona), yielding about 15,000 tons a year. Several deposits of lignite at, for example, Calaf, Sampedor and Figols yield a small annual output, and zinc found at San Pedro de Osor provides a limited but useful annual amount of about 2,000 tons. All the bauxite found in Spain (a small amount of about 6,000 tons yearly) comes from Catalonia; production centres include Mediona, La Llacuna, Font-Rubi, Santes Creus and Horta de San Juan. Minute quantities of chrome from Vimbodí are sent to the Basque industrial area, and about 1,000 tons per year of manganese are mined at Talltendre (Gerona). Potassium salts, discovered in 1912, form the greatest single mineral resource of this region. Cardona is the main centre and has a refinery and overhead cables to take the salts to Suria, another processing town. A minor production centre occurs in the mid-Llobregat valley where the salts are purer than those of Cardona. Catalonia's mineral output is not commensurate with its resources and this discrepancy is partially explained by lack of capital.

Though this area is agriculturally well endowed, its industry is more important. During the Middle Ages Catalonia was a major trading centre as it faced one of the safest stretches of water of those troubled days. The Atlantic was too rough for small sailing ships and the south Mediterranean was infested by pirates, so that only the Barcelona–Genoa route claimed any degree of safety. From those days developed a tradition of trading and business enterprise, further strengthened in the nineteenth century by the opening of the Suez Canal, and the 'quick' route to India. The loss of Cuba and the Philippines in 1898 was a serious setback, and the opening up of new routes (for example through Alpine tunnels) took some trade. More recently, however, the area has experienced better days, and its capital, Barcelona, has a population and a status almost equal to that of Madrid.

Catalonia, with an infinite variety of industry, is not only the most highly industrialized area of Spain but almost monopolizes the trade of the peninsula. The importance of the textile industry is paramount; 91 per cent of the spindles and 77 per cent of the looms of the entire Spanish cotton industry, and 86·8 per cent of all Spanish knitwear factories are concentrated in Catalonia, while all varieties of woven cloth are produced. Cotton spinning and weaving is the most important single branch of the industry, and the following list summarizes the present position:

Town	Number of spindles	Number of looms
Manresa	128,440	4,570
Puigreig	100,954	2,018
Ripoll	86,000	—
San Vicente de Torelló	71,000	286
Manlleu	60,000	227
Sabadell	43,250	1,000
Castellar	22,720	968
Reus	23,800	—

Unlike the Lancashire cotton industrial region both spinning and weaving mills are to be found in the same town; the power used is primarily hydro-electricity, and all processing is dependent on the regular flow of Pyrenean streams.

The coastal region and immediate hinterland of Barcelona specialize in knitted goods of cotton, wool, silk and rayon. Major centres include Barcelona, Mataró, Calella, Tarrasa, Gerona, Tarragona, Reus and Tortosa. A smaller branch of the textile industry is the manufacturing of woollen goods at Barcelona, Sabadell and Tarrasa, which towns account for 80 per cent of the Spanish output.

The small local supplies of coal are insufficient in amount and unsuitable in their chemical composition for the iron and steel industry. This industry is, therefore, concentrated on Barcelona, where coal, iron, tungsten and chrome are imported. The 'Pueblo Nuevo' suburb of Barcelona retains the oldest iron foundry of the province, which was originally used for constructing railway rolling stock. Hospitalet contains not only a large iron foundry, but most of the Catalan blast furnaces, which have an annual output of 10,000 tons. Badalona produces iron and steels of varied types. Engineering is similarly localized in the suburbs of Barcelona; in Barceloneta and San Andrés textile machinery, ship, aeroplane, diesel and locomotive engines are made, as well as derricks, cranes and various vehicles such as motor-cycles.

The paper industry is a Catalan speciality and the tradition of paper-making is deep-rooted; in fact, some factories date from the seventeenth century. Since vast amounts of water are used for processing, paper mills are distributed along rivers, especially the Llobregat, Ter and Fluvia. Prat de Llobregat is the main centre producing a great variety of papers; very fine quality paper, often hand-made, is produced at Gelida, Capellades and Torrelavit. Gerona and Tarragona make paper of average quality, while Barcelona specializes in a variety, including paper for cigarettes, for filtering purposes, and waxed paper and cardboard. More than 30 per cent of the Spanish output of paper is contributed by Catalonia.

Although some factories use coal or lignite, hydro-electricity is the chief source of power, and this helps to concentrate industry along valleys, for the water may be used locally from leats running off from the river to a small power station, or else used at a large centre such as Capdella, Camarasa, Pobla de Lillet or Badalona, and the electricity transmitted along lines that take the easier valley routes.

The tourist industry has become increasingly important in recent years. The mild, sunny climate, historical attractions, and picturesque scenery are obvious reasons for this growth; less obvious, but equally cogent factors are the easing of frontier restrictions and the improvement of transport which has opened up the Costa Brava to hordes of international holiday-makers. During the long summer season hotels, beaches and roads are crowded, and many new hotels have been built to accommodate the ever-increasing numbers of tourists. The main centres are Sitges, Blanes, Palafrugell, Palamós, Bañolas and Tossa del Mar, and most fishing villages now cater for tourists.

On the surface, Catalonia does not have the appearance of an industrial area. Inland rise the green grass-covered hills of the Pyrenean foothills, spoilt by neither slag-heaps nor chimneys, and the littoral retains its distinctly Mediterranean colour and charm. Industry is in fact widespread, but unobtrusive. In most towns and villages there are a few tall chimneys, and hooters blow regularly. This working to time, and general appearance of bustle, the number of bicycles seen in the streets, and the fact that people here seem to make a better living than most Spaniards, all combine to give an atmosphere alien to the rest of Spain.

The population density is high. The littoral contains many towns, often built originally on hill-tops, to resist pirates or attacking armies, while the valleys and interior 'trench' contain many more. Sometimes the difference between old and new is so pronounced as to be recorded in two names, for example Arenys de Munt, Arenys de Mar, *d'amunt* meaning the hill-top, inland and old part, and *mar* or *baix*, the beach-side and modern part. In Catalonia itself (i.e. in the provinces of Barcelona, Gerona and Tarragona) there are about 3,532,852 people. Of these cities and towns absorb the following numbers: Barcelona – 1,503,062; Hospitalet (part of the Barcelona suburbs) – 90,877 (1950); Sabadell – 78,761 (1950); Badalona – 76,331 (1950); Tarrasa – 74,449 (1950); Tortosa – 45,672 (1950); Manresa – 40,452 (1950); Tarragona – 42,138; Reus – 35,950 (1950); Gerona – 28,250; and ten other towns each account for more than 10,000 people.

Barcelona is, of course, the major centre, and in industrial and trading aspects is the real capital of Spain. With a good harbour, quite modern harbour installations, wide streets (for example the famous Ramblas) and huge buildings, many of them of historical interest, it has the atmosphere and attitude of a capital city. Here all types of metal products are made, including railway engines and nails, aeroplanes and diesel engines, engines for ships and for textile factories, typewriters and fountain pens. Cement and porcelain are made, and Barcelona is the second largest paper producer of Spain. Dyes, explosives, salts, glucose, soap, paint, glue, resin and medicines are all produced as well as various types of leather goods. Most important is the textile industry, and all types of threads, cloth and sometimes clothes are manufactured, from cotton, wool, silk, rayon, hemp, flax and other fibres. In addition to all these thriving industries one of the largest railway networks of Spain converges on Barcelona, making it a very important route centre. It has quick, direct links with France (e.g. the Barcelona express, which takes some twelve to fourteen hours to go from Paris to Barcelona). Good roads radiate from this centre to all parts of Spain, and sea communications are maintained with all parts of the world.

Sabadell contains many textile mills in addition to manufacturing flock wool, electrical fitments and various types of spirits, especially brandy.

Tarrasa is a textile centre and also produces mosaic work, a common form of domestic decoration in Spain.

Badalona produces chinaware of high quality, chemicals, some spirits and patent leather goods, and is an important collecting centre for the surrounding area.

Tarragona (the ancient Roman capital, and still a provincial centre) has a small harbour and exports wines, liqueurs, fruits, vegetables, olive oil and nuts, and as well produces some knitted goods.

Tortosa is situated on the Ebro, and contains an observatory for the study of seismological, magnetic and solar phenomena as well as potamology. It also manufactures soap, paper, porcelain, sombreros and various liqueurs, and acts as a market centre for agricultural produce, particularly olives.

Reus is an industrial centre, has over a hundred textile factories, and manufactures in addition soap, china and machinery. It also produces wine and receives the collected produce from the irrigated lands around.

The Catalans have a language and literature of their own – in fact it is said by Catalans that as many books are published in Catalan as in Castilian. The language dates from the time of the Gothic invasions, and is akin to Provençal, showing how Roman influence in Gaul brought to north-east Spain a slightly different line of linguistic evolution. Other links with the French side of the Pyrenees are architectural; the country farmhouse or *massia*, solidly built of wood and stone with two or three storeys, is similar to the *mas* of the Midi. The people themselves are rather more swarthy, more heavily built, and often darker – having jet-black hair and very dark eyes – than is usual among Spaniards. They also tend to be more hard-working and more shrewd in business transactions than the Spaniards from the south. The language, the human differences, the long tradition as a buffer state and a major trading centre – all mark off Catalonia as distinct from the rest of Spain. From the Catalan's love of independence stems a great desire for some measure of self-rule, which, under the present régime, has little chance of success. This area is a vital factor in Spanish economy but a disturbing element in Spanish politics.

THE LEVANT COAST

This area extends along the coast from the boundary of Castellón and Tarragona to Cape de Gata. Such arbitrary boundaries are taken purely for convenience, and do not always correspond with provincial boundaries. Inland the limit of the coastal area is marked by the hills and mountains of Gudar, Cuenca and the Sierra Nevada.

The region is one of quite large coastal, often alluvial, plains, separated by masses of highland which frequently extend to the sea as headlands. The main areas of lowland are those of Valencia, Alicante, Murcia, Cartagena and Vera. They are separated by the seaward extension of the highlands of Teruel, Murcia and the Sierra Nevada. A small, much eroded massif around the Moncabrer hills (4,540 feet) comes to the sea at Cape de la Nao, while a long line of hills, with the same west-south-west – east-north-east trend separates Murcia from Cartagena. Often the edges of these highlands are abrupt, giving rise to steep slopes and difficult terrain which form obstacles to communications inland. Many of these hills are of limestone which increases their aridity, and accentuates the difference between them and the greener and more fertile plains.

The numerous rivers of this area have much in common: they are all the precursors of the coastal alluvial plains; they all start in arid highland; they all flow, often through cañons, over very hilly country as they cross the steep edge of the highland rim; because of irregular rainfall, they are all seasonal in character, noted for floods as well as for droughts. The most important are the Júcar, Cabriel, Segura, Palencia, Guadalaviar (or Turia) and the Sangonera with its tributaries. There is, in addition, the large lake of Albufera, now cut off from the sea by a sandspit.

The climate of this coast is almost completely Mediterranean in character, but winter and summer temperatures show a slight rise

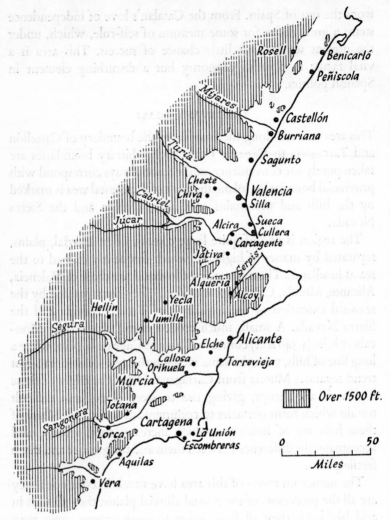

Fig. 44. The Levant Coast

in the more southerly areas, the mean maximum of the hottest month at Valencia is 86° F., and at Alicante 91° F., and, while the mean minimum of the coldest month in each case is 40° F., the average winter temperature at Valencia is 48° F., and at Murcia (close to Alicante) 50° F. The *leveche*, a warm wet sea breeze, partially contributes to this rise in winter temperatures. The rainfall of the whole area is extremely unreliable from day to day and from year to year, but as one progresses southwards drought becomes more pronounced in the summer. Valencia receives 17·8 inches annually, Alicante 17 inches, and Cartagena 13½ inches. Torrential downpours, of short duration but devastating effect, are frequent, especially in spring and autumn, and hailstones may do damage to some crops in summer. Irrigation works and dykes have an important use subsidiary to that of supplementing water resources, in diverting and stemming flood waters in times of emergency.

The Valencia region, endowed with a fertile alluvial soil, a beneficent climate and numerous irrigation works, is one of exceptional richness. In many places the system of irrigation dates back to Arab times, and several Spanish monarchs (e.g. James I of Aragón about A.D. 1239) tried to improve it. Important laws were made at the beginning of the eighteenth century and an intricate legal system has been evolved whereby, in most instances, specific water rights are given with tenure of land. This high degree of organization and system of 'rationing' ensures a fair distribution and a maximum benefit from available supplies. The system of 'canal and ditch' irrigation is in general use, and this is supplemented to the north of Valencia by water from wells. To the north hundreds of wells tap water which has seeped through the underlying fissured limestones; this water irrigates the vegas of Vinaroz, Benicarló, Alcalá de Chivert and Torreblanca. River water is used more generally and there are many barrages; the river Mijares and water from the María Cristina dam (27 million cu. metres) irrigate much of Castellón, and conditions will be even better when the Sichar (40 million cu. metres), Bechi, Onda and other barrages have been built. The river Turia fills the great Generalísimo barrage (250 million cu. metres) and irrigates a region to the north-west of Valencia; water conservation and distribution here will be completed with the construction of the Liria canal. The Júcar is the most important river, and its waters are distributed by a great network of canals covering much of the huerta of Valencia; the main barrages are those of Játiva, Énova, Meres and Cuatro Pueblos. On the river Magro, a tributary of the Júcar, the Forota barrage (proposed capacity of 30 million cu. metres) is under construction. The huerta of Gandía utilizes the water of the river Serpis which is stored behind the Beniarrés dam.

Agriculture is limited to the rich fertile lowlands, where often three or more crops a year can be raised from one piece of land. Small holdings are common, since a family can live on quite a small plot, but there are many large estates growing oranges and other cash crops.

Today the main crop of this area is the orange. Throughout the plain hundreds of groves extend in all directions, literally for miles. In winter oranges are so cheap as to be almost given away. In addition many lemons and limes are grown. The principal lemon-growing region is the vega of Segura, and the average yearly total is 8,800 tons. Blood oranges come from irrigated groves around Gandía, Oliva and Denia, pipless oranges ('cadenera' type) from Alcira and Carcagente. The bulk of the crop, however, is of the ordinary types of orange; export of all varieties continues throughout the spring season from major ports, particularly from Valencia.

Closer to the sea there are extensive ricefields, and the province of Valencia produces about 50 per cent of Spain's total. The main centres are Cullera, Sueca, Sollana, Silla and Perelló. In addition to the major cash crops, vast amounts of vegetables are produced, and are often planted as cover crops between hazel and almond trees. Many patches of land are given up to vines; the Utiel region produces light table wines and the district around Cheste and Chiva is noted for its white wines. Hemp, saffron, peanuts and the *chufa* are grown on the lowlands, while the hills remain dry, barren, and fit only for olives, *algorrabas* and heath plants that support honey bees.

The Murcia–Alicante area presents a different picture. Intense summer drought and irregularity of rainfall make irrigation essential; there is a great contrast between the extremely dry, barren limestone hills and the luxuriant growth of the irrigated vegas and huertas of the flatter regions. The major barrages serving the region are as follows; Fuensanta, on the river Segura (233 million cu. metres), Talave, on the river Mundo (45 million cu. metres), Quipar, on the river of the same name (36 million cu. metres), Puente, the oldest barrage of Spain (22 million cu. metres) on the river Guadalentín, Camarilla (39 million cu. metres), Cenajo (400 million cu. metres) and Contraparada. There are several large aqueducts, for example those of Aljufia and Barreras, which distribute these waters, and subterranean sources are tapped by wells in the Cartagena and Alicante districts. In the latter region three small barrages of Tibi, Elda and Elche store well water for summer use.

Horticulture takes place along valley floors and the coastal plain. Lemons flourish in the vega of the lower Segura, and Murcia is the primary Spanish producer with about 14,500 tons a year. Oranges of blood, pipless, mandarin and ordinary types are found around the centres of Zurcena, Totana, Guadalentín, Elche Dolores, Orihuela and Callosa. Maize, pimento, peaches, apricots and almonds are grown on the well-irrigated lowlands, while drier plains around Cartagena and Lorca produce small crops of cotton. Esparto grass grows on the more arid highlands inland, while coastal hills are utilized for olive growing. The vine is cultivated throughout the region, intensively so in the inland area between Jumilla and Yecla, where the 'Morastrell' grape produces good wines of claret type. Dates flourish in the dry climate, and Elche is especially famous for its large groves.

Fishing for local purposes takes place along the coast in small twin-sailed boats or feluccas, and the *mamparra* method of nocturnal fishing is practised, with oil or acetylene lamps to attract a great variety of fish. Cartagena is a large centre for the processing of fish; smaller ports include Aguilas, Torrevieja, Altea, Burriana, Peñiscola, Benicarló and Vinaroz. The large markets of Valencia, Alicante and Murcia absorb most of the surplus of fresh fish.

Mining is limited to one or two minerals in the hills of this area. Zinc and lead occur at La Unión (Cartagena), iron at Vera, sulphur at Hellín and Lorca, and some tin at La Unión. Lack of coal restricts smelting and almost all these metal ores are sent away, some to other countries but most to other parts of Spain.

Industry is practised only on a very small scale. Many fruits, especially apricots, and vegetables are tinned or preserved in other forms. Paper is made in Valencia, Rosell, Buriana, Buñol, Alicante, Játiva, Alcoy and Alqueria, and the increasing demand for orange wrappers has caused some expansion of the industry.

Pottery production is widespread; tiles and *azulejos* (coloured glazed tiles for interior decoration) are made in Valencia, Castellón, Alicante, Manises, Alcora and Altosano. The textile industry is small, focussing on Alcoy, Morella, Valencia and Castellón; all varieties of cotton cloth as well as small amounts of silk and woollen goods are manufactured. The iron and steel industry is limited by deficiencies in fuels and raw materials; marine and other types of engineering are carried on in Valencia, the steel coming mainly from two blast furnaces at Sagunto, while Cartagena has important ship-building yards where merchant ships and naval vessels such as submarines are constructed. Cartagena is also a metal-smelting centre, treating iron, lead, copper and zinc, and since 1950 a petroleum refinery has been in operation at Escombreros, the capacity of which will eventually reach one million tons. The chemical industry is limited to Valencia, where sulphate of ammonia is the main product.

The population of the Murcia–Valencia area is mostly rural, although towns have been attracting more and more young people in recent years. Population densities vary inversely with altitude. On the hills nucleated settlements are more usual, clustered around a well, or a hill-top, while on the irrigated lowlands population is dispersed. Near Valencia the typical country home is the *barraca*, a rectangular building with low wooden or adobe walls and a high, steep-pitched roof of reeds. South of Valencia occurs the *alquería*, a large self-contained three-storeyed farmhouse, with the workers' quarters on the ground floor, the owner's quarters on the first floor and the granary above. Altogether there are about 3,500,000 people in this region, and towns absorb the following numbers: Valencia – 571,452; Murcia – 244,683; Cartagena – 118,049 (1950); Alicante – 111,875; Lorca – 67,508 (1950); Elche – 62,910 (1950) and Castellón – 60,287. There are, in addition, 39 other towns each with a population of over 10,000 people.

Valencia is the third town of Spain, an important regional centre and natural focus of routes. It contains many famous and historic buildings, and has an important port, 'el Grao'. Its industries include those dealing with agricultural produce (for example wine-making, distilling, preserving, flour-milling), as well as ship-building, marine and other types of engineering, paper-making, cotton and silk spinning, and chemical, pottery and furniture manufacturing. The extensive damage caused by flooding in 1957 has been repaired, and steps have been taken to divert the waters of the Turia should flooding occur again.

Murcia, like Valencia, is surrounded by a fertile huerta, but lies inland. Silkworms are reared on mulberry leaves, especially around Orihuela, giving rise to a small but flourishing silk industry, and clothing, paper, and many varieties of fruit and vegetable conserves are made.

Cartagena, with its arsenal, is a military and naval base of some importance. Smelting works, potteries and a nearby modern petroleum refinery are its primary industrial activities. The port handles the export of lead, iron and manganese mined in its immediate hinterland, as well as agricultural produce from the surrounding huerta.

There are large huertas round Alicante and in this town many agricultural products are processed or preserved. It has an active port, and exports wines, fruits and salt from nearby saltings.

Castellón has a port, also called 'el Grao', and exports oranges and vines. It contains cord and sandal factories, and refines sugar and olive oil.

Elche, with its flat-roofed, whitewashed houses, is Moorish rather than Spanish in appearance, and this African affinity is strengthened by the large groves of date palms which surround the town. Sandals, cord and canvas are manufactured from local supplies of esparto grass and hemp.

CHAPTER XI

The Balearic Islands

THE THREE MAIN islands in the Balearic group are Majorca (Mallorca in Catalan), Minorca (Menorca in Spanish) and Ibiza, which is often spelt Iviza, such is the similarity between Spanish 'b's' and 'v's'. The larger and smaller islands were named by the Romans, while Ibiza was called 'Ebursus' by the Phoenicians. The islands were well known and populated, however, long before Phoenician and Roman times. Evidences of prehistoric man abound, particularly in Minorca, where the great 'Talyots' (compare the Catalan word for watch-tower – *atalya*) are spectacular archaeological structures. They are large circular or rectangular piles of huge stones, which are thought to have served the multiple purpose of watch-tower (at the top), home (in the middle), and communal grave (ground floor), although, in some, evidence of burial is not conspicuous. In addition there are stone circles, megaliths and *navetas* or burial chambers built on the plan of a ship. These constructions are contemporaneous with, and similar in design to, the *nuraghi* of Sardinia. In Carthaginian times there were already several large villages, like Mago (now Mahón) and Jama (now Ciudadela), while in Roman times Palma and Pollentia (now Pollensa) became important settlements and sent many slingers to join the Roman legions. Upon the decline of Roman influence Vandals ruled over the Balearics until, in A.D. 534, they were incorporated in the Byzantine Empire. Raids from Normans and Muslims followed, and in 903 the islands fell under the rule of the Omayads of Córdoba. From 1203 to 1349 the Balearics became an independent kingdom, and later passed under Aragón rule. In the eighteenth century they had British, French and Spanish masters, and finally, in 1802, they were incorporated in the kingdom of Spain.

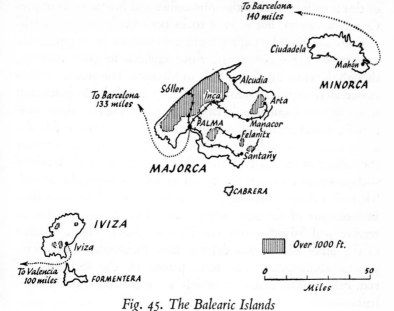

Fig. 45. The Balearic Islands

Geologically the Balearics present an interesting enigma. To some extent they seem to represent the extreme eastern end of the Betic Cordillera. Unfortunately, there is a lack of precise evidence in some vital places, which has given rise to several divergent views as to the real origin of the islands. It is now generally accepted that while Ibiza, Majorca and the western half of Minorca were formed by folding in Alpine times, the eastern half of Minorca has a totally different origin, and may be regarded as a fragment of a now vanished continent (of which Sardinia and much of Corsica formed part), in close juxtaposition to the Betic folds. Rocks in this eastern fragment include various marine sedimentaries overlying old red sandstone of the upper Palaeozoic series. Many of these rocks show evidence of fairly violent folding, while in some localities there occur flows of basic lava. Rocks in the rest of the island chain include only those from Secondary times to the present day. All these rocks were laid down beneath or at the edge of a vast sea which occupied roughly the position of the Mediterranean today, until late Cretaceous times, when the islands seem to have emerged gradually above sea level. Evidence of this is to be found in the ammonites and brachiopods of pre-Cretaceous strata, but in later rocks both marine and terrestrial remains are found ranging from nummulites to a prehistoric ancestor of the sea-cow, and from squirrels to giant tortoises, though the latter are found only in Minorca. The pressure which caused all these more recent rocks to be crumpled into mountains seems to have come mainly from the east during the Alpine oro-genesis, and it appears that Minorca felt this pressure before the other islands. In addition, Minorca seems to have been nearer the surface of the sea than the other islands, since only fossils of shallow-water creatures are found in local rocks of this period. There is a deeper channel between Minorca and Majorca than between any of the other islands, and Minorca was the first to receive real 'island' status – in Pliocene times. The separation of the other islands was delayed until Pleistocene times. This general submergence was accompanied by the formation of rias, called *calas*, many of which are today used as sheltered harbours.

From a geographical point of view it is convenient to deal with each major island separately, mentioning the smaller islands in association with the larger islands.

Majorca is the largest and covers some 1,405 square miles. Physically, the most prominent feature is the great range of mountains that runs parallel to the north-west coast for the whole length of the island. The range is moderately high, composed of jagged rocky peaks, of which one, Puig Mayor, almost in the centre, reaches a height of 4,845 feet. It forms a difficult barrier to communications, and has some effect on climate, sheltering the more southerly facing slopes from strong north-westerly winds. Since many of the rocks are formed of limestone, there is little water on the surface, only a few streams making their way to the sea or to the central plains. South of this line of mountains lies an extensive central depression, reaching the sea in several large bays, notably those of Pollensa, Alcudia and Palma. A little to the south of the island there are several hill masses, reaching no higher than 700 feet, but quite prominent since they rise somewhat abruptly above the general level of the land. Little drainage of a permanent nature is to be found, but there are several *arroyas* or *torrentes*,

i

ii

iii

XVII i Orange groves on the coastal plain near Sagunto; Moorish ruins top the distant outlier, at the foot of which lie the modern suburbs of Sagunto.

      ii Palms, local fishing boats and the Cathedral at Palma, Majorca.

     iii Wind-blown tree, rocky soil, with stone wall and 'talayot', near Ciudadela, Minorca.

i

ii

XVIII i Irrigated alluvial plain, Moorish in appearance, with arid, rolling hills of the Alpujarras in the distance, near Almería.

ii The Rock of Gibraltar, with the air-strip at the frontier; from the beach, La Linea.

which flow only after rainfall, and are dry for the greater part of the year. There are, however, good supplies of underground water, which is brought up by wind-pump for irrigation, and which may be seen occasionally deep underground in one of the caves, such as the Gorch Blau, for which the island is justly famous. There is a lagoon called 'Albufera' on the north-east coast, behind the bay of Alcudia, into which several streams drain, and there are numerous small lakes, some associated with picturesque gorges and other features of karst scenery.

The climate of Majorca approximates to that of the lowlands around Murcia and Cartagena. The average rainfall per year for the whole island ranges from over 60 inches on the northern highlands to under 20 inches in their lee and along the east and south coasts. In Palma itself there are about 73 rainy days in the year, with 1·4 days of gales. Majorca is less windswept than the other islands, since it has a sheltering range of mountains to protect it from the cold north wind that sometimes blows in winter from the Gulf of Lyons. Since it is near the sea, Palma, like most of the island, has a fairly high relative humidity, the average figure being 73 per cent for the year.

A visitor to Majorca is immediately impressed by the fertility of the island as a whole. There is little waste land except on the mountains, and the lower areas are intensively cultivated. All types of Mediterranean crops are grown with great success, and much of the surplus is exported. Six-sailed windmills near Inca grind locally-grown wheat, and the lowlands produce many varieties of vegetables (aubergines, artichokes) and much fruit (peaches, apricots, oranges, tomatoes), with irrigation playing an important part in their cultivation. Almonds grown on the hills give 12,000 metric tons a year, figs from the lowlands provide 21 per cent of the total Spanish fig crop, while a few vines and olives grow on the flanks of the mountains, although the snow cover of winter limits the upward extent of their cultivation. Several areas specialize in one crop and for this have particular fame; thus the low marshy land near Albufera produces good rice; near Benisalem, Lluchmayor, Pollensa and Felanitx there are rich vineyards; while the little town of Sóller, on the northern coast, but sheltered by a ring of hills, is noted for its oranges and lemons. Animals are

I

not important; mules, horses, sheep, goats and cattle are all kept, but purely for local use.

Natural resources in Majorca are few. Approximately 100,000 tons of lignite are obtained from small deposits, associated with prehistoric lagoons, at the foot of the central hills, near Alaró, Alcudia, Sineu, Felanitx and Benisalem. Other resources include marble, quarried near Santañy towards the south-west, and salt evaporated from coastal lagoons. Diving for sponges and fishing are important occupations along the coast. The catch averages 3,580 tons per year, and includes sardines, squid, octopi, anchovies and crustaceans such as crabs and lobsters.

Approximately 300,000 people, mainly Catalans, inhabit Majorca, and, for Spain, the island has a dense population. The largest town, which is also the capital of the island, Palma de Majorca, contains a population of 145,042 (1950, as are all figures for the Balearic Islands). No other town approaches this in size; others of importance are Manacor – 18,956; Inca – 12,522; Felanitx – 11,771; Lluchmayor – 10,094 and Sóller – 9,377. The other settlements are only little whitewashed villages, somewhat Moorish in appearance, tucked away behind some rocky inlet, or perched on some windswept hill, sites originally chosen for defence purposes, particularly against pirates.

Palma has a very good harbour and is the most important port of the three islands. It exports preserved foods, wine and liqueurs, esparto goods, baskets, tourist souvenirs and jewellery. Palma is also a noted centre for many European tourists, and is within easy and frequent sea and air communication with the mainland. There are four flights daily between Valencia and Palma, two between Valencia and Iviza, and a thrice-weekly air service between Barcelona and Iviza, and between Barcelona and Mahón, while there are additional interinsular flights. The Transmediterranea Company runs a daily service, except on Sundays, between Barcelona and Palma, a twice-weekly service between Valencia and Palma, and Barcelona and Mahón, and a service once a week between Barcelona and Iviza, Valencia and Iviza, and Alicante and Palma. The miniature railway of Majorca radiates from Palma, which is also the centre from which coach tours are organized to the more remote and picturesque parts of the island.

Imports into Palma consist of fuels such as petrol for the cars of tourists, and all types of manufactured articles including textiles, domestic hardware and bicycles, which stand up in some miraculous way to the tracks which pass for roads in much of the island.

Manacor is a collecting centre for local produce and its manufactures include the preserving of foodstuffs, the making of artificial pearls, and the distilling of various spirits. In the town itself there are several picturesque buildings, while just over 7 miles away are the celebrated caves of Drach.

Sóller is in the centre of a productive fruit-growing region, and there is some export of fruit, particularly oranges, from the small picturesque port, which is also utilized by a detachment of the Spanish navy. In addition there is a small shoe-manufacturing industry.

The island has a more dispersed population than is typical for much of Spain. Although the villages often show signs of past defences against raiders, in more modern times life has been peaceful and geared to a farming economy, so that many men have built their homesteads away from the villages, close to their fields. Thus the density of population, that at first sight appears to be small, is in fact higher than that for most of the Spanish provinces.

Majorca, with its mild, almost balmy, climate, attractive scenery and wide fertile plains, is a rich island; and, since its people are hardworking thrifty Catalans, it is not surprising that every year there is a considerable surplus of agricultural products which is sent to supply the needs of other regions of Spain less well endowed.

The rocky islet of Cabrera lies to the south of Majorca, and contains about 24 inhabitants. They are principally engaged in farming, with local shore fishing as a subsidiary occupation. There is a twice-weekly service to Palma, used for the conveyance of local crops to the Palma market.

Minorca is next in size of the Balearic Islands, and covers about 271 square miles. Much of it is covered with porous rock, often of a limestone character, which soon absorbs such rain as does fall (the average yearly amount varies from 20 to 30 inches). Winters are generally warm and frosts rare; the average annual minimum is 36° F., while at midday winter temperatures can rise well into the sixties. The summers are hot though the temperatures are ameliorated by land and sea breezes. The soil cover of the island is thin, and the land often flat, except for some wooded hills in the centre, so that the strong winds from the north have no natural barrier, as in Majorca. In addition, the ground is stony, boulders and rocky terraces stand up through the bright red earth, and the task of clearing the ground is a hard one. Much of the loose rock débris has been removed with the utmost care and used to make wells, houses, irrigation tanks and windmills (the latter seldom used today). In the little patches of soil revealed a few crops are planted – limited to the short-rooted variety, since the soil cover is only a few inches thick. Although there is very little surface water, there is a good supply underground, which is tapped by wells. Water is pumped up by motive power supplied by donkeys, machines and occasionally by human labour. Notwithstanding the great difficulties crop yields are reasonably good.

The island endeavours to be self-supporting and, to a certain extent, achieves this end. Good supplies of wheat are produced locally, although some has to be imported, and every householder has several plots of land used for growing vegetables. Peach and almond trees as well as vines are grown in sheltered places. Chestnut trees provide an alternative basic food supply, while the prickly pear is grown for its fruit as well as for hedging purposes. Many of the plants are protected from the cold winds by strong stone walls called *tancas*. Most farmers possess a pig, chickens, a few sheep and goats, and perhaps a cow. In this way a modicum of self-sufficiency is attained. There is no surplus, however, so that any expansion of the tourist trade will mean increased imports of food supplies in the season.

Other occupations vary. They include fishing around the coasts, and charcoal burning in the centre of Minorca, an important occupation in an island where there is scarcely any fuel except wood, and where even charcoal has to be used with care to maintain supplies. There is as yet a somewhat meagre tourist industry.

Of the total number of people living on the island, a little less than half live in Mahón, the capital (20,000). Situated at the head

of one of the largest and most picturesque rias of the island, Mahón
serves as the main centre of communications. The island's bus
service centres on it, and there are thrice-weekly night services by
ship to Barcelona, and other inter-island links. There is some
manufacturing of shoes and silverware in the town itself, while
the ria is utilized to a certain extent by the Spanish navy.

Ciudadela, with a population of 12,600, is the only other town
of importance. As its name suggests it was a fortified town and is
now noted for its fruit, vegetable and fish markets.

The rest of the island supports only a scanty population which
ekes out a rather meagre livelihood from an inhospitable environment. Despite the barrenness of the island, however, it is not without its beauty. Surrounded as it is by the intensely blue Mediterranean, dotted here and there with small villages and farmsteads
with whitewashed walls and wells, it lives up to its name – 'la isla
de blanca y azul'.

Iviza is slightly smaller than Minorca (209 sq. miles), but it
is more hilly; few parts of Minorca are over 1,000 feet, but
several peaks in Iviza rise above this figure, and one, Atalayasa, in
the south, reaches 1,558 feet. The underlying rocks are often
porous, particularly the outcrops of limestone, and, since the
annual rainfall seldom exceeds 14 inches, there is the same problem
of water supply as in Minorca. Winters are warm (55° F. is the
average temperature of the coldest month), and summers are hot,
so that natural vegetation is restricted to drought-resistant types
such as juniper, cistus and wild olive. The barrenness of the island
was recognized by the Phoenicians, who named it 'Ebursus' – the
Sterile.

Subsistence agriculture inland, and occasional fishing for local
needs around the coasts, are the main occupations. Iviza does not
suffer from such violent winds as Minorca, but the ground is as
rocky, and any crops grown are the result of continuous hard work
and care. Around the coasts of Iviza are important saltings, and
there is an active trade in this commodity.

Iviza, the capital, has a population of 12,283, a third of the total
for the island. Although the port has not a good site and is not
well sheltered, it is the only town of size on the island, and handles
all trade and commerce. Wine and cereals with some sawn wood

and flock wool are the main exports. Other settlements are small and of little importance.

Formentera, a name derived from the Latin *frumentum*, is an island separated from Iviza by a narrow channel, and easily accessible for small craft from the larger island. It is crowned by two central hills – Puig Guillen and Monte de Mola – but apart from these two crags it is extremely flat. The climate, similar to that of the larger island, is mild (the absolute minimum temperature is 37° F., and the absolute maximum is 94° F.), and the rainfall is slight (16 inches is the average annual total). Wheat, wine and fruit are the chief concern of the farmers, and there is generally a surplus of these commodities for export to the neighbouring island. There are about 3,000 people on Formentera, and many of these live in the tiny capital, San Francisco Javier. The coasts are utilized for saltings and, here and there, occur beaches which attract tourists.

The Balearic Islands, taken as a whole, present a picture of agricultural richness. There are many crops, varying in type from temperate to sub-tropical, and yields are generally good. The soils are mainly fertile, and the climate benign, for here the fierce Spanish sun is tempered by the sea, which increases both equability and rainfall. The people are hardworking and energetic, and this factor, coupled with favourable soils and climate, has given to the Balearics a measure of prosperity. Agricultural products, such as cheeses, sausages and tomatoes, minerals, for example salt and lignite, and manufactured goods, which include shoes and souvenirs, are exported to the mainland. Coastal scenery and inland caves, such as those of Arta, Drach, Hams and Campanet, provide unique attractions for tourists. It is not surprising to find that, with all these advantages, the islands have a high density of population – about 250 per square mile as compared with the average for Spain of 150 per square mile. On the Spanish mainland water makes 'oases' in the middle of deserts; the Balearic Islands form 'oases' in the middle of the sea.

CHAPTER XII

Andalusia

ANDALUSIA COMPRISES THAT part of Spain lying south of the Sierra Morena and west of a line of longitude drawn through Cape de Gata, and may be divided into three regions; the Guadalquivir valley, the South Coast, and the Sierra Nevada.

THE GUADALQUIVIR VALLEY

Physically this region consists of a Tertiary basin, once the floor of a sea between the Sierra Morena to the north, and the Betic Cordillera to the south. The Guadalquivir fault to the north forms a complete physical barrier, and is outlined by hills that rise abruptly from the plain below. To the north of the fault there is a sudden change in climate, crops, vegetation, and human response from Mediterranean to arid meseta types. To the south and east, however, Mediterranean features merge gradually from the lower *llanuras* of the plain to higher areas of semi-steppe, and more rugged country, until the high peaks, tremendous gorges and chasms of the high Sierra Nevada appear. Here in the south there is a zone of transition; in the north there is a line of contrast. The plain itself is not as wide as the green colouring on a map would suggest, and is confined to an area close to the river. Away from this river plain the older Tertiary beds have been dissected to form low-lying hills, minor elevations with gentle slopes, not obvious on a small-scale map, but above a level where water can be used effectively for irrigation. This is an area of gently rolling country to which such names as *campiña* are given. The seaward part of the valley consists of Las Marismas (the marshes), and a coastal fringe of sand-dunes, the Arenas Gordas, which owe their origin to winds and currents.

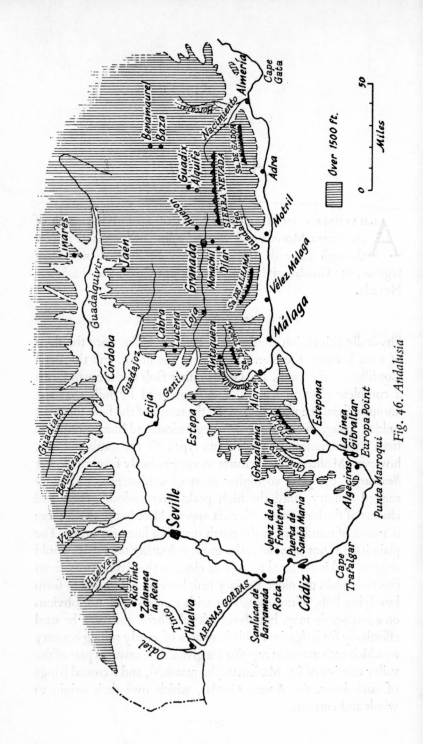

Fig. 46. Andalusia

The major river of this area is the Guadalquivir, and its most important tributary is the river Genil, which flows for part of its course along a fault-line roughly parallel to the sea. Other smaller tributaries are the Guadajoz and Carbones from the south, and the Guadiato and Huelva to mention but two of the many shorter tributaries from the north. Rivers which enter the sea independently of the mouth of the Guadalquivir include the Guadalete, the Rio Tinto (so called because of the colour of its waters, stained by minerals), which, with the Odiel, enters the Atlantic in a common estuary at Huelva.

The Guadalquivir valley is an 'island' of intense heat and insolation in summer, and, with temperatures regularly reaching the nineties at midday, and on rare occasions exceeding 120° F., it is the hottest area in Spain. Temperatures are very mild in winter, which is when most rain falls. Precipitation remains slight, however; at Cádiz there is an annual total of 18 inches, at Seville 19·5 inches (according to the Oxford Home Atlas, but 23 inches according to María de Bolós Capdevila), and 24 inches at Córdoba. The funnelling effect of the highland on winds from the south-west helps to bring in more moisture-bearing clouds than would otherwise be the case. Precipitation on the higher areas is heavier than on the lower plains, reaching 40 inches in some years, and at least a minimum of irrigation water is assured.

Agriculture in this extremely fertile area has been noted for centuries, but it is due less to natural causes than to irrigation schemes. In wide areas where irrigation cannot be practised, extensive heathlands occur, merging into steppes, especially on poor soils. Irrigation water is stored in great reservoirs, for example at Tranco de Beas, at the head of the Guadalquivir, and there are many smaller barrages on the tributaries. In addition, many canals lead directly from the river itself, some of them being of Arab origin, and a few wells are also in use. A paucity in other sources of power has led to the generation of hydro-electricity, though it is insufficient for the demands of the region as a whole, and cannot be supplemented from power stations in the north of Spain. Although there are many small power stations in the mountains, and more are being planned, there is not enough electricity for industrial expansion, or for the comfort of all the inhabitants. With rainfall meagre and unreliable it seems doubtful whether any appreciable amelioration of this situation is possible at present.

An interesting aspect of farming in the agriculturally limited areas of Andalusia is the division of land into large estates or *latifundias*. In the drier parts of the south there is a great risk of crop failure, more land is needed to feed a family, and nothing grows without irrigation. Only a man with a large amount of land and capital can withstand such natural disadvantages over a long period of time. It cannot be said, however, that these large estates are run either efficiently or for the common good. The alternative seems to be cultivation by smallholders, with the State or other syndicate acting as security against hard times.

Wheat produces high yields in the vega of Granada and along the river Genil, while both barley and maize are grown as *secano* crops, and rice, planted in the well-watered deltaic soils between Seville and Cádiz, annually provides about 70,000 tons of grain. Sugar beet reaches maximum production in the vega of Granada, along the rivers Genil and Guadalquivir, and around Baza and Guadix, while sugar cane is principally grown around Granada. Cotton flourishes in the Guadalquivir valley, and annual regional production fluctuates around 21,000 tons; flax thrives in irrigated plots around Granada, Seville and Córdoba, and hemp is an important crop of the lower Guadalquivir valley. Tobacco, an Andalusian speciality, gives high yields, particularly in the vega of Granada. Olive groves cover the hillsides surrounding the river Guadalquivir, and this area is the main world producer of olive oil; the province of Jáen is, in effect, one vast olive grove. Although situated on arid slopes, the greater proportion of olive trees (85 per cent) is irrigated. Orange trees are by no means as common a sight as in Valencia; Seville is the main centre, and produces bitter oranges used in the manufacture of marmalade, as well as several sweeter varieties. Cork oak groves extend between Seville, Cádiz and Huelva, and vines are ubiquitous, those of the Montilla district south of Córdoba producing a wine well-known in Spain.

Sherry, a wine renowned throughout the world, comes from grapes grown in the 'sherry triangle', which lies within a line

joining Jerez de la Frontera, Sanlúcar de Barrameda and Puerta de
Santa Maria. The location of the triangle is partly due to the
presence of a belt of limy soil, about 3 feet deep, beneath which is
an impermeable substratum; this combination provides humidity
throughout the summer drought. Many factors affect the ultimate
matured wine, and the element of chance is always present; harsh
burning winds, Saharan in origin, may wither leaves and fruit on
the stock; a poor autumn may restrict the natural sugar content; or
a sudden hailstorm may ruin the chances of an abundant harvest.
Plants are normally of 'Palomino' or 'Ximenes' type, grafted on
to American nursery-raised stock when the latter are two years
old, with roughly 900 plants to an acre. Pruning is vigorous, and
the grapes are cut only when really ripe, and then sun-dried for a
further two days. In the initial stages pressing is carried out by
men wearing shoes studded with round-headed nails, which do
not crush the pips, and the operation is finished by a small press.
The must passes through two stages of fermentation, and is then
carefully tasted and blended by the Solera system; the great vats
are ranged, according to the age of the wine, in tiers one above
another, and every year a certain proportion of older wine is
blended with younger wine, so that sherry of fixed type and
quality is produced. The names of the firms of Domecq and
Gonzalez Byass are well known; the latter maintains huge cellars
(*bodegas*), one of which, the Doce Apóstoles (the Twelve Apostles),
contains barrels of gigantic size – 510 arrobas. (An arroba approximates to our measure of a quarter.) Less well-known but locally
important wines include those of 'manzanilla' type from vineyards around Sanlúcar de Barrameda.

Livestock thrives in this area, and many sheep roam the hillsides
in charge of shepherds aged from ten years upwards. The merino
is the most common type, and at Carmona there is an interesting
black variety of this breed. Flocks of goats frequently run beside
the sheep, and the 'Granadina' goat is a well-known variety. Black
pigs are kept mainly for the production of sausages, and horses
are also bred. Cattle are rarely seen in Andalusia; a few oxen are
kept in well-watered areas for draught purposes, and dairy
farming has been started in the wet marshland of the Guadalquivir
delta. Bulls for the bull-ring are reared on special ranches often

renowned throughout Spain. Not every bull is chosen for fighting purposes – only those which reach the required standards of speed, size, ferocity and colour (black bulls are preferred). No bull is allowed to live after a fight, either in Spain or in Portugal, since its experience in the arena makes it too knowledgeable and too dangerous for future contests. The normal minimum number of *corridas* in Spain is 100 per year, with at least 100 lesser fights; six bulls are killed at every fight, and, allowing for extra bullfights and natural wastage due to non-selection, the number of bulls required each year is at least 2,000, and generally more. There is consequently a steady demand for such animals.

Around the coast there is an appreciable amount of fishing, and much of the catch, especially of bonito and tunny, is preserved in Huelva. Innumerable other varieties of fish are landed for local markets including sardines, hake, squid, anchovies and shellfish. Around the mouths of the Guadalete and the Rio Tinto there are extensive saltings; some of the salt is sent inland, though little is refined before use.

Small amounts of varied minerals are extracted in this area. There is manganese at Zalamea la Real, sulphur at Benamaurel, lead at Charches, Huétor and Monachil, copper at Grazalema, iron at Alquife and Hueneja, and a small amount of uranium, used for atomic power since 1960, in the province of Córdoba. Although minerals have not been exploited to the full, there is a greater variety in Andalusia than in any other province of Spain.

Industry in this area is hampered by lack of major fuel resources, since there are inadequate supplies of both hydro-electricity and coal. There is no main centre of industry; it occurs only in the larger towns, where it will be more fully described.

The general distribution of population well illustrates the importance of the irrigated lowlands, which absorb the bulk of the population. Town sites are interesting; the large capitals are along the river Guadalquivir, while another line of towns has arisen on the lower slopes of the Sierra Nevada, where incoming sea breezes first drop their moisture. Jaén, Cabra, Lucena and Estepa are examples of such hill towns. There are also several 'oasis' towns in the dry inland areas, the best example being Granada. Along the coast there is a line of important ports, for example, Cádiz and

Huelva, both of Phoenician origin. The total population for the region is about 4¾ million; towns absorb the following numbers of people: Seville – 480,213; Córdoba – 189,556; Granada – 153,409; Jerez de la Frontera – 120,021 (1950); Cádiz – 113,749 (with San Fernando 41,196 (1950)); Huelva – 71,362; Jaén – 69,066; Antequera – 43,334.

Seville, originally an Iberian stronghold, is the capital of the whole area, and contains many imposing buildings, such as the Giralda, originally the tower of the mosque completed in 1196 in the reign of Almanzor. For over two thousand years Seville has served as port and market centre for the rich hinterland of the Guadalquivir valley. Although 65 miles from the sea, it still serves as a port, being linked with the Atlantic by the Fernandino canal, while ships of large tonnage can now reach Seville by the Alphonso II canal. The main exports include wines, cork, olive oil and almonds, while coal, machinery, textiles, raw cotton and chemicals are imported. Seville has always been an important route centre, and it still forms an important focal point of roads, railways and air routes. It is also a centre for industries, some based on local agriculture and producing such goods as spirits, wines, liqueurs, flour and preserves, while others use imported raw materials to a great extent, and provide textiles (especially cotton goods), cement, iron and steel products, ranging from gun barrels to inlaid stilettos for tourist souvenirs, various acids and superphosphates. Buildings of historical interest and architectural beauty, bullfights, the annual trade fair, and the great processions during the Semana Santa, or Holy Week at Easter, ensure a regular and thriving tourist trade, which is served by a good system of cheap and (for the 'deep south') rapid transport by rail and air.

Córdoba, once a Roman town and later the capital of the Caliphate, today shows evidence of its past glories in the Mezquite (mosque) which was adorned with over a thousand marble columns and red and gold decorations. Unfortunately, later Catholic kings ruined the general effect by erecting a grossly over-decorated altar in the very centre, to the glory of God, but to the fury of local citizens. The town has grown steadily in size from a population of 8,000 in the seventeenth century to its present size of 189,556, and there are many factories manufacturing electrical fitments, bronze, aluminium and copper products, cement and chemicals. Industries based on local agriculture include fruit pre-serving, and the making of paper from straw.

Granada, the last stronghold of the Moors, still contains the Alhambra and other Moorish buildings, and is the centre of an exceptionally rich agricultural area. All varieties of Mediterranean and many tropical crops are grown by means of irrigation from the rivers Darro and Genil, which meet at this town. There are factories for making sugar, alcohol and sulphuric acid. Flax and hemp are manufactured, tobacco is cured, and there are various handicrafts such as the weaving of thick woollen cloth in tradi-tional designs, wood carving, metal working (including inlaid work) and the making of panniers and shoe soles from esparto grass. This is skilled work and can only be done by hand; if a machine is used the threads break, or tension is so slack that the soles disintegrate after they have been worn a few times. Since nearly all Spaniards in the south wear these sandals there is a steady market for such goods.

Jerez de la Frontera (the corruption of the name by British shippers gave the word 'sherry') is an important centre near the river Guadalete. Wines world-famous for quality, cognac, liqueurs and other drinks are made here, while ancillary industries include the manufacture of glass, bottles, casks, corks and labels; soap is manufactured on a small scale and there is some smelting of iron. The surrounding countryside is noted for the rearing of thoroughbred horses, well known in Spain for their strength and fine bearing.

Cádiz, situated on the tip of a narrow peninsula (the Isla de León) joined to the mainland by the 'bridge' of Zuazo, is an important port. Phoenicians built a town here (remains can still be seen) and gave it its early name – Gadir. Today it serves as port, naval station, and, to a lesser extent, as a fishing centre. A little to the south lies the industrial centre of San Fernando, which, apart from an astronomical observatory and seismological station, also contains the arsenal of Carraca, an important naval college and large shipyards, where merchant ships, oil tankers and naval vessels are built. Salt, some of which is exported to other parts of the peninsula, is evaporated from the mudflats of the lower

Guadalete. Close to Cádiz, at Rota, an American naval and air base has been constructed in accordance with agreements signed on September 26th, 1953. Generous aid, both monetary and in goods and raw materials, was given to Spain in return for the use of Spanish territory. In addition, Spain benefits from the oil pipeline constructed to other bases at Morón de la Frontera, Torreja (Madrid) and Zaragoza, since this eases the difficulty of oil transport.

Huelva is built on the Anicoba peninsula between the Tinto and Odiel rivers, and is thus surrounded by extensive marshes from which some salt is evaporated. Evidence of its early importance is seen in the Roman aqueduct. This is the port which deals with the copper and pyrites mined in the Sierra Morena to the north, and there is a specially constructed pier for handling the trucks efficiently. In addition olive oil, fruits, fish and wines are exported, and the main industries include the manufacturing of chemicals, cables and fertilizers, as well as the making of ropes. Five miles away lies the small port of Palos de Moguer, from which Christopher Columbus sailed to America on his voyage of discovery.

Jaén, the capital of the foothills, lies below Mount Jabalcuz near the river Guadalbullón. In Roman times it was the centre of a rich silver-mining region; although lead is still smelted here Jaén is more renowned for the quality of its olive oil. The steppe-like character of the surrounding countryside is shown in the abundance of flour mills, and the paucity of wine-making and preserving industries. The great emigration of population from Jaén and district has prompted the authorities to initiate the 'Plan Jaén', a scheme to bring more industry to the town.

Antequera, another town of the foothills, is situated on the banks of the Guadalhorce at the foot of the Sierra de los Torcales. It is a market centre of some importance, and contains textile factories which produce woollen and silk goods. It is an important road centre, and the main railway line from Málaga to Granada passes through the town.

Andalusia is regarded as the most 'Spanish' part of Spain, although its name is thought to be a corruption of 'Vandalicia'. Even in winter it is warm and sunny, while in summer the brilliant light reflected off the whitewashed walls produces harsh

contrasts of colour. In the countryside agricultural workers live
in 'picturesque' cottages of adobe, or in huge *cortijas*, large country
farmhouses built around a central *patio*, or courtyard, and housing
owner, workers, cattle, sheep, chickens and crops in noisy and
untidy proximity. Even more interesting to a north European are
the caves of the gipsies at Córdoba, Jaén and Granada. These are
by no means peculiar to Andalusia, and, particularly in Granada,
money from gullible tourists has brought electric light and other
modern conveniences to these otherwise primitive dwellings.
Orange trees, date palms, the dark faces of beggars (begging is
illegal but ubiquitous in Andalusia) all combine to provide a note
of oriental or at least African flamboyance in Andalusia, a note
which is augmented literally and metaphorically in well-known
restaurants by the throbbing of guitars, the clacking of castanets
and the swirling rhythm of flamenco dancers. These attractive
scenes, however, are superficial; they do not reveal the slum
tenements, the leprosy colony in the hills, the diseases, such as
rickets and blindness, for which abject poverty is mainly to blame.
Andalusia is lovely to visit, less lovely to live in.

THE SOUTH COAST

The South Coast, though smaller, has many features in common
with the Levant coast. Physically, the region consists of an alternation of alluvial lowlands and barren hills, but the plains are small,
and the uplands less pronounced, especially as they lie parallel
to the coast, and form no spectacular headlands. Of the plains,
those of Almería, Motril, Málaga and Vélez Málaga are most important. The names of the highlands backing the plains are, from
west to east, the Massif of Tolox, north of Marbella, the Sierra de
Alhama, the Alpujarras and the Sierra de Gádor. Mulhacén, the
highest peak in Spain (11,420 feet), is only 23 miles from the sea,
which is visible from villages on its southern flanks. The proximity
of sea coast to the highest peak gives an exceptionally steep gradient to the slope. Consequently the rivers of the area are short and
swift flowing. Nearly all have names with the prefix *guad*, derived
from the Arabic *wadi* (river). There are the Guadalhorce, Guadiaro,
and the Guadalfeo which comes to the sea at Motril. The Horca-
jar, which waters the Almerian plains, is also important. All are

used for irrigation near their mouths and some, for example the Guadiaro and Guadalhorce, form valuable routeways through mountain passes.

The frequent passage of depressions in winter, and its littoral position, combine to give this area a higher annual rainfall than that of parts of the Levant coast; nevertheless, the annual total still remains low – Málaga receives 18·8 inches, and Almería 18·5 inches, as compared with the very low figure of 13·6 inches for Cartagena. Summer temperatures are high, especially so inland away from the moderating action of the sea, but at the coast the high humidity in summer counterbalances the alleviating effect of marine influence.

With slopes facing the sun, valleys and coast sheltered from cold or very strong winds by high mountains, and water available for irrigation from many perennial streams, augmented by rainfall, the area is naturally well endowed for agricultural pursuits. The fertile irrigated plains are here called 'vegas', as in the rest of Andalusia; this word, believed to be Iberian in origin (the prefix *be* in Basque means low), generally refers to a low-lying, flat, open and uncultivated plain. Perhaps in Andalusia the long association of cultivation with flat lowlands has caused this slight confusion of ideas; whatever the cause, it should be remembered that a vega in Andalusia has more in common with a huerta of Valencia than with a vega (for example the desolate, barren and scarcely cultivated Vega de Tera, near the river Esla) in northern Spain.

The fertility of alluvial soil is here augmented by small-scale irrigation schemes, some of Arab origin and design, which enable a great profusion of both tropical and Mediterranean crops to be grown. Sugar cane, bananas, rice and cotton flourish, sufficient indication of a beneficent climate, while Almería and Málaga produce several varieties of grapes, those from Almería providing table grapes and a medium quality of wine, and those from Málaga providing rich sweet wines of muscatel type. Olives thrive on the drier hill-slopes, particularly at Alora and Vélez Málaga, and cork oaks occur near Málaga and around Níjar, where extensive new groves, recently planted, have not yet come into bearing. Beyond the cultivated zones there are vast areas of exceptional aridity, such as the Alpujarras, where cultivation is impossible. In fact the south coast consists of small cultivated plots of incredible fertility – oases of green in a dry, dusty upland.

Some minerals are found in this area, for example iron and a little gold at Rodalquilar in Almería, but as deposits are small they are not extensively worked. There is no industrial area, but industry, such as it is, is concentrated in the main towns. Fishing takes place along the coast, and the catch, for local use only, includes anchovies, sardines, tunny, squid and lobsters.

As few people live on the mountains there is great congestion on the tiny flat plains. There are about 1,250,000 people in the area as a whole, and towns absorbed the following numbers in 1950: Málaga – 318,102 (1960); Almería – 73,715 (1960); Algeciras – 60,456; La Linea – 58,170; Vélez Málaga – 31,610; Motril – 23,420; Adra – 13,687; Estepona – 12,913.

Málaga, lying on the Mediterranean coast east of the mouth of the Guadalmedina, is Phoenician in origin, and contains many Roman and Arab remains, some of which have been recently excavated. The blast furnaces of this town are now inactive, but there are factories for the making of chemicals, soap, cotton goods, metal goods, flour, sugar, spirits and wines of international repute. The major exports are wines, fruits and nuts. Close to Málaga is the small tourist resort of Torremolinos, which possesses a stretch of fine sand almost 4 miles long, and is one of the best-known holiday centres of this 'Costa del Sol'. Málaga is also an important route centre; it contains the most southerly of the Spanish airports, and controls the coast roads as well as those leading north to Antequera and Loja. It is, in addition, linked to Córdoba and eventually to Madrid by a railway which follows the tortuous valley of the Guadalhorce.

Almería serves the eastern end of the Sierra Nevada range, and manufactures cord, esparto goods and *azulejos*. The magnificent site of its port, sheltered by the Gulf of Almería, is wasted because of the limited hinterland and difficulty of communications with the interior. Exports include grapes, esparto goods, almonds, salt (evaporated from nearby saltings), and lead mined in the hills to the north. Like Málaga, it has a railway link with Granada and eventually with Madrid, but this line is not so well served by fast and well-equipped trains as is that from Málaga. Towns between

Málaga and Almería have to rely solely on road transport, and roads are not good, since irregular terrain makes their construction difficult.

La Linea is an important town, of recent growth, opposite Gibraltar. Originally an agricultural centre, its proximity to Gibraltar has greatly increased its commercial activity, and many of its inhabitants work in the canning factories and naval dock-yards of Gibraltar.

Algeciras is an important port for fishing and for trade with North Africa, as well as being the terminus of the trans-Iberian railway. It is an active market and commercial centre, and manu-factures corks and earthenware. The extreme warmth of the town in winter has given rise to an out-of-season tourist industry.

Estepona is a centre for the fertile land around it, where grapes, oranges and lemons are particularly important. Furniture, wooden boxes and crates are manufactured from timber obtained from the fine woods of *pinsapo* pine that clothe the slopes of the Sierra Nevada to the north of the town. Further along the coast lead is smelted and exported from Adra.

To the south of La Linea (literally 'the line' – i.e. the boundary line) lies a large rock, separated from the mainland by a flat sandy waste. It was first settled by the Moors in A.D. 711, and its present name is a corruption of the name of their leader, Tarik; 'Djebel el Tarik' (now named Gibraltar) originally meant 'Tarik's hill'. It has been a British Colony since the 1713 treaty of Utrecht, con-trols the western entrance into the Mediterranean, and is a per-petual insult to patriotic Spanish pride. The 'Rock', as its name implies, is simply a large outlier of limestone; the problem of water supply has been overcome by the construction on the eastern slope of large concrete slabs which collect dew and rain. Gibraltar's annual rainfall is high (35 inches), when compared with that of nearby Málaga (18·8 inches), and is due mainly to the easy passage through the straits of depressions, which give rise to heavy winter rain, although there are three months of drought in summer. Strategically of vital importance, economically it is of little use. There is some tinning of fish and fruit, using labour from the Spanish mainland, but Gibraltar is chiefly concerned with goods in transit and with the supplying of bunker coal and petroleum to ships entering for refuelling purposes. The peninsular railway terminus is at Algeciras, which faces Gibraltar across the Bay of Algeciras, and is also the Spanish embarkation point for North Africa. Gibraltar is linked to Spain only by a road, which crosses the air-strips built on the low flat northern end of the tiny peninsula; air services to all parts of the world are frequent, and on the western side of the Rock lie the well-equipped harbour and naval dockyards. The total population, excluding members of the armed forces, is 125,000, and in addition, about 10,000 Spanish workers enter and leave daily. The Barbary Apes live among the higher crags, existing on scant vegetation, and are occasionally enticed from their rocky heights for the benefit of tourists. The human inhabitants live in the town on the south-western side, their houses clinging precariously to the steep rugged slopes.

This south coast region, one of the richest and pleasantest areas in Spain, owes many of its characteristics to the huge mass of highland behind it. The Sierra Nevada shelters the plains from cold winds, and this, combined with a southerly aspect, ensures a high average annual temperature. The mountains attract a good deal of moisture, and retain a cover of snow well into spring, thus ensuring a perennial water supply for the plains below. In addition, they form a barrier passable only at a few points, making communication with the rest of Spain slow and difficult, but helping at the same time to preserve local customs. The sea is the other dominating influence, helping communications and ameliorating climate. South Spain looks away from the mainland over the Mediterranean to the Barbary States; and it is not surprising to find much of North African origin in the names, customs and people of this lovely Moorish oasis tucked away on the fringe of Europe.

THE SIERRA NEVADA

The Sierra Nevada consists of an enormous mass of highland extending from the village of Padul, on the road from Granada to Motril, to the village of Gergal, on the railway line from Linares to Almería, with the high peaks of Mulhacén and Veleta at the centre of the system. A great deal of research and exploration is yet to be done in the central area, but from evidence so far accumulated it seems that there has been land in this zone since lower Permian times, with intermittent invasions of the Betic sea. In Jurassic and early Tertiary times, however, this land appears to have been less extensive, and there were large geosynclines to the north and south of the present mountains, containing seas in which were laid down sediments which were later folded and incorporated into the present systems.

The major fold movements took place in Miocene times, a little after the fold movements in the rest of Spain, and from a geological point of view the mountains have one very interesting feature. They reveal definite Alpine phenomena in the structure of the folds, particularly in the nappes which outcrop in the central areas. Such intensive folding served to emphasize the line of crustal weakness underlying the whole region, so that earthquakes, while not excessive in number, occur more frequently than in other parts of Spain. The number of seismic disturbances averages three per year, but this figure may be exceeded occasionally, as in 1911, when there were eleven. The epicentre of such movements is frequently of exceptional depth. Even while they were emerging, the mountains were subject to subaerial denudation, and huge accumulations of fluvial deposits appeared on their flanks, which now form some of the arid foothills to the north of the Sierra Nevada. These later deposits are almost undisturbed and therefore horizontal, and have been deeply dissected by modern streams.

Rocks exposed in the area show great diversity of age and substance, ranging from ancient Archaean granite to younger sedimentaries, such as limestone. The folding took place without great volcanic activity so that recent volcanic rocks are absent; there is, however, a large amount of granite and other crystalline rock in the centre (as, for example, micaceous schist) associated with the Veleta nappe, where ancient underlying rock has been forced up as an extrusion and subsequently exposed through weathering. From this Archaean core the rocks become progressively younger outwards, passing through Palaeozoic sedimentary rocks, through Mesozoic to younger sedimentaries, amongst which limestone is important, if only because it gives rise to completely arid, as opposed to almost arid, hills. Various minerals like lead, zinc and

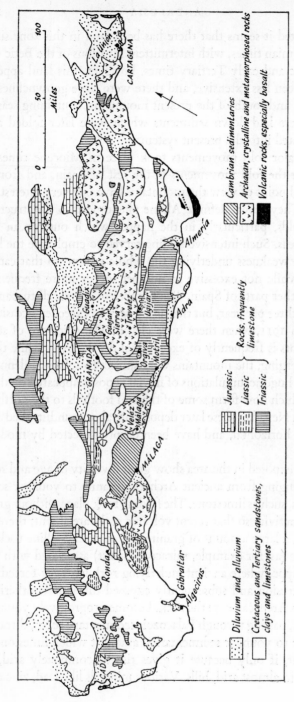

Fig. 47. The Geology of the Betic Cordillera

Diluvium and alluvium

Cretaceous and Tertiary sandstones, clays and limestones

Rocks, frequently limestone

Triassic

Liassic

Jurassic

Cambrian sedimentaries

Archaean, crystalline and metamorphosed rocks

Volcanic rocks, especially basalt

silver are associated with the older rocks, while iron occurs, though infrequently, in some of the younger rocks. Mineral waters are also found in a few places, as at Alhama, but difficulty of access prevents their being used on a large scale.

The higher region was covered by a small ice-cap during Quarternary glaciation, and ice has helped to fashion the surface features, particularly on the northern and western slopes, where insolation was less pronounced. There is much evidence of ice action; erratic blocks are sometimes found, but these are less obvious features than the mounds of glacial material, or moraine. Between the peaks of Mulhacén existed a large glacier, which has left an expanse of lateral moraine, about $1\frac{1}{2}$ miles long, between Tajo de Culo de Perro and Cortijo de las Vacas; another morainic deposit may be found below the Loma de Dilar. Many corries still exist, some, like that at the head of the valley of Siete Lagunas, revealing a stepped appearance similar to the *cirques à gradin*, or *Kartreppe* found in the French or Swiss Alps. Sometimes the corries are filled with water, such as the Lagunilla de Mulhacén, and the Laguna de las Yeguas. There still exists a small remnant of the former ice in the *hoyas*, or hollows, of Mulhacén and Veleta; in both cases ice remains in the hollows all the year round. Some geographers refer to these patches of ice as glaciers, but since they cover an area small in comparison with Alpine glaciers, and since the ice scarcely moves, they cannot be termed glaciers in the strict sense of the word.

River action is more marked than ice action in the high zones; most geographers agree that the tremendously steep-sided valleys owe their present appearance not to ice but to the work of streams, which have great force in a region of such steep gradients. The dryness of the climate compared with that of most other high mountains has prevented lateral erosion from keeping pace with vertical erosion, and has produced valleys that are almost gorges. Routeways are possible in the valleys and gorges, but the construction of roads and railways is very difficult in the land immediately adjacent to them. On the lower foothills especially, where the rock is softer, gullying is marked, a reminder of infrequent but torrential storms. Where the rivers emerge on to the plains there is usually a large alluvial fan; such features are obvious on the west side of the Sierra Nevada, where many short streams debouch on to the plain of the Genil.

The topography of this mountain range, whether in the high ranges or the lower foothills, is imposing. An atlas map shows the general arrangement of hill masses and streams; it cannot, however, reveal the interesting local details. The central ridge contains the highest peaks and acts as a divide between the rivers, climate, cultivation and human activities of the north and south slopes. It runs almost due east–west, starting at El Caballo (10,581 feet) and passing through Veleta (11,128 feet), Mulhacén (11,420 feet) and the Alcazaba (11,185 feet) continues in the same direction, but at a lower level until the Cerros de Almirez (8,400 feet) is reached. The appearance of the actual peaks is often the result of structure rather than of erosion. Thus Mulhacén, a great granitic monolith, has a relatively rounded top; Veleta, composed partly of micaceous slates, has a very gentle slope to the south but a precipitous slope to the north, while the heights composed of younger rocks show rounded monotonous outlines if derived of softer material, but sharp, jagged peaks if of limestone.

High elevation and a low latitudinal position combine to make the climate of the Sierra Nevada a unique feature of the European mainland. The climate is basically Mediterranean, but many other factors have to be considered. In the first instance height reduces pressure; this sometimes induces slight mountain sickness. The effect of pressure, however, is not as great as that of increased insolation. Above 7,000 feet the light is strong, and some protection for the eyes is advisable, while the effect on the human skin can be dangerous. There are great extremes of temperature, both annual and diurnal. By day the summer temperature in direct sun may be well over 120° F., although on the heights shade temperatures may be as little as 45° F.; at night the temperature drops very suddenly to as little as 38° F., as a result of great radiation of heat from almost bare rock into air that contains no 'blanketing' cloud. In winter temperatures in the sun often reach over 65° F., though the whole mass of highland carries continuous snow well into spring. Much of the sun's energy at this time of year is reflected back from the snow, and for this reason springs tend to be late, particularly on the northern slopes.

Precipitation occurs mostly during the winter half of the year in the form of whirling snow-storms on the peaks and heavy rain on the lower hills. Permanent snow lies for nine months above 7,750 feet, and snow in patches lies for a good eight months between 4,250 feet and 7,750 feet. Mention has already been made of the ice- and snow-filled hollows of Mulhacén and Veleta, which are perennial. Many small springs emerge from porous rock at a height of about 8,000 feet, and flow down the mountainside, watering the lower slopes throughout the year and counteracting the effect of summer drought on plant growth.

Natural vegetation of this mountain range is interesting, since during an ascent from sea level to 10,000 feet varieties of plants ranging from Mediterranean to steppe and alpine types can be found. In the Alpujarras to the south of the main ridge, natural vegetation is sparse, and the bare rock is subject to excessive gullying. Esparto grass grows in some spots, and is put to good use by local peasants. Otherwise a few stunted bushes, some coarse tufts of grass and one or two xerophytic shrubs are the only signs of plant growth. This arid or steppe type of vegetation is found in most of the foothill zone, except near rivers, where cultivation is possible. Starting from the upper Genil valley, however, it is possible to climb up past Mediterranean trees such as pines and oaks, through a temperate zone of chestnuts, firs and pines and then emerge on to the high land where such alpine flora as gentians, Pyrenean poppies and the *Ranunculus glacialis* flourish, some only a few yards away from a bank of snow.

Agriculture in such an area is bound to be limited, and can be divided broadly into three main types; that of the high northern slopes, that of the arid foothills, and that of the high southern slopes. Few people try to eke out a living on the northern slopes; those who do live either in small villages like Guejar Sierra, or else in isolated farmhouses. At lower altitudes olives and vines flourish, and small terraced plots, irrigated from tiny streams, supply all the vegetables needed, while a few cattle are kept and sheep and goats pastured on the hillsides. At higher altitudes it is too cold for olives or vines, and the staple crops are wheat, maize and potatoes, all grown on minute plots hacked out of the steep hillside and irrigated by tiny runnels led off from springs. Chestnuts give a measure of variety to local food supplies, and some sheep and goats are kept – but they are rarely to be found above 8,000 feet, since there is little grass at this height. Methods of farming are primitive; the wheat is often pulled up by hand, and then trodden by donkeys, the only beasts able to negotiate the steep slopes. On the southern slopes much more variety is possible, since it is much warmer, and it is here that a line of villages has arisen along the Rio Grande, where the streams of the mountains emerge from their gorges. Olives are grown up to the 3,000-foot contour line, oranges, vines and a great variety of vegetables flourish in the southern valleys, while chestnuts, mulberries and walnuts can be grown up to 5,000 feet, and rye and potatoes up to 8,500 feet. As a complete contrast one comes to the limited agriculture of the barren foothills, where only in the river valleys is there any extensive agriculture. A small number of sheep and goats are kept, some esparto grass is collected, and in a few spots, as for example along a spring line, a little wheat is grown; otherwise the foothills are useless for agriculture.

There are about 200,000 people in the Sierra Nevada, most of whom live in small villages on the southern slopes. The most important of these include Berja (14,000), with its lead mines, Orgiva (9,500), a small agricultural centre, and Alhama (10,000), with its mineral waters. There are other even smaller villages, such as Trévelez, an untidy huddle of houses built below the peak of Mulhacén, surrounded by small runnels of pure spring water mainly derived from snow-melt, and boasting, despite its diminutive size, of the fact that it is the highest village in Spain (5,395 feet). Another interesting village is Pitres, which retains, as do so many of these mountain villages, the original Moorish houses of its medieval occupants, still occupied by their descendants. Communication between such villages is usually only by rocky mule trail; only occasionally is there a road which can take wheeled traffic. Oddly enough there is a motor road to the top of Veleta, which was used by cars for the first time on September 15th, 1935, and has since facilitated the transport of many tourists from Granada for skiing in winter and in summer for mountaineering or sightseeing (visibility is exceptionally good on a clear day).

A good summary of the area is given by Fidel Fernandez in his book *Sierra Nevada* (Editorial Juventud, Barcelona):

Este mirador es, pues, unico en el mundo. . . . Los valles septentrionales estan petrificados por el hielo y por el frio; los meridionales, calcinados por el calor y por el sol. En los cortijas que miran a Granada se vive al amparo de fogatas, bien cerradas las puertas y ventanas; en los de la Alpujarra, se duerme a la luz de la luna, sobre montónes de paja, al aire libre. Los labradores de Guejar o de Monacil almacénan bellotas y cerezas; los de la Contraviesa almontan almendras o naranjas. Aquellos conservan patatas bajo la nieve; estos secan higos al calor del sol. Las del Mediodia son suaves lomas de alegras tonas azuladas; las del Norte son crestas terribles, sombreadas, y negruzcas.

(Moreover, this sight is unique in the whole world. . . . The northern valleys are petrified by snow and ice; the southern ones roasted by the heat of the sun. In the farmhouses around Granada people crouch beside an open fire, and keep doors and windows well shut; in those of the Alpujarra, they sleep in the moonlight, on piles of straw, in the open air. The farmers of Guejar or Monacil store away acorns or cherries; those of the Contraviesa put by almonds and oranges. The former keep potatoes under the snow; the latter dry figs in the sun. In the south there are wide rolling hills, light blue in colour; in the north menacing peaks rise up, shadowed and black.)

CHAPTER XIII

The Spanish Mesetas

THE SPANISH TABLELANDS, or Mesetas, have always held an important and influential position in the human and political geography of Spain. Structurally, climatically and economically they may be classed together as one unit; but regional differences make it desirable to divide them into three areas: the Northern Meseta, which includes Old Castile and León; the Southern Meseta, which includes New Castile and Estremadura; and the Ebro Basin.

THE NORTHERN MESETA

Physically this area consists of a large Tertiary basin surrounded by mountains composed of more ancient rocks. To the north lie the Cantabrians, which are composed in their highest part of a great mass of Mesozoic limestone, dissected by deep narrow valleys carved by swift flowing rivers. The highest peaks occur in the Picos de Europa (8,786 feet high), while to the south the Peña Espiguete reaches 8,045 feet. The height of this dissected country diminishes further east – Monte Valnera (5,636 feet), south of Santander, represents one of the highest points. Further west the rocks become progressively older until the metamorphosed schists and gneisses of Galicia are reached; the high rugged Cantabrians merge gradually south-westwards into the bold hills forming the Galician massif, where the highest summit levels reach 7,000 feet (for example, the height of Teleño, a rocky crest in the Montes de León, is 7,178 feet). The frontier hills are lower, 4,085 feet being the highest point in the Sierra de la Culebra. To the east the arid ranges of the Iberian system provide an effective barrier, the Sierra de la Demanda reaching 7,556 feet, and merging southwards into the Sierra de Guadarrama foothills. To the south

the rim of highland is more dissected, and consists of the Guadarrama range (where the peak of Peñalara reaches 7,800 feet), the
Sierra de Gredos, the highest mass, where the Plaza del Moro
Almanzor reaches 8,501 feet, and the Sierra de Gata, separated
from the others by a deep trench occupied by the Alagón, a
tributary of the Tagus.

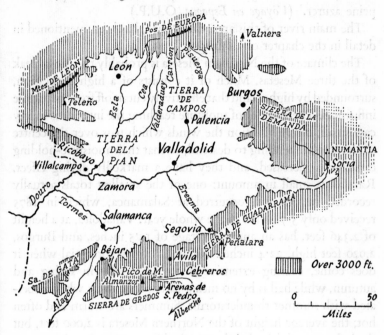

Fig. 48. The Northern Meseta

The basin itself has a straight tabular appearance, typical of
meseta scenery, caused by the horizontal layering of the surface
rocks. Excellent examples of erosion under semi-arid conditions
can be seen where rivers have cut deep gorges, or aeolian action
has created buttes and mesas. Here and there the horizontal gives
place to the almost vertical line of the cuesta, which marks the
break of slope between the high plains, or *páramos*, and the lower
areas, often called *llanuras*. The *páramos* frequently coincide with
the original level of the Tertiary plain, while the *llanuras* represent
areas lowered by erosion. More fertile riverine tracts, covered
with the alluvium of past or present rivers, are termed *campiñas*.

Such are the Tierra de Campos, Tierra del Pan and some areas near Zamora. Théophile Gautier gives a vivid and colourful description of the country: '. . . Le pays . . . avait un aspect d'une sauvagerie étrange; c'étaient de grandes plaines arides, sans un seul arbre qui en rompit l'uniformité, terminées par des montagnes et des collines d'un jaune d'ocre que l'éloignement pouvait a peine azurer.' (*Voyage en Espagne*, O.U.P.)

The main river of this area, the Douro, has been mentioned in detail in the chapter on drainage.

The climate of the Northern Meseta is probably the most bleak of the three Mesetas. Much of it consists of a high depression, surrounded by higher land that effectively cuts it off from maritime influences. The amount of moisture reaching the interior is in any case small; but in addition the winds which pass over the centre of the area are tending to descend, so that their moisture-holding capacity is increased, and they have a markedly drying effect. Rainfall is small in amount; one of the smallest totals actually recorded in the area occurred at Salamanca, which in 1875 received only 5·7 inches in the whole year. Valladolid, at a height of 2,346 feet, has an annual average of 12·5 inches, and Burgos, 2,920 feet high, 22·4 inches. Rainfall is often torrential when it does come, causing extensive floods, especially in spring and autumn, while hail is by no means rare, particularly when associated with summer thunderstorms. Summers are warm and often hot; the average height of the Northern Meseta is 2,000 feet, but the influence of altitude is less marked in summer than in winter, and average temperatures rise into the seventies for most towns, while midday temperatures are frequently much higher. At Burgos the average August temperature is 66° F., but 104° F. has been recorded. Summer heat is made less bearable by strong winds that stir up the dust, covering men and crops with a thick brown layer, and helping to cause the *calina*, a type of heat haze. Winters are cold; the average temperature at Burgos in January is 36° F., but January minima of 11° F. and 12° F. have been recorded in Burgos and Valladolid, and the cold is made less endurable by the frequency of grey skies. Temperature inversion also occurs, and mountain slopes may be warmer than the lower plains which are covered by a dense mass of freezing stagnant air. The annual and diurnal range of temperature is great, the former averaging 35° F., the latter reaching and often exceeding 20° F. A climate with such continental characteristics naturally presents many and varied problems.

Agriculture is a somewhat hazardous undertaking, for all the natural elements seem to conspire against man. To the traveller passing through this area the monotony of scenery is accentuated by the similarity of crops grown – almost always wheat or some allied cereal. The great fields, without even fences to break the sky-line, stretch literally for miles. The peasants who cultivate them have long journeys to make by mule or ox before they begin their day's work, and then have to endure the vagaries of the meseta climate, particularly strong winds, since there is no shelter on the open *campos*. Despite their hard work yields remain pathetically small; on the high *páramos* from 6 to 10 quintals per hectare; in the more fertile places, such as the clay zone of the Tierra de Campos, from 10 to 15 quintals per hectare. These low yields are primarily the result of climatic factors (especially scanty rainfall, desiccating winds and abrupt changes of temperature), although methods are primitive and there is room for improvement. Vines grown by *secano* methods occur near Burgos, Ávila and Vallado-lid, while Ávila lies in an important olive-producing region. In general, however, the Northern Meseta is too cold for the growth of olives. Irrigation in this area is limited, since the land is porous, and the steep slopes leading from one plain level to another hinder the building of canals, while rainfall is not only small in amount but very irregular in fall. Irrigation schemes have already been mentioned; but even when all possible use has been made of available water, the fact remains that much of the Northern Meseta is not and never can be irrigated. On the lower areas, where irrigation does exist, many crops can be grown on an intensive basis – vines, maize, sugar beet, fodder crops and all kinds of vegetables for local markets. The drier uplands, although carrying only a sparse covering of natural vegetation, form ex-tensive pastures for flocks of sheep and goats, the former providing a high proportion of Spanish wool. Transhumance takes place annually, the animals wintering in Andalusia or Estremadura. Pine forests can be found on the higher slopes of the peripheral mountains, particularly in the provinces of Soria, Ávila and Segovia, and provide valuable charcoal for domestic use and resin for industry.

Mineral wealth is confined to the bordering hills. To the north, on the flanks of the Cantabrians there is a small amount of coal and anthracite of good quality, which is transported to other parts of Spain by the railway passing through La Robla. Hydro-electric power stations are scattered throughout the region, and the station at Ponferrada provides the necessary energy for aluminium smelting at Valladolid. Insignificant amounts of iron ore are mined at Barruecopardo and Lumbrales, and lead at Losacio, all near the Portuguese frontier.

Industry in the Northern Meseta is confined to the towns and will be mentioned in connexion with them.

From the point of view of population several interesting facts emerge. This is one of the most scantily populated areas in the whole of Spain – on an average there are 34 people per sq. km, and in the province of Soria only 16 per sq. km. Two factors are responsible for this and for the actual distribution of population. In the Middle Ages the Northern Meseta was the scene of many battles, and people tended to gather together on some hill-top for defence, first founding a castle, and then building a walled town. Numerous examples of these ancient castles, from which came the name of Castile, and walled towns still remain. The other requirement was a source of water, and later towns and villages arose along spring lines or beside rivers. Small though it is the population is concentrated in towns and large villages; even today there are few isolated settlements. Of all the main regional capitals only one, Valladolid, is centrally situated; the others are to be found in the foothills of the bordering mountains, where gaps in the sierras facilitated communications, and goods from both highlands and plains could be exchanged. The total number of inhabitants in the region is about 2,500,000, most of them urban dwellers distributed in towns as follows: Valladolid – 132,526; Burgos – 89,864; Salamanca – 89,085; León – 78,111; Palencia – 50,392; Zamora – 44,957; Segovia – 34,711; Ávila – 25,021; Soria – 21,546; Béjar – 15,666 (1950).

Valladolid is the largest and is situated at the confluence of the

i

ii

iii

XIX i The vega of Granada, with snow-covered Sierra Nevada in spring.
    ii Fish-wife of Huelva drying fish by bales of cork.
   iii Andalusian gipsy dancing before a village audience.

i

ii

iii

XX i Cutting wheat-chaff by sledge, near Medina del Campo, Northern Meseta.

ii Valladolid, with Castilla Canal in foreground and typical meseta skyline.

iii Shaduf irrigation used to obtain a small crop of wheat near Salamanca.

Pisuerga and Esgueva, 2,056 feet above sea level. It is an important industrial centre, deriving fuel (coal and electricity) from the northern coalfields, and contains iron foundries, R.E.N.F.E. workshops, and factories producing agricultural implements, paper, silk, and soap, while aluminium is smelted and manufactured into domestic goods and aeroplane parts. Surrounded by wheatfields, Valladolid is naturally a trading centre for all types of cereals, especially wheat, while flour-milling is important, and foodstuffs such as pasta and biscuits are made. The town is also an important route cente, lying at the centre of the extensive road system of Old Castile, and controlling railway routes to France, Portugal, Madrid, and to south, north and west Spain.

Salamanca lies on the north bank of the river Tormes, 2,514 feet above the sea. It contains many buildings of historical interest, including a Roman bridge, 472 feet long with 27 arches, medieval mansions such as the House of Shells, and an important University, founded in 1215. It is the collecting and cultural centre for the province, but for its size contains relatively few industries; these are mainly concerned with the products of the surrounding plains (wheat and cattle), and include the manufacture of pasta, flour, meat extracts and leather goods, as well as fertilizers, pottery and glue.

Burgos is a gap town on the edge of the Meseta, at an altitude of 2,807 feet. It was the first capital of the kingdom of Castile, and contains some interesting Arab remains as well as a very imposing cathedral. During the Spanish Civil War it was the headquarters of the Nationalist forces under General Franco, and much attention has been paid since the end of World War II to the building of new barracks and sports grounds for soldiers stationed here. Industry has been encouraged also; Burgos is one of the few towns in the Northern Meseta with a steadily growing population, some of whom are employed in the new industries manufacturing photographic film and paper, cellophane, playing cards, and artificial silk, as well as in the older, well-established potteries and iron foundries.

León, the Legio Septima of Roman times, lying 2,796 feet above sea level at the confluence of the rivers Bernesga and Toria, has a very fine Gothic cathedral. It is situated at the junction of meseta

K

and hill country, and deals mainly with cereal and animal produce, serving also as a collecting centre for the coal of surrounding mines. Its industries include the manufacture of chemicals, as well as penicillin.

Palencia, the Roman Pallantia, is situated in the Tierra de Campos on the river Carrión. It is a very important agricultural centre; not only does it contain experimental centres for research into grape and silk production, but it is also a trading centre for livestock as well as for cereals. Cartridges, railway machinery, bells and cast iron are produced here, and there is a small textile industry, based on local wool, for the manufacture of blanket material, baize and serge, the latter group all being intended for the home market.

Segovia, 3,277 feet above sea level, and at the confluence of the Eresma and Clamores, rises majestically above the vast wheatfields surrounding it. It is dominated, and almost dwarfed, by the great Roman aqueduct. Huge unmortared blocks of granite, coming from the Sierra de Guadarrama, were used to make the 148 arches, some nearly 288 feet high. The great cathedral, begun in 1525, is also an outstanding building. There is a small amount of industry in Segovia, which includes the production of rough textiles, paper, bricks, tiles, glass and pottery.

Zamora lies at an altitude of 2,132 feet on the north bank of the Douro a few miles before this river leaves the meseta section of its course. It is important chiefly as a collecting centre for wines, cattle, sheep and wool as well as for honey from the surrounding heathlands. There are in addition several factories for the manufacture of shoes, caps and sails, while the nearby hydro-electricity stations at Ricobayo and Villalcampo produce sufficient current for local needs and even have a surplus for transmission to Bilbao and Madrid.

Ávila, where strong granite walls, built between 1097 and 1101, top the river Adaja, lies 3,692 feet above sea level, and has the distinction of being the highest provincial capital in Spain. It is chiefly an agricultural centre, but also has factories for the production of rough cotton and leather goods. There are several small villages in the hills to the south of Ávila which are of some importance, such as Cebreros, in the high valley of the Alberche, which produces grapes, wine, temperate fruits, cheese and cereals, and Arenas de San Pedro, at the foot of the highest peak in the Sierra de Gredos, where fruit and cereals are produced and copper utensils and sombreros manufactured.

Soria, 3,460 feet above the sea, lies on the upper course of the Douro, not far from its source. The ruins of the Iberian city of Numantia lie 5 miles away. It deals chiefly with agricultural produce, particularly with cereals, beeswax and livestock, and has a timber trade based on local pine forests.

Béjar has a fine defence site on top of a rocky eminence which still retains the ruins of its castle and walls; after Valencia and Barcelona it is the most important wool-manufacturing centre in Spain, and also produces cotton goods as well as soap, hams and canned meats.

There is no other important town in this area with a population exceeding 10,000; an indication of the great barrenness of the area as a whole, which cannot support a large population, as it has no large industry and little agriculture. Castilla la Vieja is a land of dusty, grey horizontals, where the monotony of flatness is only occasionally broken by a line of hills or by a residual crowned with the ruins of one of the 'castles of Spain'.

THE SOUTHERN MESETA

The Southern Meseta consists of a large proportion of the provinces of New Castile and Estremadura (i.e. the land far beyond the Douro, as it was known in Roman days). Geographically the area has a somewhat indefinite boundary owing to the complexity of the underlying strata. In the west there are mostly Palaeozoic rocks of a hard and non-porous nature, crumpled into intricate folds in Hercynian times; in the east as well as in several places in the west, occur the softer, more porous rocks of the Tertiary basins. There is one marked geological boundary to the south, that of the Guadalquivir fault, the extreme limit of the Sierra Morena. To the east are the rocky hills of Cuenca and the Montes Universales, formed of moderately hard and porous rocks, often limestone. To the north are the Central Sierras, those of Gata, Gredos and Guadarrama. In the centre of these sierras occur masses of very ancient sedimentary and metamorphic rock, and some granitic intrusions which are used today as a source of road metal. These sierras occasionally reach heights of over 8,000 feet, and are the highest in the region; another transverse range occurs between the rivers Tagus and Guadiana, comprising the Sierra de Guadalupe (where the peak of Carboneras reaches the height of 4,734 feet) and the Montes de Toledo, which do not exceed a height of 5,000 feet. The Sierra Morena consists of a series of hills with a gentle gradient to the north, but descending abruptly to the Guadalquivir valley; the most important ranges are those of Cambrón (3,502 feet), which is marked to the west by the pass of Despeñaperros, the main pass into Andalusia from north Spain, Alcudia (or Almadén) and Madrona (4,341 feet), Tudia, and Aracena near the Portuguese frontier. The Serrania de Cuenca forms the eastern boundary of this region, culminating in a central mass of highland, the Montes Universales (6,089 feet), while to the west there is no marked topographical boundary, the rolling hills extending into Portugal without a break. Typical meseta country exists in the eastern section of this region, where the district of La Mancha exhibits characteristic land forms, such as cuestas, *páramos* and *campiñas*.

The main rivers of the Southern Meseta are the Tagus and the Guadiana, which, with their tributaries, have been mentioned earlier.

Climatically the Southern Meseta is similar to the Northern Meseta, semi-continental in type. Winters are cold; Madrid sometimes has snow, and its mean daily maximum in January is 48° F., while the mean daily minimum is only 33° F. The sierras may be covered with snow during a freak storm even in late May. In this Southern Meseta, however, the winters are a little shorter than in the northern areas, while the summers are hotter. For days on end the sun blazes from a cloudless sky, and light surface winds whip the dust along in miniature 'dust devils', while at times visibility is obscured by the *calina*. The mean daily maximum in Madrid is 93° F., the absolute maximum 111° F.; nevertheless, nights are frequently cool, and if for any reason the sun is obscured the temperature drops rapidly – Madrid's mean minimum temperature in July is only 61° F. In spring and autumn the weather is most changeable, and it is then that the influence of the

Fig. 49. The Southern Meseta

cold mountain winds is felt most keenly – the 'Guadarrama sutil, que mata un hombre, y no apaga un candil'; the 'treacherous Guadarrama wind, which can kill a man, but will not blow out a candle'. Most rain in this area comes in spring and autumn, with a small amount falling in winter, and a summer drought sometimes broken by violent thunderstorms, torrential in character, which are of little use to the crops that need rain so badly. Badajoz, lying in a small rain-shadow zone, receives 14·9 inches per year, Madrid 16·4 inches; the highlands and areas more open to the rain-bearing winds from the west receive more – Cáceres' annual total is 29·8 inches. By the time such humid winds reach La Mancha, however, they have lost most of their moisture, and the eastern part of the region is extremely arid.

In the high sierras, where the snow lasts well into spring, and temperatures are modified by altitude, there is a good deal of heath and moorland, used as pasture for sheep and goats. Ibex exist in the Gredos ranges, but a far more dangerous enemy is the wolf, which is sometimes forced by hunger at the end of a hard winter to ravage even lowland flocks. Wolf hunts are regularly organized in the Central Sierras to try to exterminate this pest. Pine forests in some areas, notably those in the Serrania de Cuenca near Cañete, Mira, Palancares, Villova, Yemeda and Carbonera, provide fuel, timber and resin; granite outcrops supply road metal and stone for constructional purposes. The upper valleys of the tributaries of the Tagus form valuable 'oases' of agriculture amongst the heath and woods, although cold winters prohibit the cultivation of olives.

Around the upper Guadiana lies the arid area of La Mancha, an Arab name signifying 'wilderness'. Here surface water is rare, and although there are underground supplies, care is needed in using them. This is the home of Don Quixote, but the celebrated windmills, so often associated with him, are now only found in isolated outlying districts or along the main tourist roads, as at Madridejos. They were introduced in 1575, an innovation from the Netherlands, and their place is now taken by modern machine-driven mills in the main towns. Formerly vast areas in this region were covered by barren steppe or semi-desert; today, with the help of irrigation schemes already mentioned, many parts of the waste land are irrigated and produce good harvests. Of all the irrigated areas the huerta of Aranjuez is one of the most important, producing sugar beet, potatoes, saffron, strawberries and many vegetables for the Madrid markets. Other irrigated areas occur along the valley of the river Tagus. Wheat and allied cereals are a prominent feature of the Manchegan landscape, particularly in the La Sagra and La Mancha districts, but vines are grown extensively in the southern zones, around Valdepeñas, Tomelloso and Manzanares, while the slightly warmer winters make possible the production of olives around Daimiel, Campo de Calatrava, Orgaz and Mora. Sheep of 'Manchego', 'Merino' and 'Churro' breeds are reared on the drier uplands, and trans-humance is universally practised, the sheep leaving their summer pastures in the mountains to winter in the valley of Alcudia, and in the Campo de Calatrava. Although there are still a few stock routes left, the majority of the sheep are transported to their summer or winter pastures by rail, and R.E.N.F.E. generally offers reduced rates in the season. A small but flourishing occupa-tion is the utilization of the aromatic plants which cover the more arid tracts of heathland; some are collected for drying, cleaning and packing for export, but many of these plants, especially lavender, thyme and rosemary, provide nourishment for bees, which produce the honey for which the Alcarria region is particularly noted. Birds, too, are trapped in the Ciudad Real district for sale at local markets – a bird in a minute cage is a common sight on most of the tenement walls in Spain.

In Estremadura conditions are somewhat similar to those of New Castile, although the underlying rock, being non-porous, retains more surface water and thus allows of more profuse natural vegetation, particularly tree growth. In the irrigated areas, such as those of the Tiétar district, good crops of maize, vegetables, cotton and tobacco are obtained, and when the Plan Badajoz reaches completion this now small zone will be greatly extended. Vines are grown in the Tierra de Barros district, around Almendralejo, and south of Badajoz large groves of olives are encountered which flourish on the warmer south-facing slopes of the Sierra de Gata, in the Tierra de Barros district and in the Hurdes zone. Wheat, the typical meseta crop, is extensively grown, the main centre coinciding with the fertile clay soils of the Tierra de Barros, while oats is grown as a fodder crop. Cattle are allowed to roam over the drier heathlands, and there are many flocks of sheep, most of them of merino type, which are pastured on the rather sparse vegetation of the Helechosa de los Montes, Castilblanco, Tierra de Barros, la Serena and Plasencia districts. The cork groves in this area provide acorns for the numerous herds of swine, including the black 'Extremeña' type, which provide hams famous in the peninsula, and good-quality leather. The cork oaks, which in general grow wild, are especially noticeable near the Portuguese frontier; the trees live for 150 years and provide cork on an average every ten years, the later strippings providing the better-quality cork. Natural resin in the cork melts when heated, and several thin pieces can be quickly and easily pressed to form one thick piece with a minimum of machinery. Only the highest grades are made into corks, the more general uses being in the refrigeration, insulation and shoemaking industries.

Many minerals occur in the Southern Meseta, especially in association with the older rocks of the Sierra Morena. Coal is mined at Puertollano and in the Peñarroya – Espiel district, and, although the coal is sulphurous in content, it is effectively used in local electricity stations. Smaller coal-mining areas occur further west at Zafra, Llerena and Fuente del Arco. Iron ore is extracted at Vilches, Guarroman, El Pedroso and Jerez de los Caballeros, while there are important copper workings in the Rio Tinto area, where the rock is so near the surface that it can be stripped off in layers by the 'bull-dozing' technique. Almadén produces almost half the world's mercury, while lead is widespread, though small in amount – the main centres include Linares, Peñarroya and Azuaga to the south, and the smaller centres of Granadilla and Madridejos to the north. Antimony is mined between Almuradiel and Torrenueva and at Puebla de Alcocer, while manganese occurs at La Joya, Soloviejo, El Granado and Campofrio near the Portuguese frontier. Wolfram is obtained in the valley of La Serena, and rock salt at Minglanilla.

There is little industry in the Southern Meseta, despite the varied natural resources. Coal at Puertollano, used in generating electricity, as well as the petroleum now provided by the American-subsidized oil pipeline from Rota to Zaragoza, provide power for the smelting works and iron foundries to be found in this town and others in the Sierra Morena. Much industry is centred on Madrid; its natural resources are meagre, but using raw materials imported from other parts of Spain, or from abroad, and power in the form of hydro-electricity from the Guadarramas, and oil from the pipeline previously mentioned, industry is now increasing within the capital, and, though artificially fostered, is likely to prosper. Apart from these two centres industry is distributed among the main towns, in connexion with which it will be mentioned later in greater detail.

The natural disadvantages of aridity, infertile soil and lack of natural resources have combined to make this a sparsely populated region. The peasants living in the countryside rarely inhabit isolated dwellings; small nucleated settlements are more typical. Some consist of one-storeyed houses built of adobe, around a central courtyard; in the mountains houses have to withstand really hard winters, and are usually two-storeyed, built of stone and timber, with the upper storey serving as store-house. In

i

ii

iii

iv

XXI i Vines on rocky soil with gullied páramos beyond, near Daimiel, La Mancha.

ii Abandoned meander of Tagus near Toledo. Compare the flat fertile alluvial patch with barren eroded hills beyond.

iii Cave village near Venta de Baños, Northern Meseta.

iv Old and New in the Plaza de España, Madrid.

i

ii

XXII i Suspension bridge over the Douro and barrels and bottles of port wine
for export, Oporto.

ii Typical fishing boats on the Tagus, Lisbon.

several areas in La Mancha and near Cuenca villagers have carved houses for themselves out of Tertiary limestone or sandstone; these cave dwellings provide warmth in winter and the rock tempers the extreme heat of summer. Each house has wooden jambs and lintels (although doors and glass windows are occasionally lacking) and is clearly marked by a colour-washed postal number. One such cave village near Cuenca is called merely 'Las Cuevas' – the Caves. The population of the area as a whole is a little under 5,000,000, and towns absorb the following numbers: Madrid – 1,966,070; Badajoz – 110,580; Albacete – 79,875; Cáceres – 52,020; Toledo – 46,465; Ciudad Real – 35,539; Puertollano – 34,884 (1950); Cuenca – 24,969; Guadalajara – 15,730.

Madrid, built on the banks of the insignificant river Manzanares, now partially canalized, lies at a height of 2,148 feet, and is a capital surrounded and supported by the most barren land in the country, and linked only with difficulty to the richer periphery. Human rather than geographical factors prevailed in the choice of Madrid as capital – Philip II, establishing his court there in 1560, recognized the site as being near the mathematical centre of the Iberian peninsula, and appreciated the advantage of centralized communication linking each separate province. Madrid is now the great peninsular route centre; lying at the intersection of two main Iberian routes – that of the Tagus–Henares valleys leading via the Jalón valley to Zaragoza, and that which crosses the Sierra de Guadarrama by passes to the south of Ávila and Segovia – it soon became the focal point of a network of routes which superseded and supplemented the original lines of communication. With readily available flat ground and no liability to fog Madrid also possesses good airfields, the most important being that of Barajas, and is the centre for peninsular and extra-territorial services.

The town has few geographical advantages, apart from a central position, and has no deep historical roots. The first definite mention of it dates from the latter half of the tenth century, when it was known as Majrit or Magerit, and occupied by the Moors, who surrendered it to Alphonso VI in 1085. The old castle (now the Royal Palace) formed the original nucleus, and for over 400 years the town served as a minor market and route centre, visited occasionally by royalty who hunted in the wooded vicinity. Philip II first gave it the status of a capital, although it was never called a city (*ciudad*) but always referred to as a town (*villa*). Philip III moved the court to Valladolid in 1601, stayed there for six years, and then returned to Madrid, and rebuilt the royal residence of the Pardo, 12 miles outside the town. Philip IV surrounded the town with walls which were maintained until the nineteenth century. Most of the important civil and religious buildings date from the eighteenth century. The fierce pride of the Madrileños, typical of the inhabitants of Castile, has been revealed twice in recent history; once when untrained civilians rose in 1808 against the forces of Napoleon, and again in November 1936, when the dogged resistance of poorly armed city dwellers held back General Franco's Nationalist forces, despite the now famous remark of General Emilio Mola, who declared that his 'fifth column' of sympathizers inside Madrid would soon bring about its surrender. This proved to be incorrect; the town endured a bitter siege for over two years before surrendering on March 29th, 1939.

From an industrial point of view Madrid has had few geographical advantages; distance from the sea necessitates the transport of raw materials by rail, adding to their cost, and the main Spanish coal deposits lie far to the north in Asturias. Industries have arisen more in response to demand than to any easy combination of raw materials. In the future, however, fuel problems will be considerably eased; new hydro-electric power stations recently inaugurated in the Guadarrama ranges will provide adequate electricity even in times of extreme aridity (in recent years power cuts have inevitably succeeded drought), while the new American-financed oil pipeline from Rota via Madrid to Zaragoza will provide a convenient minor source of fuel, which will, however, be dependent on a constant supply of imported petroleum. The industrial pattern of Madrid is typically that of any main capital; certain industries, often classified as luxury, produce such goods as leather, perfume, fans, artists' requisites, guitars, high-grade cigarettes and cigars, silk scarves and stockings, jewellery and gloves. There is a small textile industry, and papermaking and bookbinding cater for the needs of cultural and governmental departments. Glass of many types is manufactured, ranging from artistic souvenirs to the *securit* glass for cars, lorries and railway carriages, while laboratory glass is manufactured at Villaverde, which also produces acids and other chemicals. More important industries have arisen in the suburbs, especially various branches of the iron and steel industry, which utilize iron brought by rail from the Ojos Negros mining district. Villaverde produces railway rolling stock and other machinery, ball bearings and diesel engines are made at Barajas, and Getafe, to the south of Madrid, specializes in the manufacture of aeroplanes.

Badajoz, larger than most towns in the area, is situated 4 miles from the Portuguese frontier on the river Guadiana, 600 feet above sea level. It is surrounded by some of the most fertile land of the Southern Mesetas, and will have even greater significance as an agricultural centre when the extensive irrigation schemes envisaged in the 'Plan Badajoz' reach completion. It manufactures leather goods and is a minor tourist centre.

Albacete, at a height of 2,247 feet, commands the gap between the Serrania de Cuenca and the foothills of the Betic Cordillera, and thus controls traffic passing from La Mancha to the Levant coast. The land around is fertile, and irrigated by the María Cristina canal; an experimental farm and an aerodrome have been established just outside the town. Famous in medieval times for its swords and daggers, Albacete still continues to manufacture knives and scissors.

Cáceres lies 19 miles away from the Tagus, 1,440 feet above sea level. Erected in 75 B.C. by the Romans as Castra Caecilia, it still retains Roman walls and an aqueduct, and is a thriving agricultural centre, its factories producing corks and the *azulejos* used in local buildings.

Toledo lies on a rocky prominence above the Tagus, where this river curves in a wide meander before passing through a narrow gorge. This is one of the oldest inhabited sites in Spain, and the town still retains evidence of its glorious history in such architectural features as Roman ruins, the Gothic cathedral, and many fine churches. Today it is famed as a tourist centre (many special trains and coaches run to Toledo from Madrid), and much of its wealth is so derived. In addition there are a few industries on a small scale and of an artisan nature; inlaid knives, brooches and clasps now take the place of swords and daggers that once had international fame, and coarse woollen cloth is also manufactured. There is a seismological station at Toledo, and because of its unique archaeological and historical remains the whole town has been declared a National Monument.

Puertollano is a town with a rapidly growing population, owing to its proximity to coal and lead mines, the former being used to generate electricity for smelting the latter. A subsidiary source of fuel is the oil pipeline from Rota to Zaragoza. The town is situated at a height of 2,322 feet in a deep valley carved by the river Jándula, at a point near the divide separating this river from the river Valdeazogues, and, as its name implies (literally 'door to the plains'), commands the routeway into the mid-Guadiana plains, a route taken by the main railway line from Madrid to Badajoz and Portugal.

Ciudad Real (2,093 feet) lies in the Campo de Calatrava, and is an important agricultural centre. It produces flour and some leather goods, but the barren nature of the land around it precludes a large population, and the new industries of Puertollano, 23 miles away, have encouraged a steady 'drift' of population away from agricultural pursuits to the better-paid industrial occupations.

Cuenca, 3,024 feet above the sea, is picturesquely situated on the slopes of a rocky gorge where the rivers Huécar and Júcar meet. This somewhat remote capital, seldom visited by tourists, was joined to Madrid and Valencia by railway as recently as World War II. It is an important collecting centre for agricultural produce, and has a small textile and leather industry.

Guadalajara, today one of the smallest of Spanish provincial capitals, is one of the oldest; the Iberians called it 'Arriaca' (in Basque *arriak* means 'stones'), and the Moors also emphasized its stony site by renaming it 'Ouad el Hajara', or 'river of stones'. It is surrounded by extremely arid land, and has a small paper and textile industry.

THE EBRO BASIN

The limits of the Ebro basin are obvious on most maps; to the north are the high ranges of the Pyrenees, to the south and west are the rocky hills of Teruel, the Sierra Cebollera and Sierra de la Demanda, while to the east, and cutting off the basin effectively from the sea, lie the Catalan hills. Within these bordering highlands lies the triangle of the Ebro basin, a country of flat or gently rolling plains, with here and there a steep-sided, flat-topped range of hills breaking the skyline. The average height is less than in either the Northern or Southern Meseta, descending gradually from 1,500 feet in the north-west to 700 feet in the south-east. To the north of the basin the rocks have been associated with the folding which helped to create the Pyrenees, and as a result the hills occur in definite ranges, generally running east–west, as for example the Sierra de Andia, the Sierra de la Peña and the Sierra de la Guara (highest point 6,814 feet). In some cases weathering has so picked out the differences between hard and soft rocks that not only are the hills parallel, but also parallel are the dips and scarps that form the main mass of hills. In this area the consequent rivers have cut through the main escarpments to join the Ebro, making a tortuous gorge at every 'break-through', but subsequent rivers eroded the softer rocks and so flow parallel to the hills and at right-angles to the main rivers, for example the Aragón and Gallego. This country is extremely difficult to cross, as major routes are forced to follow the main rivers. Highlands to the south consist more of flat tablelands, dissected by rivers which, in an area of great aridity, have carved gorge-like valleys which often serve as the only possible routeways.

The rivers of this area all form part of the Ebro drainage system, but there is a great contrast between the many swift-flowing northern tributaries, fed perennially, and the more slowly moving southern tributaries, which are sometimes almost dry in summer, and are few in number.

The Ebro basin contains one of the largest expanses of steppe country in Spain, which results from the arid nature of the climate and the porosity of the surface rocks. Rainfall is very variable, and annual amounts range from under 10 inches to over 20 inches

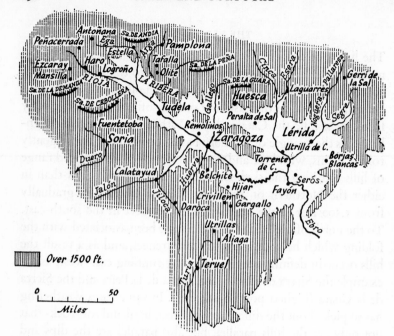

Fig. 50. The Ebro Basin

on the plains, rising to 40 inches on the higher, more exposed ranges. Zaragoza receives 13 inches annually, Lérida 14 inches. Temperatures are similar to those of the Southern Meseta, although frost is more frequent in the Ebro basin, and summers are a little cooler in the Southern Meseta. A large annual and diurnal range is common, and snowfall is by no means rare, even in the lower areas. The absolute minimum and maximum temperatures at Zaragoza are 3° F. and 117° F. respectively, and at Pamplona (1,472 feet) and Huesca (1,518 feet) the average minimum temperatures for the coldest month are the same – 20° F., while for the hottest month the average maximum temperatures are 98° F. and 99° F. respectively. Lérida, nearer the coast and affected to a slightly greater extent by marine influence, still retains marked continentality of temperature, the average minimum for the coldest month being 20° F., and the average maximum for the hottest month being 90° F. Despite great ranges of temperature, olives grow well on all the lower land, and can even be found in some sheltered places up to 4,000 feet on the Catalan side of the Pyrenean foothills. This region, like the other Mesetas, is a windy spot; one of the most characteristic winds is the *cierzo*, a fairly warm but boisterous gale blowing in spring, generally from the north or north-west. Another strong wind, which often blows in winter, is the *tramontana*, comparable in origin and effects with the *mistral* of the Rhône delta. The *tramontana* normally occurs in connexion with the 'back' of a depression passing over the Gulf of Lyons, and although the air is slightly warmed by its descent over the Pyrenees, it remains cold by comparison with the air of the warm sector of the depression which preceded it, and can have adverse effects on plant growth.

Agriculture in the Ebro basin is as difficult as in the other Meseta regions. The natural vegetation, where such occurs, is steppe, interspersed with regions of semi-desert where salt deposits may be found. On the other hand this aridity lies adjacent to a perennially wet region, that of the Pyrenees, from which streams pour forth to meet the Ebro. With accessible water supplies and long periods of sunshine, natural conditions favour crop growing wherever irrigation is possible. This area contains the largest extent of irrigated land in Spain, and produces a rich variety of crops. Maize is widespread, being grown normally as animal fodder; sugar beet is important, the main centres of production including Caspe, Hijar, and the valleys of the Cinca, Jalón, Jiloca, Huerva and Ebro. Flax and hemp are grown near Zaragoza, and there is an important fruit centre near Daroca on the river Jiloca, extending along this valley into that of the river Jalón, where such temperate fruits as apples, pears, peaches, apricots, cherries and figs are grown. Some vines in the Rioja district near Logroño are grown by means of irrigation, and there is market gardening outside Zaragoza.

Wheat is the main crop of the *secano* areas; grown on an extensive basis on the lower hill-slopes it yields a rather poor return. In some districts the spring floods of the Ebro are utilized by planting wheat in the waterlogged soil of the alluvial fan of some small tributary; the wheat soon sprouts, a small blue-green triangle among the dusty brown of the surrounding fields, and the water lasts just long enough for the wheat to reach a good size before the hot summer sun ripens it. Olives thrive on the lower slopes, the region extending between Belchite and Borjas Blancas, near Lérida, being particularly important. Vines predominate further upstream, especially in the Rioja district near Logroño, and along the valleys of the Arga and Ega, around Estella, Tafalla and Olite. On higher ground, where semi-desert vegetation provides rough pasture, sheep of the 'Raso' or 'Karakul' type are allowed to roam, providing good wool and some meat each spring when surplus lambs are killed. Transhumance is widespread, the animals remaining on the lower plains during the winter, and being herded slowly up the *cabaneras*, or well-defined trails, to the cooler and richer pastures of the lower Pyrenean slopes in summer. Cattle are reared in the extreme west of the region for draught purposes and for milk, and some are kept near the major towns for dairy products.

Natural resources of this area are few; a broad zone containing lignite extends from Capella and Laguarres in the eastern foothills of the Pyrenees through Torrente de Cinca, Velilla de Cinca, Serós, Fayón, Alloza and Estercuel to Utrillas and Aliaga in the Teruel hills. Much of the lignite is sulphurous and there are no large reserves. Small amounts of asphalt are found on either side of the Ebro basin, at Fuentetoba and Torrelapaja in the Soria hills and at Peñacerrada and Antoñana south of Vitoria. Small deposits of iron are worked at Haro, Ezcaray and Mansilla, north-west of Soria, while copper occurs at Los Arcos, and manganese at Gargallo and Crivellen. Rock salt is widespread, being mined at Remolinos (Zaragoza), Forcada, Peralta de Sal (Huesca) and at Gerri de la Sal (Lérida); sulphur is extracted at Libros (Teruel). The most important single resource of the region is water. In medieval days one of the *fors* (charter of laws) of Navarre decreed that, after a torrential spate had diverted a river's course, the new course could be claimed by the owners of the land it crossed, but only when the old one had dried up to such an extent that a hen could cross it with her brood of chicks. Today, man does not need to depend on the whims of nature; both irrigation and hydro-electricity schemes ensure a fair and extensive distribution of this primary source of power and agricultural wealth.

The Ebro basin, like the Mesetas, is one of the most sparsely populated areas in Spain. Country dwellers generally inhabit small compact villages, each with a church as a nucleus, often on some hillock for defence purposes, with the older houses clustered around the church and the newer houses occupying the lower ground. In some isolated villages water is still delivered daily direct from the neighbouring stream by a water-carrier and his donkey. Although nucleated settlements are typical of the region, a few isolated dwellings can be found; in Aragón those occurring in the drier hills are called *mas* or *masadas* (cf. the *mas* of Catalonia and south-west France), while in the irrigated zones they frequently bear the name of *torre*. The Ebro basin contains approximately 1,300,000 people, and towns absorb the following numbers: Zaragoza – 291,181; Pamplona – 84,936; Lérida – 66,547; Logroño – 58,180; Huesca – 25,428; Teruel – 21,566; Calatayud – 18,764.

Zaragoza, the capital of Aragón, and the Caesar Augusta of the Romans, was built on the banks of the Ebro close to the confluence of this river with the rivers Gallego and Huerva, and close to the junction of the Jalón and Ebro. It is a key town in this area, with a long history, as some of its famous buildings reveal, for example the Moorish palace of the Aljaferia and the Basilica of Pilar. It is an important route centre, commanding all traffic passing down the Ebro valley, over the Pyrenees via Canfranc or Sallent, over the eastern hills via the Jalón or Huerva valleys to Teruel, Calatayud or Madrid, and over the Catalan hills to Tortosa, and it lies on the direct and much-frequented route from Barcelona to Madrid. The irrigated land around is very fertile, and Zaragoza is naturally a collecting centre of size and importance. Recent improvements in the supply of power – electricity from Pyrenean rivers and petroleum from the oil pipeline from Rota to Zaragoza – have encouraged the expansion of its industries, which include the manufacture of textiles, cement, paper, railway rolling stock, agricultural machinery, glass, chemicals and sugar refining. The town forms an important tourist centre, particularly for French visitors.

Pamplona, capital of Navarre, is built at a height of 1,788 feet on the banks of the river Arga, a tributary of the Aragón.

Topographically and climatically it belongs more to the Ebro basin than to the Basque provinces to the north, although it lies in the 'no-man's-land' between these two regions. Its factories produce chocolate, made from imported cacao and local milk and sugar, watches and clocks, agricultural machinery, chemicals and furniture made from timber supplied from nearby woodlands. It is, in addition, an active agricultural and commercial centre, and tourists are annually attracted to the *encierros* of the feast of San Fermin, when the small but courageous Carriquiris bulls from the Ribera zone near the Ebro are let loose between their corral and the bull-ring, and are preceded by young male runners, to the frenzied delight of thousands of excited onlookers.

Lérida, the Ilerda of the Romans, owes much of its prosperity to the rich irrigated plains which surround it. It serves as route and collecting centre for both the huertas and the higher and more barren plains, and contains many preserving factories for vegetables and fruits.

Logroño, a thriving town situated on the south bank of the Ebro, is the main town of the Rioja area. It is an important collecting centre, and its industries include those depending upon local produce, such as barrel- and cork-making for the great quantity of wine which comes from this area, flour-milling and the preserving of fruits and vegetables, as well as the production of chemicals and textiles.

Huesca, 1,528 feet above sea level, was built by the Iberians on a rocky eminence above the 'Hoya de Huesca' – the deep Huesca valley – on the right bank of the river Isuela, and at one time contained the royal residence of the kings of Aragón. Today it is a busy agricultural town, and holds regular fairs and markets. It is also a centre for bus routes to adjacent parts of the Pyrenees not served by railway.

Teruel, capital of the mountain province of that name, stands 3,091 feet above sea level, at the confluence of the Alfambre and Turia rivers. Small in size, and surrounded by bleak highlands, it is a collecting centre for local produce, but contains no industry of importance.

Calatayud, once named Bibilis, stands on the Jalón, and is an important route centre, controlling traffic bound from Zaragoza to Madrid and Valencia. It also processes the cereals, vegetables, sugar beet and fruits grown in the irrigated lands nearby.

The tablelands of Spain are vast and unchanging in their desolate monotony. The harsh climate, with its violent contrasts, serves to emphasize the essential barrenness of this tawny wilderness. By day, the ground cracks in the heat and plants wither; in the evening the lurid colours of the sunset cast a deep vermilion glow over ground which is already becoming cold. In summer the beggars seek shade under some convenient rock or bridge; in winter they huddle for warmth against the buildings last touched by the sun's rays. This is a land which gives no quarter; the Castilian peasant justifiably describes the year as 'nueve meses de invierno y tres meses de infierno' (three months of hell and nine months of winter). The difficult environment has helped to foster and encourage the obstinate pride and independent spirit of Castilians, a characteristic which dates from their origin. Yet, for all their pride, their noble escutcheons and their love of anarchy, the inhabitants of Castile have always remained poor; Cervantes' portrayal of Don Quixote's meals as '. . . hash most nights, boiled bones on Saturdays, lentils on Fridays and a young pigeon as a Sunday treat . . .' was probably nearer the truth than the descriptions of many more serious 'Romanceros'.

CHAPTER XIV

Portugal

PORTUGAL, LYING BETWEEN latitudes 37° North and 42° North, faces the Atlantic and the riches of North and South America, with the prosperous countries of North West Europe situated to the north and the Strait of Gibraltar, through which pass the main trade routes to the Mediterranean, the Middle East and the Far East, situated to the south. This has given Portugal a position eminently suitable for trading purposes. From Phoenician times onwards, successive peoples have put in at ports along the western seaboard and traded with the native inhabitants, continuing their journey northwards to the remoter islands and peninsulas of France and Britain, and returning again with furs, wood, amber, slaves, curiously wrought weapons and finely woven cloth. Though Portugal was subjected to Iberian, Roman, Visigoth and Moorish rule this north–south route always remained open and important. After the expulsion of the Moors and the emergence of Portugal as a separate country the trade route was gradually extended. Under the leadership of Prince Henry the Navigator expeditions of discovery were fitted out to sail around the African coast, and settlements were established at strategic points. While the Portuguese were gradually mapping the African coast the Spanish discovered the West Indies and the Americas, thus adding a further extension to the original trade route. Ships crossed the Atlantic blown by the trade winds on their outward journey and by the westerlies on their return. In this way the Portuguese coast became the terminus for transatlantic voyages, and the volume of trade increased greatly, making Portugal one of the richest nations on earth. Some of this wealth was used in building cathedrals, towers, castles, palaces and halls, where the originality and ornateness of design (now called

Manueline after King Manoel I, 1495–1521), reveal the impact of new scenes from abroad and the romantic adventure of overseas travel.

This wealth and power diminished in four centuries, colonies were lost and earthquakes at home (particularly that of 1755) destroyed many fine buildings. Today the Atlantic port of Lisbon, though admittedly an international port, lacks an adequate hinterland and contributes little to world trade; in fact the main trade routes now by-pass the Portuguese coast. Climatically, however, Portugal is well situated. A warm current washes the Atlantic seaboard, helping to ameliorate winter temperatures, and maritime proximity causes a slightly higher rainfall than is usual in Mediterranean lands. One of the wettest areas of the Iberian peninsula is the Serra da Estrêla, with an annual rainfall of 113 inches. Equable temperatures, combined with an annual rainfall which never falls below 20 inches and is, over most of Portugal, well above this figure, give rise to a lushness of vegetation seldom encountered elsewhere in Iberia. Vineyards, fields of cereals, and orchards flourish, while natural vegetation is so varied and profuse that no adequate survey has yet been made. In spring, when the wild flowers appear, the whole country is a patchwork quilt of colour; there are irises, poppies, anchusa, moon daisies, field chrysanthemums, asphodel, white lavender, as well as pink bluebells of the Sierra Caldeirão and rare wild narcissi of the north.

With an area of 34,207 square miles Portugal is a small country, yet within its narrow confines there is a wide geographical diversity. The underlying structure varies from an extension of the Iberian granitic core in the north to the softer Triassic sandstones of the Barlavento coast; the bleak heights of the Serra da Estrêla rapidly give place to the wide alluvial plains of the Tagus or the salty lagoons of Aveiro. In the south, almond trees blossom in February and there is summer drought; in the north, depressions bring cloud and rain even in summer and winter frosts occur on the hills. The people, too, have very diverse racial origins; many reveal in their dark eyes and sallow skin the effect of the domination of the Moors. In the north, there are fair-haired, blue- or grey-eyed people; along the coast, especially in the south, negro traits may be seen, a legacy of the lucrative eighteenth-century slave trade, while at Nazaré the population is reputed to be of Phoenician origin. Even the language, which at first sight appears so directly derived from Latin, contains a number of Teutonic and Arabic words. These differences in physical environment and human response make it possible to divide Portugal into two major natural regions, which can be further subdivided as follows:

1. South Portugal. Algarve
                     Alentejo and Tagus Plains
2. North Portugal. Coast and Coimbra Plains
                     Serra da Estrêla
                     Douro Region

N.B. All population figures quoted in this chapter refer to the year 1958.

SOUTH PORTUGAL

The Algarve

To the Moors this sun-drenched southern coast appeared as a remote western extension of their Iberian Empire; they accordingly gave it the name El Gharb – the western land – the modern equivalent of which is still retained. To the north of the province underlying Palaeozoic sediments come to the surface in the Serra de Monchique and Serra do Malhão, two hilly masses which reach an average height of 1,500 feet, and serve as an effective barrier to cold northerly air masses. The major part of the Algarve is formed of Triassic and Jurassic rocks which, along the coast, give rise to rocks and promontories, as at Lagos, where the Ponta Piedade has been eroded to form fantastic spires and arches. Elsewhere along the coast a westwardly movement of sea water, in combination with the alluvium brought by such rivers as the Odelouca, Fernioca and Guadiana, has resulted in the formation of extensive sandspits, lagoons and low-lying islets, especially at Tavira, once capital of the Algarve, where silting has been so extensive that the town is now 2 miles from the sea. This sedimentation is particularly noticeable along the Sotavento coast from Faro to Vila Real de San António.

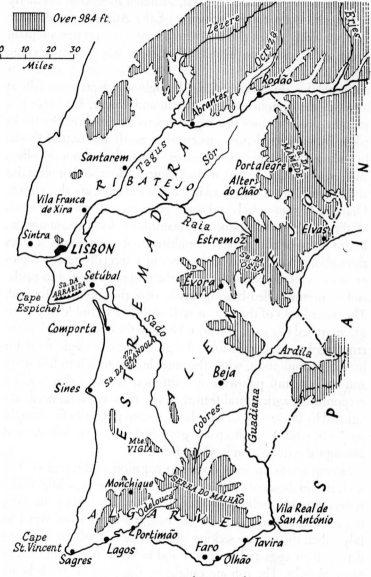

Fig. 51. South Portugal

Lying in the south of Portugal, sheltered from cold northerly winds, and open to the influence of the Atlantic, the Algarve enjoys a sunny warm climate, where winter temperatures remain above 48° F., with no likelihood of frost, where springs come early (January to February), and where the heat of summer is tempered by sea breezes. Rain brought by depressions falls at intervals throughout spring, autumn and winter, but there is a summer drought since this region lies to the south of the tracks taken by summer depressions crossing north and central Iberia. In such a climate oranges, peaches, vines, figs, almonds, olives and cereals (wheat, barley, maize) naturally flourish, but plantains and bananas, normally found in tropical climates, are also grown. Oranges, figs, muscatels and some grain are exported, but much of the agricultural produce is retained for local consumption. Maize in particular serves a multitude of purposes as it does throughout Portugal: sown in rows in a specially reserved plot or as a catch crop between olives, the thinnings are fed to cattle, and so are the pollen-bearing tassels, once the cobs have formed. The outer husks of the cob, as well as the stalks and leaves when green, are fed to cattle, or used as bedding for stock when dry; the empty cobs are used as fuel; the grain forms a staple food for human consumption, while the inner husk is torn into fine strips and used to stuff pillows and mattresses. Stock-rearing is not a predominant agricultural feature in the Algarve; local needs are satisfied by the rearing of long-horned oxen primarily for draught purposes, while pigs, sheep and goats find pasture on hillsides and amongst the stubble on lowland fields.

Fishing forms the second main occupation of this region. The sea is rich in shoals of sardines, anchovies and tunny, while coastal waters provide shellfish, lobsters and crayfish. Tunny are very important commercially and are caught mainly from April to July, when the fish are seeking muddy river mouths in which to deposit their eggs, and are larger and in better condition than in other months. The fish are caught by the *battue* method, being driven into nets which are then drawn towards a line of boats. As the tunny surface they are harpooned by fishermen who, clinging perilously to rigging or to the very edge of their craft, soon become berserk at the sight of the carnage and sing and yell

i

ii

iii

XXIII i Saltings, Aveiro, Portugal.

     ii Baroque library, Coimbra.

    iii Typical mountain farm in the Serra da Estrêla.

i

ii

iii

XXIV i Funchal, Madeira, from the sea. Note typical cloud and mountainous
         terrain.

      ii Street scene, Tetuan, former capital of Spanish Morocco.

      iii Coconut palms, Mozambique.

as the tunny thresh the bloody water in their death throes. Every part of the tunny is used; the fine fillets are preserved in olive oil for export; the offal is dried and used as a fertilizer rich in phosphates. Vila Real de San António is the fishing centre of this coast, an artificial town in the sense that it was built in 1774 in five months from prefabricated parts on the orders of the Marquis of Pombal. Other fishing centres include Olhão (31,903 inhabitants), where, true to the roving instincts of their seafaring ancestors, the men go on long-distance fishing expeditions every summer, some even reaching North American waters; Portimão, one of the main centres for the sardine-tinning industry; Faro (33,749 inhabitants), where only small ships can safely negotiate the ever-changing sandbanks that form a barrier across the entrance to the harbour, and Lagos, where both tunny and sardines are processed and exported. Locally evaporated salt helps in the preserving processes at all these towns.

The landscape of the Algarve is reminiscent of Morocco; date palms, fig trees and bananas introduce an exotic note into otherwise typically Mediterranean agriculture; square, white-washed houses with flat roofs, narrow alleys flanked by tall bare walls, bare-footed women dressed in long flowing robes – all might be found in Tetuan or Marrakesh. These are conspicuous and picturesque details attractive to tourists, yet the most interesting corner of the Algarve is frequently overlooked. Projecting almost as far as 9° West Cape St Vincent stretches into the Atlantic forming a barren, windy promontory. The Earl of Essex rounded this historic point on his way to Faro, which, in 1596, was under Spanish domination. Books belonging to the Bishop of nearby Silves found their way as loot to England and helped to form the nucleus of the Bodleian library at Oxford. Off Cape St Vincent Rodney defeated the Spaniards in 1770, and in 1797 Lord Jervis and Nelson routed the French. An even more interesting promontory is that of Sagres, twin of Cape St Vincent. Here Prince Henry the Navigator, third son of Philippa of Lancaster, John of Gaunt's daughter, and King John I of Portugal, had his fortress, chart-room and look-out post. When new territory was discovered, he colonized it. The great Portuguese Empire was founded in 1420 with the acquisition of Madeira and the addition in 1432 of the Azores. Prince Henry did not live to see the completion of his work; he died in 1460, and it was not until 1497-9 that Vasco da Gama rounded the Cape of Good Hope and sailed on to India. Sagres, however, remains a silent testimony to his greatness; from this remote gale-swept outpost he kept watch over the uncharted ocean, looking for the tiny sails and decorated poops of caravels returning from the expeditions of discovery inspired by his intellect, determination and faith.

The Alentejo and Tagus Plains

The Alentejo comprises a belt of land approximately 50 miles wide extending from the Serra do Malhão to the river Tagus, and parallel to the Portuguese–Spanish boundary. Here the pre-Cambrian and Palaeozoic rocks of the Spanish Mesetas are exposed, and hard intrusive granites give rise to the highest points of Serra d'Ossa and Serra de Mamede, 3,363 feet. Evidence of metamorphism due primarily to igneous intrusion is found in several places; the marble quarries of Évora produced stone used in building the Escorial. A little gold is found near Évora and there are also small deposits of copper, iron, manganese and asbestos, but these are not yet fully exploited. Copper is mined in particular south of Beja, where the copper-bearing Palaeozoic strata of the Rio Tinto area of Spain extend into Portugal. The landscape, in general, is one of high rolling plains descending gradually to wide valleys. The higher parts of the Alentejo act as a watershed, dividing rivers flowing to the Guadiana, which include the Cobres and Caia, from those which flow out to the western seaboard like the Sado and tributaries of the Tagus such as the Tera and Sôr. In the north, at Portas de Rodão, the Tagus has cut a deep gorge in the hard rocks which form the edge of the Spanish Meseta, and is crossed by a new bridge which, owing to high seasonal floods, had to be constructed well above the river level.

The Alentejo lies from 50 to 100 miles from the sea, and has a drier and more continental climate than regions further west. In winter frost affects the higher uplands and some snow falls on the Serra de Mamede. Annual rainfall seldom exceeds 25 inches, and in a few places east of Évora, in the rain-shadow created by the Serra d'Ossa, it is occasionally less than 20 inches. Summer is a time of complete drought; rain comes in the winter half of the year, but a slight continentality of rhythm is shown in the tendency towards spring and autumn maxima. In this climate natural vegetation is restricted to such drought-resistant species as gum cistus, umbrella pine (*Pinus pinea*) and various types of heather including *mata* and *carqueja*. The quicker-growing variety of pine (*Pinus pinaster*) has for many years been used for replanting, whilst, in some places, eucalyptus has replaced the stretches of original conifers. Most varieties of pine yield prunings which supply almost all Portuguese bakeries, whilst the trees are tapped for resin for periods varying from twice a year to twice in the lifetime of the tree. Taken together pine tree products, including resin, turpentine and pit props, form Portugal's fourth most important export.

Of all the trees that grow in the Alentejo the cork oak is the most important, both regionally and nationally, since cork is one of the most valuable of Portugal's exports, bringing in approximately $1\frac{1}{2}$ million escudos per year as revenue. The cork oak (*Quercus suber*) grows to a height of from 30 to 40 feet, and the cork of commerce is the bark of the tree. This bark is stripped from the trunk and lower limbs by making a delicate incision with a special axe the full length of the trunk or branch. Lateral incisions are then made and the bark carefully peeled off with the flattened handle of the axe. A strip of bark may be converted by the worker into a rough basket by the addition of thongs at each end. The trunk and branches of the tree, thus denuded, turn in colour from rich vermilion to brick-red and eventually to brown, while the cork, reddish brown in colour, resumes its original curved shape. The tree is first stripped when it is between five and twenty years old; this stripping produces cork deeply pitted, and of inferior quality. The tree is stripped every eight or ten years and the quality improves at every stripping up to the fifth or sixth, after which it remains stable. Bark from small branches, or bark that is thin or damaged in any way, is known as *refugo*, and is used generally when crushed or cut into small pieces. There are several factories for processing cork in the Alentejo, like the Robinson factory at Portalegre, where corks, table mats and tiling are among the goods produced. Much of the cork is exported, however, baled in its crude state, and later used for insulation products. Well-tended trees live for more than 150 years and their acorns provide valuable food for local hogs.

Agriculture in these wooded heathlands is necessarily restricted. Cereals, primarily wheat, barley and maize, are grown in small plots or between cork and olive trees. The grain is cut by sickle or scythe, threshed by flail or by the treading of oxen, and ground in windmills, set on one of the numerous hills. The straw, however, is baled by machine, since mechanization in this one instance proves quicker and more effective. Other crops include pulses, a few vines, and field cabbages used as a fodder crop. Irrigation is necessary for full utilization of flat land and fertile soil. The *shaduf* method is used on outlying farms, while the aqueduct at Elvas, built on Roman foundations by the peasants themselves between 1498 and 1622, provides water for gardens, fields and the celebrated plum orchards. More recent enterprises on a large scale have been undertaken, and now water from the Serra da Estrêla is used in much of the northern Alentejo. Sheep and goats are pastured on the higher slopes, while the Alter do Chão region is noted for the rearing of the 'Alter' variety of horse. Oxen are used for ploughing and the whole region is noted for swine. Wild pigs, frequently dangerous, are hunted as game in the remoter areas, while the domesticated animal, black and voracious, is tended carefully in herds, and fattened on cork oak acorns before being slaughtered in winter.

As yet the minerals of the region have not been fully exploited (some copper is mined in the hills near Beja and silver and sulphur pyrites near São Domingos). Such industries as there are reflect local agricultural pursuits. Woollen cloth is woven in Beja, wood and cork are carved into articles for domestic use and tourist souvenirs, and *azulejos* are made for local use in the larger towns. Population is sparse in this land of heath and woods; the general figure lies between 175 and 265 per square mile. Some of the people live in isolated farmsteads, but the majority live in small villages and the regional centres of Évora (47,387), Beja (42,703), Portalegre (28,074) and Estremoz (6,929).

The Tagus Plains: Estremadura

Estremadura consists primarily of the plains lying around and south of the Tagus; it is bounded to the west by the Atlantic, to the south by the Algarve, to the east by the Alentejo and to the north by the Serra da Estrêla, 6,530 feet high, and the Serra da Lousã, 3,942 feet high. In this ancient province the river Tagus enters the sea passing over country which, geologically, presents a mirror image of the structural elements found at its source. The major part of Estremadura is composed of a Tertiary basin in which occur almost horizontal limestones and sandstones. Rocks other than those of Tertiary age include Palaeozoic sandstones and shales, which form the Serra Grandolas and Monte Cereal, and Jurassic sandstones and limestones which occur along the coast from Cape Espichel to Setúbal. The whole region is one of instability, due in part to faulting of Mesozoic strata north of the Tagus, and in part to the inevitable weakening of the earth's crust caused by the juxtaposition of the rigid Archaean mass underlying the Iberian peninsula and younger peripheral folds. Small tremors are fairly common; the most disastrous earthquake occurred in 1755, when Lisbon and surrounding towns were almost completely demolished. Buildings situated on older rocks – hippurite limestone or the nearby sheet of basalt which separates the Tertiary and Secondary rocks – were less affected; nevertheless 30,000 people died and the extensive damage was caused primarily by the *tsunamis* or seismic sea wave which rose to a height of 40 feet.

In general the land is fairly flat and low-lying, seldom rising higher than 500 feet, except in the south and west, where Monte Vigia, Serra do Cereal and Serra da Grandola reach 1,000 feet. The coast of Estremadura is smooth, with few promontories, and is divided into two parts by Cape Sines. To the south, the older Palaeozoic and Secondary strata give rise to cliff formation, while to the north the softer Tertiaries have, in the main, been eroded, and prevailing westerly winds have been instrumental in forming extensive sand-dunes in the north, including a large sandspit almost 10 miles long extending from Comporta to just south of Setúbal. This sandspit partially blocks the estuary of the

Sado, and has created a sheltered tidal lake south-east of Setúbal. West of Setúbal extends the limestone crest of the Serra da Arrabida, ending at Cape Espichel, which in turn descends northwards to a flat plain, ending eventually at the estuary of the Tagus. The main rivers include the Sado, which enters the sea between Alcácer do Sal and Setúbal, draining into the bay of Setúbal, and the Sôr, Sêda and Zêzere, all tributaries of the Tagus, which enters an extensive tidal lake before passing through its 'bottleneck' shaped estuary to the sea.

Climatically Estremadura is typically Mediterranean. The temperature and rainfall statistics for Lisbon are as follows: average temperature for January 50·5° F., for July 71° F., and the average annual rainfall 29·7 inches. The climate is mild in winter and rainfall is adequate; indeed, floods often occur in February on the low-lying meadows (*lezirias*), temporarily cutting off outlying farms and tending to submerge the narrow islands (*mouchoes*). These floods, however, subside by March and spread fertile silt over the land.

Much of the region is cultivated, but, where natural vegetation has been left untouched, Mediterranean species predominate. Sweet chestnuts, Mediterranean pines, sessile oaks, bay, ilex and tree heaths (such as the *Erica arborea*) combine with smaller heathers, gorse, aromatic shrubs and occasional evergreens to give a dusty green background to the profusion of colour seen in February and March, when wild flowers of many varieties come into bloom.

Agriculture in this region is important; much of the land is flat and rivers provide water for irrigation. In 1955 a new hydro-electric power station was opened at Cabril on the Zêzere, the waters of which can now be regulated for irrigation. Wheat, barley and maize are predominant cereals and are ground in large windmills fitted with whistles or a clacking device which warns their owner of a wind change even though he is at work in fields half a mile away. On the marshy river banks extensive ricefields have been created, particularly in the Sado valley. Every farm has its patches of vines, lemons and oranges are grown in sheltered areas, and olives are planted on the hill-slopes. On either side of the Tagus extend the plains of the Ribatejo, vast, flat, heath-covered and sparsely populated. Here graze the bulls for the Portuguese *corrida* (bullfight between bull and horseman) and *pega* (struggle between bull and group of men). The bulls, scarcely ever killed in the ring, are tended by *campinos*, cowboys who still wear their traditional dress of short breeches, white hose, short bolero and green or red stocking cap. Vila Franca de Xira, about 18 miles north-east of Lisbon on the river Tagus, is the main centre for bullfighting. Apart from the bulls, fine horses are also bred in the Ribatejo, while the more mundane work of ploughing and cart-pulling is left to the patient long-horned ox.

Abrantes (population 48,925), situated in the eastern part of the Tagus valley, is an important centre for olive growing. Here, as in the rest of Portugal, the fruit is beaten from the trees on to hand-woven rugs, or *liteiros*. It is then taken to a nearby pressing mill which consists of two huge stone wheels revolving vertically within a high metal border, crushing the olives against a horizontal stone slab. When properly ground the pulp is put into coiled rope containers, about 2 feet in diameter, and slowly pressed hydraulically. The oil is then 'drawn', that is run off into butts of hot water. Inferior oil is produced by regrinding the pulp once or twice more. The strongly rancid flavour which is characteristic of most locally produced Portuguese olive oil is a result of the time lag between harvesting and grinding, which allows the olives to deteriorate rapidly. The hot water into which the olive oil is poured only serves to emphasize the flavour and odour, which, although repugnant to tourists, is agreeable to the Portuguese palate. When good oil is required for export or for high-grade fish-tinning, only two hours elapse between harvesting and grinding, and the oil is cold-drawn.

There is a rich harvest to be gained from the Atlantic along these coasts, and fishing is a thriving occupation. In Lisbon itself the *varinhas* or fishwives hawk their sardines and anchovies from door to door, after acquiring the fish at dawn from quayside fishermen. In Sines, birthplace of Vasco da Gama, lobsters are a speciality, caught around the coast and kept alive in vast nets beneath wooden floats until required for the Lisbon market. Tunny are also caught, but sardines are more important. The young of the sardines, *pilchardus*, are particularly sought, and the large shoals to be found annually off the coast form the basis of the sardine-canning industry in Portugal, with Setúbal (55,637 inhabitants) as the main centre. In 1956 the catch was 100,633 metric tons valued at 326,000 escudos; the value of tinned sardines, Portugal's second most important export, was 901,672 escudos, though the weight was only 42,411 metric tons. Cheap labour, mainly female, together with proximity to high-quality olive oil and cheap salt evaporated from sea water at Setúbal and Alcácer do Sal, are the factors responsible for the importance of fish preserving along this coast.

The main centre of this region is Lisbon, the capital of Portugal. Situated at a point where the inland tidal lake, the Rada da Lisboa, narrows to form the Tagus estuary, Lisbon is sheltered from western storms and cold northerly winds by the Cintra hills, a ridge of barren highland behind it. Its latitude, 38° 44′ North, and its easy access to the Atlantic have throughout its history caused Lisbon to be a major port of call for all types of ships. Before Roman times there were Celtic settlements in this area and trade with Britain and north-west France flourished. In Roman times Olisipio, as it was called, was a small seaport in the remote western province of Lusitania. In this capacity the town continued to flourish under Visigoth and Moor, until, after the Christian reconquest of Spain, Portugal became independent and acquired capital to fit out voyages of discovery. The tower of Belem, rising dramatically above the Tagus, a little to the west of Lisbon, is the spot from which many expeditions set sail, including that of Vasco da Gama. Today Lisbon is the only major port along the west Iberian coast, forming an important passenger port, refuelling station and entrepôt port, with a river frontage of 5 miles. The main road and railway routes of Portugal converge on Lisbon. The international railway routes are as follows:

From Lisbon northwards via Oporto, through Valença and Túy to north Spain.

From Lisbon north-north-east to Coimbra and thence through Vilar Formosa to Salamanca, Madrid or France.

From Lisbon north-east via Abrantes to Valencia de Alcántara and thence to Madrid.

From Lisbon north-east via Abrantes and thence via Elvas to Badajoz, Seville or Madrid.

From Lisbon south via Faro to Villa Real de San António and then by ferry to Ayamonte, thence to Seville or Málaga.

In addition to the major land routes there is local but irregular coastal transport and frequent national and international air services. The main international route from North West Europe via Lisbon, the Azores and Bermuda to North America is particularly important.

Lisbon with its population of 783,226 presents to the visitor a relatively modern aspect. The devastation caused by the earthquake of 1755 and the clear-sighted town planning which followed are responsible. Colour-washed houses of pastel shades rise in terraced fashion above the Tagus, and in many vantage spots *miradors* have been constructed to afford a view over the river. However, the old quarter of Lisbon, the Rossio, is a tortuous maze of alleys flanked by tenements which occasionally give place to ancient and now somewhat decrepit palaces. The climate is so mild along the coast that increasing numbers of North Europeans come every year for the winter months. The countryside around Lisbon presents varied and attractive scenery including the wild limestone Serra da Arrabida, the rocky cliffs of Cascais, and the cool and wooded Cintra hills. In peacetime Lisbon forms an ideal tourist centre; in wartime, Portugal has generally chosen neutrality, and Lisbon has enjoyed the somewhat hazardous advantages of a port open to all commerce. In World War II thousands of members of the allied armed forces and refugees made their way by devious underground routes through France and Spain to one of the few free capitals of Europe.

NORTH PORTUGAL

North of the river Tagus the land becomes transitional in character between Mediterranean and north-west European types of climate. Rainfall generally exceeds an annual average of 30 inches, while the average summer temperature seldom exceeds 70° F. Furthermore, the occasional fogs and frequent cloud associated with an oceanic cool temperate climate become more

L

and more pronounced. With climate as the criterion for a national division, geology forms the criterion for a regional division. A great fault extends for approximately 110 miles from a point just south of the mouth of the Douro south-south-east as far as the

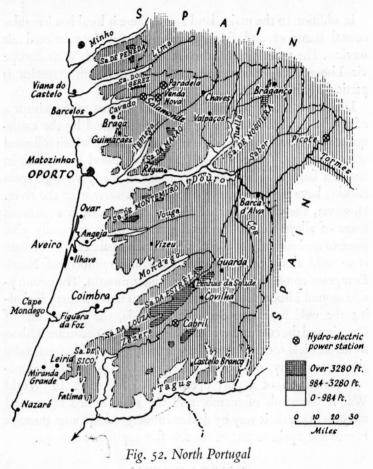

Fig. 52. North Portugal

Tagus near Abrantes, where it disappears beneath Tertiary sediments. This fault marks off the younger rocks of the west from the older Palaeozoic and crystalline rocks to the north and east, and makes possible a subdivision of North Portugal.

The Coast and Coimbra Plains

This region includes all land bounded by the Atlantic to the west,

the above-mentioned fault to the east, and the Tagus to the south. The high central serras formed of Jurassic sandstones and limestones extend from Coimbra to Lisbon and trend from south-west to north-east, continuing eastwards as the mountains of the Serra da Estrêla. Locally these serras are referred to as the Serra de Sico between Coimbra and Leiria, and the Serras de Candeiros and Montejunto (Monte Junto, 2,184 feet) between Leiria and Lisbon. Before the draining of the coastal and Tagus plains these serras formed the main highway to Lisbon and it was here that two major engagements for Portuguese freedom were fought – that of Aljubarrota, August 15th, 1385, when Portuguese bowmen routed Spanish cavalry, and that of Torres Vedras (1810), when Sir Arthur Wellesley successfully opposed Napoleonic forces.

More important than the hill country is the coast. Here, covering the basic Secondary and Tertiary sediments, vast piles of sand have been heaped up to form extensive dunes. Aveiro was completely blocked in 1575 by a freak storm, and its port ruined until three centuries later when another storm washed the sand away. Ovar was once a thriving fishing port and gave the name *varinha* (fishwife, originally from Ovar) to Lisbon; now, like Ilhavo and Angeja, it lies well inland. The dunes have always threatened encroachment on the rich farmland behind and fixing them has been the aim of successive rulers of Portugal. King Diniz, 'o Lavrador' (the husbandman), planted a forest of pine trees from 1297 till 1325 to protect the farms between Leiria and the sea, and the modern State Forest of Leiria has the unique distinction of having been maintained continuously for six centuries. Modern methods are sometimes quicker; between Figuera da Foz and Aveiro a sandspit $15\frac{1}{2}$ miles long and a little over $\frac{1}{2}$ a mile wide has been both fixed and planted in six years. The modern method of fixing includes creating 'false dunes', growing sand-fixing plants under patches of cut heathers in the space thus protected until the soil is sufficiently fixed for tree-planting. The *Pinus pinaster* is the tree most generally used for this purpose. Despite the valiant attempts of the Portuguese Forestry Service large sandy wastes still exist. Where the two main rivers of the area, the Vouga and the Mondego, come to the sea there are, in addition, extensive lagoons and salt-marshes which, in summer, harbour malarial mosquitoes.

Farming and fishing form the two basic occupations. The farms are small, set in the midst of their fields, and methods, though well suited to the size of the farms, are often primitive. The hoe is frequently used in preference to the plough, and the *shaduf* method of irrigation is generally employed, although some farmers make use of blindfolded donkeys to turn water wheels. Variety rather than specialization is characteristic; good crops of maize, wheat, barley, pulses, figs, vines and vegetables are obtained on the lower farms; those higher up grow more olives while those almost at sea level produce rice. To the north the sweet chestnut becomes increasingly important. Cattle-rearing is carried out on the rich pastures around the Aveiro lagoon. This vast expanse of extremely salty water fringed by villages and windmills provides local farmers with a useful fertilizer in the form of water-weeds and algae. Oxen help to drag it with wooden rakes across the lagoon, and flat-bottomed craft called *moliceiros* take it to its destination up one of the innumerable creeks. In the north of this area flax is grown and pulled in autumn. There is no commercial outlet for this product and it serves a purely local market. Methods are therefore simple but effective; after pulling, the flax is dried, the seeds being retained separately, and the stalks steeped in water for several days. They are then dried again, ground in the local mill, and beaten (or scutched) with a flat chestnut-wood axe, or *espada*. The flax is teased by being passed over a nail-studded board, and is then ready for spinning and weaving into good, hard-wearing linen.

Along the coast there are a few small fishing villages, but, in general, the coastline does not provide good harbours. At Nazaré the catch is hauled up by oxen kept on the beach specifically for that purpose, while Figuera da Foz (pop. 56,862) and Aveiro (pop. 40,187) both have small fishing fleets of tiny brightly coloured craft, each with an eye painted on the bow to ward off ill-luck. Jão Alfonso, a native of Aveiro, was one of the first navigators to reach Newfoundland, and his home town still maintains this link by sending a certain number of craft every year to Newfoundland for the cod fishing. Apart from fish the coast of this region provides an abundant supply of salt. At both Figuera da Foz and Aveiro there are extensive saltings which provide much of Portugal's salt by evaporation from sea-water. This takes place primarily in summer as the winters are frequently cloudy, if not always pluvial.

There are few industrial activities. Resin is obtained from the trees of the larger forests and a limited supply of timber is cut every year, while olive oil and wine are both produced locally. Mineral resources are few – copper and lead are found around Aveiro, but the deposits are small. Coal of inferior type and iron are mined near Moncorvo, while near Cape Mondego and Coimbra poor coal and lignite are obtained. The salt from Aveiro and Figuera da Foz is used at Marinha Grande, between Leiria and the sea, in the glass factory, which was started by an Englishman, John Beare, in 1748 and is now State-owned. Tourists visit Coimbra, Nazaré, where the inhabitants claim direct descent from Phoenician ancestors, and the religious centre of Fatima. Near this village, on May 13th, 1917, three children tending their flocks on the barren, windy moors saw a vision of the Virgin Mary. Disbelieved at first, and punished for their supposed mendacity, they insisted on the truth of their story, and were believed when others told of similar manifestations. Portuguese bishops, at first sceptical, finally countenanced official recognition of the miracle, and now the tiny hamlet ranks next to Lourdes as the largest pilgrimage centre in Europe.

Coimbra, the fourth town of Portugal, with a population of 98,027, is the main centre of this area. It lies on the river Mondego, 25 miles from the sea. Situated almost 9 miles north of the excavated site of Conimbriga, the great Roman town, Coimbra became its medieval successor. The university, founded in 1290, is one of the oldest in Europe. The great baroque library built between 1717 and 1728, and containing 50,000 volumes, is particularly renowned. Apart from its importance as a cultural centre, Coimbra serves as a focal point of roads and railways in central Portugal, the main routes being those to Oporto in the north, to the Spanish frontier via Guarda in the north-east and to Lisbon in the south. Local farmers find a ready market for their wares, while as a tourist centre it has much to offer: its central position in Portugal makes it a suitable base for excursions; it is surrounded by beautiful and varied scenery; the climate is generally mild, particularly in the winter half of the year; and it contains, apart from the library, an imposing cathedral which incorporates parts of a former mosque.

The Serra da Estrêla

The old crystalline and Palaeozoic core of Iberia gives rise in Portugal to a high, dissected mountain mass, trending as in Spain from north-east to south-west. The really high mountains end in the west with the termination of the Archaean rocks at the Tagus–Oporto fault-line, and there is a graded descent southwards to the Tagus and to a small Tertiary basin near the frontier. To the north and east the rocks remain predominantly crystalline, and height alone marks off mountains from uplands. Two main rivers drain this region; the first, the Zêzere, divides the southern Serras of Morada and Guardunha (highest point 4,015 feet) from the northern Serras of Lousã and Estrêla (highest point 6,530 feet). Since the completion of the hydro-electric power station at Cabril, this river has provided much of central Portugal with both electricity and water for irrigation. The second river is the Mondego, 125 miles long, and navigable for small craft for 52 miles. Future schemes will, no doubt, harness its waters for electricity but at the moment it serves to irrigate local fields by means of water wheels of a type seen more frequently in Turkey and Yugoslavia. A huge wooden wheel, 20 to 30 feet high, is turned by the water alone; the current is often directed on to the wheel by brushwood and rocks strategically placed. Tied to wooden slats are earthenware jars which scoop up the water and tip it into long runnels made of hollowed logs, which conduct the water through the fields up to 300 yards from the river. In this way land even 20 feet above river level is easily and cheaply irrigated.

With an average height of 4,000 feet the mountain ranges of Portugal are far cooler than the surrounding countryside. In summer the average temperature is about 60° F., although south-facing slopes receiving the full force of a Mediterranean sun can become as hot as the lower plains. In winter it is very cold; snowfall is heavy and the snow lies on the peaks from November to April. Rainfall is also heavy, over 100 inches a year in really exposed areas, and although some falls throughout the year, there is a winter maximum. To the east, near the Spanish frontier, there is a rain-shadow area where only approximately 25 inches of rain falls annually. Plant growth is naturally adapted to this change of climate with altitude. On the lower slopes there are heathlands and woods of pines, cork oaks, sweet chestnuts, beeches and elms; higher up the warm temperate species give way to the conifers, which, in turn, disappear at about 4,000 feet, where meadows continue until the high crests are reached. The short turf produces, every spring, a carpet of alpine flowers, while the small streams and lakes contain good trout. Unfortunately wolves and a few lynxes still exist in these granite highlands, and local sheep-dogs are specially bred for valour and strength to protect the flocks.

The sparse population of this bleak, grey countryside is primarily engaged in agriculture, often of subsistence type. The small stone-built farmsteads, or *quintas*, are generally situated near a stream which forms the main water supply, and crops grown include wheat, barley, lucerne, roots for the animals and vegetables for human consumption. Cereal production generally ceases at 4,000 feet, but in sheltered spots barley will ripen at 5,000 feet if autumn-sown. Oxen and mules form the beasts of burden, and provide the manure without which the soil, derived mainly from granite, would be sandy and infertile. Flocks of sheep and goats are pastured on the higher slopes, frequently guarded by shepherds in traditional clothes.

Apart from farming there is a little mining for tin and iron ore at Barca d'Alva and for tin and wolfram at Guarda (51,468 inhabitants), Castello Branco (63,305 inhabitants) and Vizeu (76,816 inhabitants). Other minerals exist, as might be expected from the geology of the region, but as yet are little exploited. In winter a few intrepid skiers visit this region, despite a paucity of maps and hotels of Alpine standard. The headquarters of the Portuguese skiing club is at Covilhã (68,522 inhabitants) and the only winter sports hotel of Portugal lies 4,500 feet above sea level at Penhas da Saude.

The Douro Region

The northern part of Portugal consists almost entirely of granites and schists belonging to the Archaean core of Iberia. These rocks have been so dissected by rivers that the countryside consists of rolling uplands, very difficult to cross, with steep-sided V-shaped valleys alternating with high, windswept crests. The average height of the ridges is 4,000 feet; they trend, in general, from north-east to south-west, and the main ones include:

Serra de Peneda (4,503 feet)
Serra do Gerez (4,817 feet)
La Raya Seca and Laronca (4,390 feet) ⎫ North of the
Serra de Marao (4,642 feet) ⎬ Douro
Serra de Padrela (3,763 feet) ⎭
Serra de Nogueira (4,331 feet)
Serra de Lapa ⎫ South of the
Montemuro (4,534 feet) ⎬ Douro

The major river is the Douro, which, for the first part of its course in Portugal, acts as a boundary between Portugal and Spain, and receives as tributaries the Tâmega, Tuella and Sabôr from the north, and the Paiva, Távora and Côa from the south. The rivers Minho, Lima and Cávado reach the sea independently, the former marking the Portuguese–Spanish border for most of its lower course.

The increasing influence of depressions from the Atlantic is shown in climatic statistics; winters remain mild with lowland average temperatures ranging from 45° F. to 50° F., summers are warm or hot, lowland regions having an average of 70° F., and rainfall is not only greater in amount (40 to 60 inches a year), but more persistent, as are mist, fog and cloud, than in the rest of Portugal. The high and steady rainfall coupled with impermeable rocks and steep-sided valleys gives ideal conditions for the creation of hydro-electric power stations. Until recently lack of capital has been the main problem; the Portuguese government has, however, sanctioned several major hydro-electric power schemes, some of which have already been completed. These include the Caniçada and Salamonde stations on the river Cávado, the

Venda Nova on the Rabagão, the Paradela in the Cávado basin, one of the largest stone-built dams in the world, and the Picote, built among the rapids (*pontos*) of the upper Douro and completed in 1958.

The rough dissected nature of this countryside has tended, in the past, to produce hardy, self-sufficient farmers who try to wrest a living from infertile, sandy soil. Fields are small and crops are grown mainly to feed the farmer's family, so that variety is important. Maize, barley, potatoes, vegetables and chick-peas are the more usual crops, and most farms have, in addition, some vines, a plot or two for flax or hay, and one or two long-horned oxen, adorned with fox-skin headgear as a partial protection against flies. In the drier interior, near the upper Douro, cork oaks are grown extensively, while sweet chestnuts form a ubiquitous addition to a somewhat monotonous diet. Some fruits, such as cherries and apples, are grown at higher altitudes, while at lower levels near the coast oranges and apricots may be seen, though not in profusion. Local barns are often built on four stout posts or on stones topped by a millstone to prevent the depradations of rats; such structures are a familiar sight in Galicia too, and many other similarities help to emphasize the affinity existing between these politically different but geographically similar regions.

The mineral wealth of North Portugal is very varied, but transport and labour difficulties preclude any extensive exploitation. Gold is mined on a small scale at Tres Minas near Valpaços, about 700 tons of uranium are extracted annually at Urgeirica, and a few tin mines occur in the eastern hills. There are many spas in the area, including among others Gerez, renowned for the strength of its waters, Vidago and Chaves (population 54,406), originally the 'key' to Portugal through the northern 'door', and now thriving as a result of the hot springs in its immediate vicinity. Much afforestation has been undertaken by the Portuguese Forestry Service and timber felling is carried out on the plantations. Coastal villages and towns like Viana do Castelo (population 70,331) are concerned with fishing; sardines, tunny and local delicacies such as crab and lamprey form the bulk of the catch, but there are no large fishing centres as Setúbal further south, because the wide, sheltered harbours provided by the rias of Galicia are not found along the north Portuguese coast. The textile industry is important locally; Guimarães (pop. 96,064) is the chief centre of the Portuguese linen industry, Braga (pop. 84,142) contains cotton factories, and firearms and cutlery are also manufactured there. Heavy, richly coloured models of oxen, chickens and other creatures are made in the potteries at Barcelos. Oporto, apart from making textiles, manufactures cement, *azulejos* and all the requirements (bottles, corks, barrels) of a flourishing wine industry.

The production of port wine and all its associated industries is primarily responsible for the density of population in the coastlands of North Portugal, particularly around Oporto. Wine and brandy form the third export of Portugal, but their preparation demands far greater skill and organization than does that of cork and sardines, the first and second exports respectively. The localization of the port wine industry is the result of geographical factors; the local vine stock, descended from that originally imported from Burgundy 800 years ago, requires soil derived from schist, great heat in late summer, and less rainfall than is characteristic of most of North Portugal. All these conditions are fulfilled in the rocky, arid Paiz do Vinho, beginning approximately at Régua, 45 miles east of Oporto, and continuing up the Douro for about 15 miles. Here there is no soil – merely a thin covering of schist flakes preserved from downwash by terraces which occur on all hills. Every shipper of port today owns a series of farms or *quintas*, and often buys a growing crop to supplement his own harvest. The grapes are small, dark and tightly bunched, but strong and sweet, having received during the long summer months intense insolation and little rain to make them watery.

Picking is carried out with the help of seasonal workers from other provinces; women and girls fill the smaller baskets, while men carry the larger ones, sometimes weighing 150 pounds, to the treading vats. Although they work hard all day, the pickers gather round the vats at night to encourage the treaders. After their feet have been inspected and washed, the treaders link arms, enter the the granite vats (*lagares*), and slowly trample the black, sticky, intoxicating mass. The grapes are trodden for four hours and 'rested' for six; grapes for port wine must always be trodden by human foot, since the skins of the grapes must be broken but not the pips. Once the thick mass becomes liquid it is referred to as the *lagrima*; after fermentation begins the word *masta* (must) is used. The *lagrima* is cold but fermentation generates heat, at the same time eliminating all impurities. At this stage the temperature and sugar content of the must is frequently measured. Ordinary must is run off at 7 to 7½ degrees of sweetness, and fermentation is stopped by the addition of grape brandy. A small quantity of must is run off at 4½ degrees for blending purposes, while at the other extreme, some *lagares* produce must of 12 degrees, which is very sweet.

The must is eventually run into *tonels* or vats, and kept until April, when it is tasted, 'refreshed' with more brandy, put into casks and taken downstream by rail, or floated down in the large-sailed *rabelos* – vessels which seem to negotiate the dangerous rapids of the Douro casually but safely. The wine lodges of Oporto are on the south bank at Vila Nova de Gaia (pop. 133,760); here the wine is rested, matured, tasted, blended, revived, tasted and blended again until, after several years of quiet, unhasting, but purposeful skill on the part of the wine shippers and tasters, the wine is bottled and exported. There is, ordinarily, no such thing as a 'vintage' port on account of continuous blending, but occasionally in a good vintage year a certain crop will be treated individually to produce this noble rarity. Port is traditionally associated with Englishmen; its importance dates from 1678 when a trade agreement was signed to facilitate the exchange of English cloth and Portuguese wine, and this bargain received official recognition in the Methuen Treaty of 1703. Most of the great wine lodges owe their foundation to Englishmen and still bear English names (Sandeman's, Gilbert's, Cockburn's).

Oporto (pop. 281,466) forms a natural centre for this northern region. Its position as a port has suffered from the gradual silting up of the Douro estuary. Leixões, 5 miles to the north-west, is now its artificial outport, designed for heavy ocean traffic. Three main railway lines converge on Oporto; one from Spain in the north via the frontier town of Túy, one from Spain and the Douro via the frontier towns of La Fregenada and Barca d'Alva, and one from Lisbon and Coimbra to the south. Road traffic also converges on Oporto following the same routes, and its passage within the town is facilitated by suspension bridges (which help to unite the steep and rocky banks of the Douro) like the bridge of São Luis, which was built by Eiffel.

APPENDIX A

The Spanish Possessions

URING THE SIXTEENTH and seventeenth centuries when Spain was at the height of her power she had an extensive and far-flung empire. Much land in the then known parts of the American continents, many stations around the coasts of Africa and the Philippine islands, and even their hinterlands were under Spanish sway. Since those days there has been a gradual diminution in the extent of these lands, and now only remnants of the African possessions are left. These include the Canary Islands (named after the native dogs), places of sovereignty in Spanish Morocco, the enclave of Ifni, Rio de Oro, and the West African territories of Rio Muni and Fernando Po.

The Canary Islands, first occupied by Spaniards in 1479, form an archipelago lying athwart latitude 28° North, approximately 72 miles off the north-west coast of Africa. Agriculture is a flourishing concern, despite an average annual rainfall of from 5 to 20 inches, because in many places the weathered volcanic soil is extremely fertile. The islanders depend on agriculture for their living and there is a surplus of crops for export, considerable both in quantity and variety, the latter due to variations in relief, which includes flat alluvial plains as well as high volcanic peaks such as Teide (12,185 feet). The coastal lowlands, small plains tucked in between rocky hills, produce most tropical crops, for example, bananas, dates and sugar cane. These crops are grown with irrigation from local supplies of water, such as wells or small streams. At higher altitudes Mediterranean crops are grown – oranges and lemons, figs and tomatoes, while on the more barren slopes vines are cultivated. The local wine, however, does not compare favourably with its Spanish counterpart, since the climate does not give the necessary tang or 'body' to the grape juice. Wheat, barley,

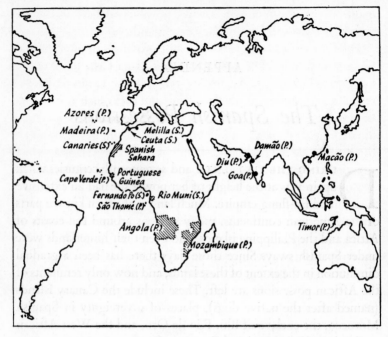

Fig. 53. Portuguese Possessions, 1960; Spanish Possessions, 1960

maize, peaches, apricots and almonds are among the crops grown to provide for the needs of the local people. Of all the variety and profusion of crops, however, only the banana and tomato are grown in large quantities to supply a wide and continuous demand from overseas buyers.

In the volcanic rocks of the islands little in the way of mineral resources is to be expected. There is no fuel of any kind, if one excludes tree growth, and the only natural resources of importance are pumice stone, sulphur, mineral waters, and some granite at Galdar. Hence there is little industry on the islands, most of the manufactured goods being imported from Spain.

Two other occupations in the islands are fishing around the coasts, where a variety of fish are caught, often unintentionally including flying fish, and the tourist industry which flourishes wherever there are additional attractions, for example, the eyeless fish in the underground lakes at Lazarote, or the snowy summit of Teide often seen as a mirage over the sea. Distance from the main ports and capitals of Europe, however, debars all but the wealthier tourists from visiting these islands.

The Canaries today form two major provinces of metropolitan Spain, the provinces of Las Palmas and Santa Cruz de Tenerife. Las Palmas includes the islands of Gran Canaria, Lazarote, Fuerteventura, and a group of smaller islands and rocks such as Graciosa, Lobos and Roque del Oeste. Together these islands cover 1,565 square miles and contain about 967,000 people, most of whom are of Spanish origin, speak Spanish and live on Gran Canaria, which supports a population of 419,250 (1960 estimate), of which 193,000 (1960 estimate) are absorbed by the capital, Las Palmas, a dazzling white town stretching for some 5 miles along the coast between the sea and a line of inland cliffs. Its port, La Luz, deals with an appreciable tonnage of shipping each year (about 2,500 ships of all types). In the town are iron foundries and factories for the manufacture of machinery, leather goods and fertilizers. On the island of Lazarote live 331,654 people and Fuerteventura contains 18,541 inhabitants.

The province of Santa Cruz de Tenerife is smaller, less rich and less populated than that of Las Palmas. It includes the islands of Tenerife, Gomera, Palma and Hierra, and contains 1,329 square miles of territory and about 446,000 inhabitants. The largest island is Tenerife, with a population of 320,000, of which 193,984 (1960 estimate) live in the capital Santa Cruz, a relatively modern town which is expanding upwards instead of along the coast as is the case in Las Palmas. There is a good port, visited by some 2,100 ships a year, and it is from here that the major export of bananas and tomatoes takes place. In addition there is a petroleum refinery where various derivatives of petroleum are made and several factories are engaged in the manufacture of food products. La Laguna (31,000) is another town of importance and was once the capital of the island. Here is an aerodrome, and several factories manufacture mosaics, rough cloth and canvas. Orotava (19,000) is an important tourist centre lying at the foot of the peak of Teide, in a valley of rare beauty where flowers abound throughout the year. Icod (15,000) is famed for its ancient Dragon Tree, and is a collecting centre for local produce. The island of Palma is occupied by about 77,000 people of whom 10,000 live in

Santa Cruz de Palma, the main town. The island of Gomera has about 32,000 inhabitants, and the island of Hierro contains some 13,000 people.

The Canaries are unique possessions combining a warm, balmy climate with a profuse variety of natural plants and great agricultural wealth. Lying on the main shipping lanes between Western Europe, South America, and West and South Africa, they are well situated in regard to world trade routes.

The loss of Spanish Morocco in 1955 has left only five zones

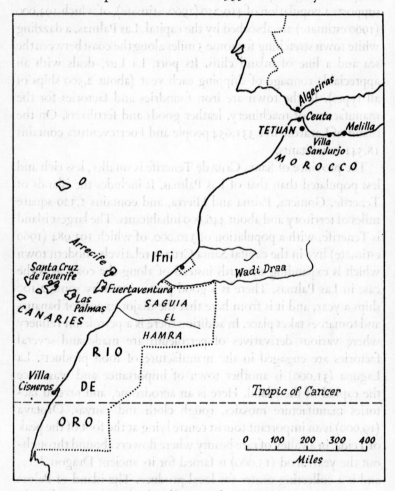

Fig. 54. The Spanish Possessions

of Spanish sovereignty on the North African coast: Melilla, Ceuta, the Chafarinas Islands, the Peñon of Alhucemas and the Peñon of Velez de la Gomera.

Melilla, which became Spanish in 1470, has a population of 85,010 (1955 estimate), and is an important commercial port and route centre. A small railway network links the town to the iron-mining region which lies to the south, and there are regular services by ship and air to Tetuan, capital of this section of Morocco, and to Málaga, Madrid and Valencia. Iron ore of average quality is mined in the vicinity of Beni-Bu-Ifrur, a region south of Melilla. During their occupation the Spaniards have improved agriculture by constructing irrigation channels and dams, such as the Pantano Najilo near Tetuan, and the river Muluya provides water for crops growing on either side, as well as hydro-electric power for Melilla. The town forms a good market for the sale of local produce – cereals, tobacco, some cotton, figs, olives, dates, and even bananas from the irrigated lowlands, and goats, sheep, leather goods and wood from the hills. In addition Melilla serves as a fishing centre, dealing with about 8,000 tons of fish a year.

Ceuta lies opposite to Gibraltar, forming one of the 'Pillars of Hercules'. It has a fine natural harbour, but the competition of Gibraltar and absence of a wealthy hinterland prevent the full utilization of its resources. The town, like Melilla, is a route and market centre, containing 64,485 inhabitants, of whom approximately 15 per cent are Moslems, living in a small *barrio* (native section) which contains the mosque of Muley Hassan. As a fishing centre the town deals with about 6,000 tons of fish a year.

The Chafarinas Islands are situated in the western Mediterranean north of Cape Agua and comprise three small islets – Congresso, covering roughly $\frac{1}{8}$ of a square mile, Isabel II, with a perimeter of just over a mile and 500 inhabitants, who use the even smaller islet of Rey as a cemetery. The Peñon of Alhucemas, situated in the bay of Alhucemas, covers an area of approximately 4·7 square miles and contains a small village, Andalusian in appearance. The Peñon of Velez de la Gomera lies 50 miles from the north African coast, and its tiny village is dominated by a castle. All these islands, once the haunts of Barbary pirates, became

Spanish possessions in 1848, and are now used as minor fishing centres.

The enclave of Ifni lies to the north of the river Draa, and comprises some 741 square miles of territory. Although it lies in desert latitudes it faces the Atlantic and receives the benefit of moist sea breezes. Agriculture is quite flourishing and there is scattered cultivation of cereals, grapes, tomatoes, esparto and the 'argan tree', from which comes an edible oil. Fishing off the coast produces an annual average catch of 40,000 tons. There are about 44,686 inhabitants, mostly Berbers, and Ifni, with a population of 1,032, is the main town and port.

The Rio de Oro, a Spanish possession since 1885, is considerably larger, covering approximately 73,362 square miles, and, with the adjoining tract of Seguiet (or Seguia) el Hamra (32,047 square miles), comprises Spanish Sahara. It is simply part of the vast Sahara desert, and correspondingly barren. Nomadic pastoralism is the main occupation, but some settled types of agriculture are practised around the oases. After the rains about 31,000 nomads enter the area to make use of the short-lived grass. On the coast is the hamlet of Villa Cisneros (about 300 inhabitants), where in its market wool, sheep, goats, camels, cattle, ivory and ostrich feathers are usually bartered and rarely sold. In addition, off the coast, and following the plankton found in the cool waters of the Canaries current, are many shoals of fish, which give rise to an important fishing industry. Fishing extends as far as, and is worked in conjunction with that of the Canary Islands. There are no facilities for dealing with fish on the coast of Rio de Oro except those for salting and preserving in oil at Villa Cisneros.

The other African possessions of Spain lie in the area of the Gulf of Guinea. For the most part they consist of islands and parts of the mainland. The islands in the Gulf form an archipelago, starting from the mainland near the Cameroons, and continuing into the sea in a south-westerly direction as far as the Spanish island of Annobon. Of these islands that of Fernando Po is the largest, becoming a Spanish possession in 1778. Its position is potentially an important one, commanding the trade of the Guinea coastlands; in addition, the height of the island (Clarence Peak, or the Peak of Santa Isabel, reaches 9,369 feet, and others rise over 8,000 feet) ameliorates the climate and makes it suitable for European settlement. These advantages, however, have not yet been fully exploited.

Of the major products entering into commerce cocoa is the most important (about 18,000 tons a year), followed by coffee, sugar cane, cotton, copra, palm oil, vanilla, tobacco, oranges, bananas and other tropical fruits. In addition, the native inhabitants, the 'Bubis', cultivate all their own food crops. The thick tropical jungles that cover most of the island are a rich source of timber, but at the moment are little exploited, because of shortages in labour, transport facilities and capital. Since the island is volcanic, containing many craters and much volcanic débris, there are few mineral resources. The main towns of the island are Santa Isabel to the north (11,098 people) and San Carlos on the west coast (10,000 people). There is a great concentration of population in these two ports, for the total population of the island in 1950 was only 40,475.

The archipelago also includes Annobon, a small island with a population of about 1,400 negroes, mainly concerned with fishing and sheep-rearing, Corisco (5 square miles in area), Elobey (covering 480 acres) and Little Elobey, the two latter being mere islets off the mouth of the river Muni.

On the African mainland there is a small enclave around the river Muni which belongs to Spain. This covers 11,040 square miles of territory bordering the Cameroons and French Equatorial Africa. There is a profusion of natural vegetation and the dense forest cover is the greatest asset of this country, providing gum, rubber, palm oil, ebony, ivory, cocoa and tropical fruits. As yet there is little attempt to establish agriculture on a plantation basis. Mangrove swamps occur along the coast, and rivers are often narrow and full of rapids, so that communications are impeded. However, the main river, the Benito, or Volo, is navigable inland for nearly 8 miles, and is over a mile wide at its mouth. The capital of the territory is Bata, which contains about 20,400 inhabitants, 97 per cent being negroes. The population of the territory is about 156,785 people, of whom only 1,805 are whites.

Taking the Spanish possessions as a whole, the major obstacles to progress seem to be of a geographical nature; in North Africa shortage of water is the main problem, while in West Africa the extreme heat and humidity make it difficult for even the negro population to work with energy. Human problems, however, do exist, especially in the Guinea area, where a decrease in the negro population is seriously depleting the supply of cheap labour. Many reasons have been put forward to account for this population trend. In any case the natural increase among the negroes has never been great and the vices introduced by the whites have not helped to increase it. Moreover many negroes are descendants of people comparatively recently driven south by invaders and they are not yet fully acclimatized to excessive heat and moisture.

The contribution of the Spanish possessions to Spanish economy, although small in amount, is important. The supply of iron ore obtained from the mines of the Rif and exported from Melilla exceeds that of Vizcaya, and other mineral products help to augment home supplies. From the Guinea lands come all types of tropical products which, in general, supply a luxury market in Spain. At her present standard of living Spain is, in fact, almost independent of outside sources of tropical products, and, since the possessions are assured of a steady market, a harmonious *status quo* has been reached, which, nevertheless, deprives both sides of competitive stimulus.

APPENDIX B

The Portuguese Possessions

PORTUGAL, ONE OF the least important countries in Western Europe, is the third biggest colonial power in the world after Britain and France. The intelligent curiosity and daring character of individual Portuguese seafarers in the fifteenth and sixteenth centuries were primarily responsible for the existence of this empire, while the papal treaty of Tordesillas, A.D. 1494, which declared the Portuguese sphere of influence to be east of a line 370 leagues west of Cape Verde, limited it to Brazil, to Africa and to Asia. The Portuguese introduced to Africa several basic food crops like maize and manioc, and, according to some authorities, bananas and palm oils from the West Indies.

Their possessions are fragmentary, not because of loss of territory, as is the case with Spain, but as a result of the Portuguese interest in exploring coastlines and establishing forts (as far distant as, for example, Fort Jesus at Mombasa and Goa in India), rather than in colonizing hinterlands. Towns along the coast, especially in Angola and Mozambique, are busy modern centres, but until recently little had been done to develop the backward interiors of these two large provinces.

The Portuguese treatment of natives is unusual and in some ways illogical. In Portuguese Africa there is press censorship, much poverty (wages average about ninepence a day), a degree of illiteracy higher than in any comparable region of the continent, and forced labour, though the Portuguese prefer to call it directed labour. Yet there is no colour bar, no segregation and little social distinction. One unique system is that of the *civilizado* or *assimilado*, whereby selected natives are given European privileges, a passport, permission to travel, the right to vote and free education for their children, and, in return, assume European responsibilities such as

329

military service and payment of a higher income tax. However few natives have reached the required selection standard, 30,000 in Angola, 4,378 in Mozambique and 1,478 in Portuguese Guinea.

Mozambique, discovered by Vasco da Gama's fleet in A.D. 1498, was proclaimed, with its western counterpart Angola, a province of Portugal in June 1951. It extends from Tanganyika in the north to Natal in the south, and has a coastline of 1,626 miles and a western boundary so irregular that the width of the country varies from 56 to 718 miles.

Mozambique has the triple advantages of a fertile soil, a reliable limate and a semi-skilled labour force, but agricultural progress has been impeded by lack of Portuguese interest and by African labour troubles. Native farmers grow a great variety of crops including maize, millet, manioc, rice, simsim, groundnuts, tobacco and cotton, mainly for their own use, though cotton, groundnuts, simsim and cashew nuts are exported, the last named being destined chiefly for India.

In the mangrove swamps around Beira mangrove bark is gathered, from which cutch is extracted for use in tanning and as a preservative of sails. Forests in the uplands supply a little beeswax and wild rubber as well as hard timber, resistant to the white ant, especially used for railway sleepers and for constructional purposes.

Most European farming centres on the Manica Highlands where tobacco, temperate cereals and maize are grown, the last named being especially important around Chimoio and Neves Ferreira. Animal farming is almost entirely restricted to this region because of the prevalence of the tsetse fly at lower altitudes, and there are only three-quarters of a million cattle in Mozambique. Plantation crops include tropical fruits such as bananas and pineapples, and citrus fruits, the Incomati valley being especially famous for oranges, sisal to the north of the Zambesi round Mozambique and Quelimane, cotton in the Zambesi valley and at Sofala further south, tea on the Nyasaland border and at Gurue, coffee in the Inhambane district, coconuts along the coast especially north of the Zambesi delta (the world's largest coconut plantation is at Quelimane), and sugar round Sena in the Zambesi valley. To these cash crops can be added tobacco, kapok and castor oil. Vast irrigation schemes are developing on the Incomati river and on

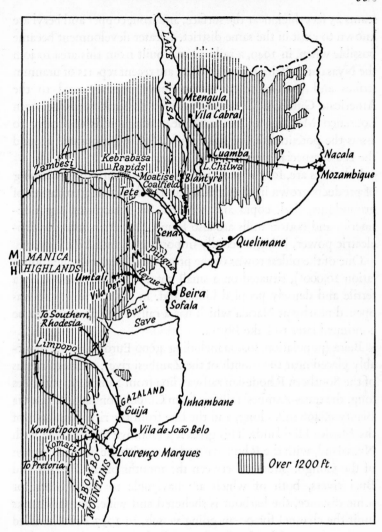

Fig. 55. Mozambique

the Limpopo river, the latter being dammed below Guija for the cultivation, by European farmers, of a large area of rich alluvial land above Vila de Joâo Belo.

There is some mineral wealth in the country; gold is mined in the Manica Highlands and panned in the Revue river, silver being obtained as a by-product. The Moatise coalfield near Tete has seams 25 feet thick near the surface, and iron, copper and beryl are known to exist in the same district. Greater development became possible when, in 1949, a railway was built from this area to join the Nyasaland–Beira railway. There are recent reports of uranium strikes and petroleum concessions have been granted to the American Gulf Oil Company which has sunk wells between Lourenço Marques and Inhambane, though it is too early to assess the potentialities of this oilfield. Salt is evaporated around the coast, especially near Mozambique.

Industries are, for the most part, concerned with the processing of products grown in the territory and include the preparation of groundnuts, sisal, copra and tobacco. Soap factories, sugar refineries and cotton mills are also found, the latter, using hydro-electric power, being especially important around Vila Pery.

One of the oldest towns of the province is Mozambique (population 10,000[1]), situated on a small coral island surrounded by a fertile and densely peopled hinterland. In 1951 a new port was opened nearby at Nacala which has a railway to Cuamba, to be continued later to Lake Nyasa.

Beira (population 40,000 including 4,000 Europeans) is favourably placed near the mouth of the Zambesi river, at the terminus of the Southern Rhodesian railway line from Salisbury, 374 miles long, the trans-Zambesi railway from Chipoka on Lake Nyasa via Blantyre, 496 miles long, and the line from the rich farmlands of the Manica Highlands. This gives it a lucrative transit trade with Nyasaland, with the Rhodesias and even with the Katanga region of the Congo. Situated between the mouths of the Pungue and Buzi rivers, both of which are navigable to small boats for some distance, the harbour is sheltered and wide, but sandbanks limit the channel for ocean-going vessels. In 1957 Beira handled 3,258,376 tons of freight, Southern Rhodesian chrome ore, asbestos, tobacco and Northern Rhodesian copper being included among its exports, and machinery, motor-cars, petrol, iron and steel goods, and railway equipment forming the bulk of its imports.

Lourenço Marques, with a population of 100,000 including 16,000 Europeans, is the capital of the country. It is a fine modern

[1] Population figures are for 1950.

city, and its wireless station is to the Union of South Africa what Radio Luxembourg is to Europe. The town and its beaches are so attractive, its vegetation so luxuriant, its hotels so well equipped, that it is a popular holiday resort in the cool season of the year between May and September, especially for visitors from the well-populated Witwatersrand region of the Transvaal. It has several industries, chief among them being flour-milling, cement-making, and the production of agricultural implements. Its greatest asset is its harbour, one of the best on the east coast of Africa, with a stretch of water 26 miles long by 22 miles wide in Delagoa Bay. It is the terminus of the main line from Pretoria via Komatipoort, 352 miles long, making it the nearest port to the gold-mining district of Johannesburg and the coal-mining centres of Witbank and Springs. It is also the terminus of a railway from Southern Rhodesia via Guija, giving it a transit trade with the Rhodesias. In 1954 it handled 4,988,978 tons of freight, more than Beira, including exports of sugar, sisal, citrus fruits, copra, vegetable oils, coal, chrome ore, Southern Rhodesian asbestos and Northern Rhodesian copper, and imports of petrol, motor vehicles and machinery.

Mozambique possesses an extremely useful coastline, and in order to gain access to it Britain and South Africa have done much to develop the territory. The Mozambique Company, in which British interests predominated, did valuable work until its concession expired in 1941, British firms were responsible for the building of the Zambesi Bridge, one of the longest bridges in the world, opened in 1935, and the Union of South Africa has helped to develop the port of Lourenço Marques, especially the coal bunkering jetty.

The trade of the country is not large and 30 per cent of it is with the mother country.

Until recently imports have exceeded exports, and the trade balance has been made up from the transit trade and from the earnings of the 80,000 natives who leave the country annually to work on Rand mines under the arrangements of the Mozambique Convention of 1909.

The total area of Mozambique or Portuguese East Africa is 297,731 square miles and its population 5,738,911, including 48,910

Mozambique: Imports and Exports for 1959

Imports		Exports	
Railway rolling stock and		Copra	201,345
lines	168,773	Tea	144,003
Cotton goods	64,519	Cashew nuts	121,802
Wine	51,864	Sisal	115,014
Iron and steel goods	44,210	Raw cotton	24,774
		Wood	21,897

Figures refer to millions of escudos, according to *Boletim Mensal do Instituto Nacional de Estatística*

Europeans, concentrated in Lourenço Marques and Beira, and an equal number of Indians and Arabs scattered throughout the coastal plain. The territory is too unhealthy for a large European population though conditions have improved since 1829 when 34 out of 40 European residents in Lourenço Marques died of fever.

Portuguese traders first visited the coastlands of Angola in 1482, though actual colonization did not take place till the beginning of the seventeenth century, and a real interest in the country has only been evident during the last few years. Subsistence farming on the part of the natives produces crops of manioc, maize, beans, groundnuts and tobacco. The natives also collect beeswax and rear cattle and sheep on the interior plateau. Cash crops are grown on European farms; these are especially concentrated on the Bihé Plateau, at a height of 5,000 feet, along the railway line from Katanga to Lobito Bay, a region which is developing rapidly. Maize and tobacco are cultivated, wheat is grown as a winter crop, and cattle-rearing is becoming very important. On the better-watered plateau slopes with up to 50 inches of rain, coffee, sugar, cotton and sisal are grown. Cotton and sugar are also cultivated with irrigation in the dry south-west where the rainfall is only 2 inches a year. The Cazengo district is especially famous for coffee and the Cabinda enclave yields other tropical products such as cocoa, palm oils and kernels.

The extent and value of Angola's mineral resources, likely to be great, have not been adequately assessed. Malachite, copper, iron, gold and lignite are mined, but most important are diamonds, chiefly for industrial purposes, panned in the alluvial field near

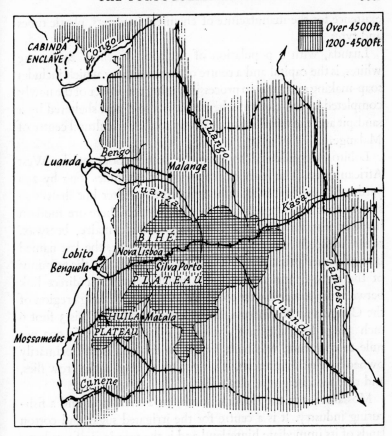

Fig. 56. Angola

Luanda and from which in 1956 there were 743,930 carats for export. Salt is evaporated from coastal lagoons and fishing takes place along the coast.

Industry is expanding with the development of hydro-electric power. Power plants have been built on the Dande river at Mabubas and at Muceques on the Cuanza river, and a similar station at Cambambe is designed to develop an aluminium industry at Luanda. With cheap and abundant hydro-electric power the Portuguese are planning an electro-metal industry using the iron ore deposits of Pungo–Adondo. Gum copal is obtained from surface rocks for use in the production of varnish, a large oil refinery is being built near Luanda, and new factories are coming into existence for the manufacture of chemical fertilizers, plastic tubes and tyres.

Luanda, with a population of 140,000, of which 20,000 are whites, is the capital and a centre of light industry which includes soap-making and tobacco processing, using the power of the newly completed hydro-electric schemes. It is also a port sheltered by a sandspit and the terminus of a railway to the agricultural centre of Malange.

Lobito is considered to have the best harbour of the West African coast. The harbour is fringed by a 3 miles long by 250 yards wide sandspit which not only affords shelter but shelves so steeply that large vessels can dock alongside. There are modern harbour installations, and its exports include maize, beeswax, sugar, oil seeds, sisal, hides, salt and manganese, the last named being destined primarily for the U.S.A. Lobito is also the terminus of the trans-continental railway which provides a direct link between the east and west coasts by way of the Katanga region of the Congo and Northern and Southern Rhodesia. This 3 foot 6 inch gauge line, the first few miles of which cost £9,000 per mile to construct, was built by the British and is still primarily owned by British interests. It is 1,700 miles long, as the crow flies, and reaches a height of 6,081 feet.

Mossamedes in the extreme south has a small port and a fish-curing industry. It is a centre for the irrigated sugar and cotton lands of its immediate hinterland and is the terminus of a railway to the agricultural region of the Huila plateau farmed by Boers who trekked north from South West Africa.

Nova Lisboa on the Benguela railway is a road and rail centre with railway workshops, and a centre for the newly developed European farming area on the plateau. In such a position it is likely to become the future capital of the country.

An expansion in trade is a very recent feature in Angola's economy. Most of it is with Portugal which receives preferential treatment.

In this vast, potentially rich area the Portuguese are hoping to promote great development schemes. This includes more railways, without which further mineral exploitation is impossible, and extensive irrigation and settlement in the Cunene river valley

Angola: Imports and Exports for 1959

Imports		Exports	
Wine	272,258	Coffee	1,014,613
Motor vehicles	192,094	Diamonds	500,945
Cotton goods	176,515	Sisal	225,968
Machinery	175,885	Maize	184,688
Railway rolling stock and		Fish meal	168,832
lines	126,276	Raw cotton	73,174
		Dried fish	59,499
		Iron	57,334

Figures refer to millions of escudos.

based on a dam at Matala, and in the Cuanza river valley. Limiting factors are lack of Portuguese capital and lack of enthusiasm on the part of Portuguese immigrants. This was well illustrated in the colonization project of 1953 near Cela. Generous gifts of land and animals were offered but, out of 1,000 colonists expected, only 124 availed themselves of the opportunity.

Angola or Portuguese West Africa is Portugal's largest possession, covering nearly half a million square miles (481,351 square miles), and including the Cabinda enclave north of the Congo mouth. It is fourteen times the size of Portugal and has a coastline of a thousand miles. For so extensive a country population figures are small, only 4,145,266, of which 27,000 are half-castes and 80,000 Europeans, chiefly Portuguese.

Portuguese Guinea was discovered by Nuno Tristão in 1446. Much of it is too humid (sometimes reaching saturation point) and too low-lying to be sufficiently healthy for European settlement. There are no large estates and agricultural companies as in Angola, and farming is almost entirely in the hands of natives. Bananas, oil palms and palm kernels are grown and exported. Groundnuts are the chief crop of the interior plains and plateaus especially round Farim, Bafata and Gabu. Rice is the most important crop, cultivated extensively around the coasts and estuaries where periodic flooding is possible, and as rice cultivation extends more mangrove is cleared. Not only are they self-sufficient in rice, but it is estimated that the district around Catio could supply the entire Portuguese demand.

There is virtually no industry in Portuguese Guinea, though concessions have been granted recently to a Dutch organization

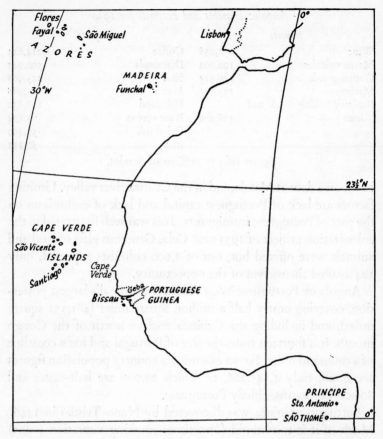

Fig. 57. Portuguese Atlantic and African Possessions

to prospect for bauxite, and to a Luso-American company to drill for oil.

Bissau, on a densely populated island in the Geba estuary connected with the mainland by a causeway, became the capital in 1941–2. The economic centre of the country, Bissau has a meteorological station and observatory nearby, an airport and a good port. The streets are wide and lined with shady colourful flamboyant trees, the houses solid and well built, avoiding the corrugated iron roofs so ubiquitous and detrimental to the appearance of urban areas in most parts of Africa. Other towns include Bolama and Bafata.

Communications are limited to 2,000 miles of dirt roads (but including one tarmac road linking Bissau with its native quarters), and to three rivers, the Cacheu, Geba and Corubal, each navigable for about 100 miles, and providing cheap and easy transport.

Portuguese Guinea, about half the size of Portugal, has an area of 13,948 square miles and a population of 510,777, including 2,263 Europeans. It remains today an African backwater where lack of incentive and abundance of government monopolies have a deadening effect on its administrative and economic development.

The Portuguese islands of the Gulf of Guinea associated with the volcanic activity of the nearby Cameroons (on the mainland of Africa 125 miles away) include two, São Thomé and Principe, discovered by the Portuguese in 1471 and settled by them in 1485. They soon established a prosperous trade in sugar, importing slave labour for the plantations from Guinea, the Gabon and Angola. Later competition from Brazil and the rebellion of Angolan slaves caused a decline, and sugar was replaced in the early nineteenth century by coffee, and especially by cocoa which proved so successful that by 1905 the islands were the world's leading cocoa exporters. This position was lost after 1912 as a result of declining fertility of the soil, limited space owing to the mountainous nature of the land, the competition of the Gold Coast (now Ghana) and the refusal of British chocolate manufacturers to buy from these islands on the philanthropic grounds that labour conditions in the plantations were appalling. Cocoa, however, still provides three-quarters of the total exports, the Netherlands and the U.S.A. being the chief customers. Many of the 125,000 acres under cocoa are in the north-east of São Thomé; plantations, or roças, are large – one covers 25,000 acres or one-tenth of São Thomé. They are owned by companies or by absentee Portuguese landlords and are worked by Angolan and Portuguese East African contract labour. The government is encouraging these people to stay and farm land offered to them in the undeveloped areas of the south. Plantation labour is augmented by deportees from Angola and Mozambique who are treated almost as slaves, and only after serious rioting in 1953 was there any amelioration of their working conditions. Anxiety lest the

domination of one crop should cause economic instability and
uncertainty has led to the cultivation of others including coconuts, rubber, sugar, oil palms, bananas, spices and cinchona at
altitudes of 3,000 feet, and coffee on Monté Café and in Trás-os-
Montes. The usual African subsistence crops are grown on native
farms, and from agricultural products soap and maize flour are
manufactured. Fishing is a minor occupation off the coast.

The capital of São Thomé is a town of the same name at the
head of Ana de Chaves Bay. It is linked by rail with Trindade and
has air communications with Fernando Po, Angola and Portugal.
There is no coastal road round São Thomé, but as many plantations have their own beaches canoes and coastal steamers form a
useful type of transport. Santo Antonio, at the head of a bay of the
same name, is the chief town on Principe and the terminus of the
coastal road.

São Thomé, the larger island, is 30 miles from north-east to
south-west and 20 miles across, while Principe, 90 miles to the
north and so named because it was once an hereditary possession
of the heir to the Portuguese throne, is only 10 miles from north-
east to south-west and 5 miles across. The total area is 372 square
miles, and the total population is 60,159, of which 53,000 inhabit
São Thomé and only 7,000 live on Principe.

The Cape Verde Islands derive their name not from the natural
vegetation but from the green Sargasso weed which drifts there
from further west. Lying 310 miles to the west of Cape Verde on
the African continent, they were first settled by the Portuguese in
1462. They consist of ten large inhabited islands and five small
uninhabited islets, divisible into two distinct groups – Barlavento
(windward) including Santa Luzia, Sal and Boa Vista, Santo Antâo,
São Vicente and the Sotavento (leeward), including Santiago,
Maio, Fogo and Brava.

The islands are volcanic and contain several high peaks, among
them Fogo, an extinct volcano over 9,000 feet high. The offshore
north-east trade winds prevail over the islands and dry conditions
are general. There are, however, several fertile valleys watered
by mountain streams and in these high-quality crops are grown.
These include coffee, sugar, maize, manioc, tobacco, oranges and
castor oil. Labour has always been a problem, and slaves from

Portuguese Guinea were employed in the plantations, their descendants forming the Creole population of today.

Praia, on the island of Santiago, is the capital, but St Vincent, population 20,000, is the chief port with a refuelling station and a cable station for South America and West Africa. Recent improvements on the islands include the airport at Ilha do Sal opened in 1949 and 340 miles of road completed in 1955. The total area of the Cape Verde Islands is 1,557 square miles and the population 148,331, of which 103,255 are half-castes and 2,909 are Europeans.

The Azores consist of a group of nine volcanic islands on the northern Mid-Atlantic Ridge, 1,000 miles west of Portugal. The first Portuguese to land here in 1432 found flocks of vultures encircling the cliffs, hence the name Açores. Much of the soil is poor, being of a volcanic nature, and vulcanicity is still apparent. Even as recently as 1957 a submarine island began to take shape off Fayal, streams of lava extended for 3,000 feet and a dense cloud rose 24,000 feet. At the end of a week the island was 300 feet high. A warm equable climate (temperatures range from 57° F. to 71° F.) and an adequate annual rainfall of 39 inches facilitate cultivation in small fertile areas including terraced slopes on the mountains. São Miguel has pineapple, tobacco and tea plantations. Wheat, maize and several Mediterranean fruits such as citrons are grown on Terceira where there is also pasture land for cattle and sheep. Oranges form the chief crop of São Jorge, but dairy cattle are pastured on the hills in summer and butter and cheese produced. The dwarf cattle of Corvo are unusual, looking like Lilliputian Jerseys.

Several handicrafts are found on the islands. Potters use local clay to make crude earthenware and the red clay of the Villa do Porto district of Santa Maria to make ceramics, while São Jorge specializes in the making of quilts woven from linen and wool. Wine-making is also important and mineral waters are exported.

São Miguel, which rises to 5,600 feet, is the largest and most densely populated island, having 120,000 inhabitants, many of whom live in the capital Ponta Delgada. Angra is the chief town of Terceira (population 70,000), the third island to be discovered. Horta, the largest town of Fayal, has the best harbour of the

M

Azores, sheltered by lava-formed headlands. This port was chosen to be the transatlantic cable station linked with Brest, Lisbon, Halifax and New York, and it has an airport lying on the routes between Europe, West Africa and South America. Collectively the Azores cover an area of 890 square miles and have a population of 318,000, which is densest around the coasts.

The name Madeira, 'island of woods', is an unusual name for an island with little of this type of vegetation. Popular opinion has it that rabbits living in the woods were so destructive to crops that the farmer inhabitants took the drastic step of burning the woods, causing a conflagration that lasted for seven years. It is likely, however, that the less sensational but more persistent cutting of timber for fuel and the removal of woods for further cultivation have been equally, if not more, responsible for this deforestation.

Madeira, discovered by the Portuguese in 1419, consists of one large and four small islands. The soil is fertile and the climate mild, with average temperatures from 59° F. to 71° F. The annual rainfall, however, is only 25 inches and the dry heat in summer makes irrigation essential for successful cultivation. Madeira shares with the Canaries the unusual system of *levadas*, or open channels into which water from mountain torrents is directed and distributed over much of the island, each district having a fixed time of supply. Cultivation extends along the coast and to a height of 2,000 feet on terraced slopes up to the woods of pine and eucalyptus. Wheat, barley, sweet potatoes and many types of fruits such as figs, avocados, guavas, pineapples and bananas are grown.

Cane-sugar production brought Christopher Columbus to the island and he later married the daughter of the governor of the Ile de Porto Santo. Many negroes were imported for work on the plantations where even today production and transport of sugar are primitive, men often having to carry the cane on their backs to waiting lorries. There is, however, the very modern processing factory of William Hinton and Sons in Funchal.

Vines, too, have prospered. In *Henry the Fourth Part I* Poins chaffs Falstaff about 'a cup of Madeira and a joint of cold chicken'. Napoleon showed sufficient foresight when putting in at the island to take on board vast quantities of Madeira to drown his sorrows on St Helena. The success of viticulture has led to the danger of Madeira possessing a one-crop economy, and to lessen the risk coffee and various fruits are grown extensively. Again, primitive methods are used – the grapes are crushed by human feet and often put in goat skins and carried on sledges, but in the Lodge of the Madeira Wine Association processing eliminates impurities using modern scientific methods. Types of wine exported include Malmsey, Bual, Sercial and Verdelho.

Industry is of the artisan type; the men are engaged in woodwork, wicker work, and the plaiting of straw hats, while embroidery and lace-making are a female prerogative. These articles are produced primarily for tourists.

Funchal, population 90,000, built on a steep slope, has a good harbour, though large ships usually anchor off the port. The transport system within the town is unusual. Bullock-drawn carriages or *carros* negotiate the gentle slopes while wicker sledges drawn by men bounce rapidly down the lava cobbles of the steeper slopes, much to the delight of tourists. Funchal is also the centre of the island's meagre road system. There are only two good motor roads, one from Ribeira Brava over the Encumeada pass to São Vicente, and the other from Funchal through Ribeiro Frio to Faial and Santana. The total area of Madeira is 314 square miles and the mixed population of Jews, Moors, Italians and Portuguese numbers 250,000, giving a density of population twice that of the Azores, though one island, rightly named Desertas, is uninhabited.

Portuguese India dates from 1505 and although these possessions are small and scattered they have survived longer than have British and French possessions on the sub-continent. They consist of Goa and the islands of Angediva, São Jorge and Morcegos on the coast of Malabar; Damão, Dadrá and Nagar-Aveli on the gulf of Cambay; and Diu with the enclaves of Gogola and Simbor on the coast of Gujarat.

Farming is almost limited to the cultivation of rice and coconuts and few minerals are found here. On the peninsula of Marmagão manganese is mined and salt evaporated. On this peninsula is the town of Marmagão, population 3,865, which has the largest and best-equipped harbour of Goa. Two miles away is the larger town of Vasco da Gama, named after the famous Portuguese discoverer of Goa. It has a population of 6,719 and has oil installations. At the furthest extension of the Marmagão peninsula is Margão, population 11,002, a route centre and a market centre for the Salcete district. The modern capital of Goa is Panjim on the river Mandavi.

Exports from Goa include coconuts, copra, cashew nuts, salt and fish, and an average of nearly 900 ships visit Goanese ports each year, and about a half a million tons of goods are handled. Goa has lost a lot of its transit trade with the Deccan of India, though this should be counterbalanced to a certain extent by the trade agreement made in 1958 with Pakistan which provides for the export to Pakistan of iron ore from Goa, especially if improved port facilities contemplated at Marmagão materialize.

Goa, the largest territory – 60 miles long by 40 miles wide – is 1,268 square miles in extent and has a population of 550,000, most of whom speak Goanese and 43 per cent of whom are Christians.

Timor, measuring 300 miles along its north-east–south-west axis, forms part of the East Indies group. It became Portuguese in 1586, but much of it is now part of Indonesia, and Portuguese territory is limited to the eastern part, together with the two small islands of Pulo Cambing and Pulo Jako and the enclave of Okusi Ambeno in the north-west.

Portuguese Timor, like the rest of the island, is covered with thick monsoon forest, and agriculture is limited to small clearings where the natives practise shifting cultivation to produce subsistence crops. Where conditions are slightly drier and at higher altitudes a savanna type of vegetation is found which supports a few animals.

Dili, population 7,000, is the capital and chief port of Portuguese Timor, exporting sandalwood, coffee and copra, and accommodating about 50 ships a year. The total area of the territory is 7,332 square miles and there is a population of 442,378, including 568 Europeans.

To the east of the Canton river mouth lies the British-held island of Hongkong. To the west is the Portuguese peninsula of Macão, where permission to settle was granted by the Chinese in 1557 but full possession only recognized in 1887. Macão consists of a rocky peninsula linked to the mainland by a narrow neck of land, and the two small islands of Taipa and Coloâne.

The town of Macão is a cultural centre rather than a busy commercial town. Its industries are few – the making of fireworks, matches, incense candles and the drying of fish. Macão has a small harbour (to be improved by the construction of a dry dock) which accommodates fishing vessels and passenger steamers plying between Macão and Hongkong rather than trans-ocean liners and merchant ships. The total area is 6 square miles and the population 187,772, of which 2,719 are Europeans.

Portugal's fragmentary possessions in India and South-East Asia have prestige value but little strategic or economic importance. The Atlantic islands are sufficiently near to form outer territories of Portugal itself, to supply raw materials and receive the manufactured goods of the mother country in exchange. This reciprocal trade is of advantage to both sides. The African possessions of Mozambique and Angola offer vast potential wealth but only in recent years has Portugal focussed serious attention on Africa and shown a willingness to pour capital into development schemes. In the second development plan of 1960 to 1964 Portugal is investing more than 9,000,000,000 escudos in her overseas provinces, of which a third goes to Mozambique and a half to Angola. Many examples of government enterprises have been given in regional accounts but they are of such recent origin that their achievement is difficult to assess. One major problem is the sparse native population which limits the supply of cheap labour. Another is the unwillingness of Portuguese to immigrate and their incapacity for hard protracted manual labour, so necessary in the early stages of colonial development. If, however, prosperity can be achieved it will go far to alleviate the financial difficulties of the mother country.

Bibliography

Enciclopedia Geográfica de España MARÍA DE BOLÓS Y CAPDEVILA
Grasso Hnos., Barcelona, 2nd edition, 1958
Geografia Especiel de España JOAQUIN IZQUIERDO GROSELLES
Editorial y Libreria Prieta, Granada
España – Geopolitica del Estado y del Imperio DR J. VICENS VIVES
Editorial Yunque, Barcelona
Geografia Económica de España F. C. REUS Arimany, Barcelona
Más Allá de la Prehistoria GMO. COLOM Colecciones Cauces, Madrid.
[A survey of the Balearic Islands]
Riqueza y Economía del Pais Vasco ANDOM DE SORALUZE Editorial
Vasca Ekin S.R.L., Buenos Aires
Sierra Nevada FIDEL FERNÁNDEZ Editorial Juventud S. A.,
Barcelona
Valle de Aran NOEL CLARASÓ DAUDÍ Ed. Arimany, S.A., Barcelona
El Parque Nacional del Valle de Ordesa (Comisaria de Parques
Nacionales) Arnaldo de España, Madrid
Diccionario Vasco-Castellano P. BERA-LOPEZ MENDIZABAL Ed.
Icharopena, F. Unzurrunzaga Zarauz (Guipuzcoa)
Don Quixote CERVANTES Trans. by J. M. Cohen, Penguin Classics
Oxford Book of Spanish Verse Clarendon Press, Oxford
Alpes et Pyrénées VICTOR HUGO Nelson, Paris
Voyage en Espagne THÉOPHILE GAUTIER Oxford University Press
La Mediterranée et le Moyen Orient BIROT and DRESCH Presses
Universitaires de France
Géographie Universelle Tome VII, Part I Armand Colin
Historia d'España y de la Civilizacion Española R. ALTAMIRA Y
CREVEA Barcelona, 1913–14
A History of Europe 1494 to 1610 A. J. GRANT Methuen
Europe in the Nineteenth and Twentieth Century 1789 to 1932 A. J.
GRANT and H. W. V. TEMPERLEY Longmans
A History of Europe H. A. L. FISHER Arnold

History of the Conquest of Mexico and *History of the Conquest of Peru*
W. H. PRESCOTT Everyman's Library

Hunters and Artists; The Steppe and the Sown; The Way of the Sea
PEAKE and FLEURE Clarendon Press, Oxford

Prelude to History A. COATES Methuen

The Conquest of Morocco VICE-ADMIRAL C. V. USBORNE, C.B.,
C.M.G. Stanley Paul

The Spanish Tragedy E. ALLISON PEERS Methuen

Spain: A Companion to Spanish Studies E. ALLISON PEERS Methuen

Portugal J. B. TREND Benn

The Statesman's Year Book for years 1947 to 1960

The Encyclopaedia Britannica

Britannica, Book of the Year for years 1947 to 1959

Southern Europe M. NEWBIGIN Methuen

A Geography of Western Europe edited by E. D. LABORDE University
of London Press

A Systematic Regional Geography, Vol. II Europe J. F. UNSTEAD
University of London Press

Groundwork of Modern Geography WILMORE Bell

Geology in the Service of Man W. G. FEARNSIDE and O. M. B.
BULMAN Pelican Book

South America E. W. SHANAHAN Methuen

Africa W. FITZGERALD Methuen

The Mediterranean Lands D. S. WALKER Methuen

West Africa R. J. H. CHURCH Longmans

India and Pakistan O. H. K. SPATE Methuen

Asia; a Regional and Economic Geography L. DUDLEY STAMP
Methuen

Daily Weather Reports of the Meteorological Office

Spain MARTIN HÜRLIMAN Thames & Hudson

The Spanish Temper V. S. PRITCHETT Chatto & Windus

The Selective Traveller in Portugal A. BRIDGE and S. LOWNDES
Chatto & Windus

Spain W. B. FISHER and H. BOWEN JONES Christophers

Blue Moon in Portugal W. and E. YOUNGER Eyre & Spottiswoode

Grapes and Granite N. EPTON Cassell

Navarre; the Flea between Two Monkeys N. EPTON Cassell

Pyrenean Holiday R. P. TAYLOR Robert Hale

Through the High Pyrenees H. SPENDER and H. LL. SMITH A. D.
　Innes
Brochures of 'Direccion General de Turismo'
Anuario Estadistica de España
Anuario Estadistica del Comercio Exterior de España
Brochures published for the Spanish Pavilion at the 1958 Brussels
　Universal and International Exhibition
Boletim Mensal do Instituto Nacional de Estatística
Various articles in *The Times*, *The Times Educational Supplement*,
　the *National Geographic Magazine*, the *Geographical Magazine*

MAPS USED

Bartholomew *Spain and Portugal* 1 : 1,600,000
National Geographic Society *Western Europe* 1 : 2,500,000
Foldex *Portugal* 1 : 700,000
Firestone *North-west Spain*⎫
　　　　Western Pyrenees｜
　　　　Eastern Pyrenees⎬　1 : 500,000
　　　　Balearics｜
　　　　Murcia-Almeria｜
　　　　Valencia⎭
Michelin　*Western Pyrenees*⎫
　　　　Eastern Pyrenees⎬　1 : 200,000
　　　　Madrid-Zaragoza⎭
Oxford Economic Atlas Clarendon Press
Oxford Home Atlas O.U.P.
Columbus Atlas Bartholomew
University Atlas GOODALL and DARBY George Philip & Son
The Oxford Advanced Atlas Bartholomew, O.U.P.
Mapa Geológico de España Instituto Geológico y Minero de
　España, Madrid, 1932

Index

★ – temperature figures
† – rainfall figures